THE
EVOLUTION
OF
GENETIC SYSTEMS

THE
EVOLUTION
OF
GENETIC SYSTEMS

C. D. DARLINGTON

BASIC BOOKS, INC., PUBLISHERS

NEW YORK

FIRST EDITION 1939

SECOND EDITION, REVISED AND ENLARGED 1958

PREFACE

New discoveries in science are first recognised by the fact that they seem to answer questions that we have long been asking ourselves. It is only when—after many days—we find them answering questions that we had *not* been asking ourselves that we begin to know them as something fundamental. Such discoveries were made in the study of life a hundred years ago by Mendel, Darwin, and Pasteur. And of their work it is no longer enough to say it is answering questions. What it is doing, and doing now more than ever, is to force new questions on us and thereby to alter the scope and meaning of the human mind.

The same transformations are happening in the physical sciences, the same recognitions of contradictions and paradoxes, the same surprising reconstructions, the same revelations of unexpected worlds beneath the worlds we knew. But in the physical sciences these transformations do not necessarily destroy the treasured beliefs of the past. In biology they destroy beliefs, rules, axioms, definitions, arguments, and conclusions which have been treasured as much by the instructed few as by the less instructed many.

What is this world of biology in which turmoil has been raging with increasing intensity throughout the present century? When the century began, biology consisted of a hundred disciplines. These disciplines had a general interest in life which they could not define, a general belief in evolution about which they could not agree, and a general fear of experimental methods which they did not understand. Today biology has common interests and beliefs and understandings which have arisen from the intervening conflicts on the material processes underlying life. Today the deepest properties of life, which are properties of heredity, development, and infection, are in process of being related to a physical and chemical basis. And this is what gives a kind of unity, one kind of unity, to the study of life.

There is, however, another kind of unity which rests on the physical and chemical basis but has a radically different quality, a quality that is utterly peculiar to life itself. This is the quality of related,

v

interacting, and ultimately organised change—change to which we give the name of evolution, covering, no doubt, with the name many deep abysses of our own ignorance.

It is the purpose of this book to join together the two worlds, the relatively fixed world of physics and chemistry and the undoubtedly moving world of biology, with some of the threads which are needed to join them. It is a hazardous attempt. In making it, I have been led by a belief in the connectedness of the processes of life for which it would be tedious to offer the rational evidence. It is also now unnecessary. For when I first made the attempt to write an account of what I called *The Evolution of Genetic Systems*, the chemical basis of these systems was virtually unknown. Their unity rested on the uniformity of visible cells and nuclei and chromosomes and the uniformity of the laws of heredity. Today the unity and the connectedness are chemically established.

The researches which are responsible for this new unity of science are not, of course, brought to a standstill by their own success. New vistas at once open to our eyes at each step forward. Most of those who are now leading the advance, men whose work we so much admire, are too busy to look back. They are too busy even to look sideways. It is again the purpose of this book to do both and to see, indeed, how the shape of our knowledge is being changed today just as it was changed in the past by the work of Mendel, Darwin, and Pasteur.

Botany School, Oxford   C. D. Darlington
17th January 1958.

Acknowledgements: Figure 1 is reproduced from Darlington: *Recent Advances in Cytology*, by permission of Messrs J. & A. Churchill; Figure 12 is reproduced from *Nature*, v. 138, p. 402, by permission of Messrs Macmillan: Figure 21 is based on that in *Hereditas*, v. 22, p. 223, by permission of the Editor.

CONTENTS

END-PAPERS

*The course of meiosis shown for one
pair of chromosomes in ten stages*

1. Pairing and left-hand relational coiling of partners (pachytene)

2. Division of chromosomes into chromatids now showing right-hand relational coiling

3. Crossing over has taken place between chromatids of partners, and a chiasma appears (diplotene)

4. Relational coiling undone, spiralisation begun and also terminalisation of the chiasma

5. Centromeres mutually repelled (diakinesis)

6. Terminalisation complete, major coiling developed, and centromeres co-orientated on the spindle (first metaphase)

7. Chromatids separate and centromeres move apart to opposite poles (first anaphase)

8. Centromeres of the two daughter chromosomes prepare to divide, only minor coiling preserved (second metaphase)

9. Centromeres move apart (second anaphase)

10. Four haploid nuclei reconstituted each with one chromatid from each pair of chromosomes (second telophase)

quippe, ubi non essent genitalia corpora cuique,
qui posset mater rebus consistere certa?

For if each organism had not its own genetic bodies,
how could we with certainty assign to each its mother?

nil ideo quoniam natumst in corpore ut uti
possemus, sed quod natumst id procreat usum.

For nothing is born in the body in order that we may be
able to use it,
but rather, having been born, it begets a use.

Lucretius: *De Rerum Natura* I, 167-8; IV, 834-5

1
PREMISES OF GENETICS

LIVING organisms as we know them are things derived by breaking off or reproduction from their like and usually capable of giving rise to their like for an indefinite time. This is the genetic way of defining life. The degree to which organisms arising in this way are like their parents is said to be due to *heredity*. The degree to which they are different is said to be due to *variation* in this heredity.

One proviso must be added to this definition: that conditions outside the organisms be not changed. In nature the differences between organisms depend on differences outside as well as inside them. Smaller size may be due to bad heredity or bad food. We therefore separate these two factors as *Genotype* and *Environment*. Genetics rests on the axiom that the character of an organism depends on the reaction of its genotype and its environment. Where a plant is propagated by grafting or cuttings all over the world and for a great space of time, its environment and its observable characters change continually but its genotype remains the same. When it is brought back to the old conditions its old character reappears. We therefore say that there must be material particles within the organism which reproduce themselves without change and determine this constancy within it. That at least was the simplest assumption and one that was made long before any such particles were seen. The *corpora genitalia* of the ancients became the ids of Weismann and the genes of Johannsen. Now, however, we find that all plants and animals are made up of cells and all these cells contain nuclei. These bodies alone are indispensable to the reproduction of a cell or of a whole organism. They are characteristic and similar in their behaviour in plants and animals. We therefore assume that the nuclear particles are responsible for heredity. The nucleus is in fact the seat of the genotype very much as the brain is the seat of the mind.

When we look deeper into this matter we find that the notions of genotype and environment introduce us to a variety

1

of other problems. In the first place the organ of the genotype is not one but many nuclei distributed throughout the body. These nuclei are surrounded by a material, the cytoplasm, through which they exert their effect on the organism and on one another. They must be capable of interacting in the course of development. The cytoplasm is therefore the agent through which differentiation is established between the parts of the organism. It constitutes an inner environment coming between the organs of the genotype and the outer environment. On these properties depend the adaptations of genetic systems to the great variety of conditions of development we are going to consider in various organisms.

Thus environment has other meanings which have nothing to do with our axiom. The environment for particular purposes depends on whether we are speaking of the whole or of a part of an organism, or indeed of the whole or a part of a species. It may depend also on the stage of development and the relations of parent and offspring. And lastly, by a paradox, it depends on the genotype from which we thought to have separated it. For when we change the genotype we throw the organism into a new environment. A dwarf bean does not meet the same world as a scarlet runner.

Before we go any further let us recall the three vital experiments on which genetics is founded. The first experiment provided the evidence for Johannsen that the genotype is independent of the environment. Johannsen took a stock of beans (*Phaseolus vulgaris*) descended by self-fertilisation for several generations from one plant. This he described as a *pure line*. He found the seeds produced differed in weight. Moreover plants differed in the average weight of the seeds they produced. But plants grown from the heavier-seeded parents produced seedlings with no heavier seeds than those from the lighter-seeded parents.

This experiment Johannsen repeated for several generations, but selection continued to have no effect. The new sub-lines within the old pure line had all the same seed weight. Why? Because the genotypes of all the plants in the pure line were the same and the differences between them were due merely to differences in the environment. These effects were not inherited. The environment is therefore powerless to produce a change in a group of organisms without selection; selection is powerless to produce a change without variation amongst the genotypes. And variation is not inherent in heredity in the sense in which Darwin imagined it to be. When, on the other hand, a population containing different pure lines is bred selectively, it is changed as a whole, because the differences between its constituent lines are genotypic: they are not environmental.

The second experiment (although earlier in date) provided the evidence for Mendel that the genotype is composed of indivisible parts. Mendel crossed members of two pure lines of peas (*Pisum sativum*) which differed in one recognisable respect: one was tall, the other dwarf. The first generation, or F_1, progeny were all tall, but when they were self-pollinated they produced second generation, or F_2, progeny three-quarters of which were tall and one-quarter dwarf. The dwarf all bred true, and so did one of the three quarters that were tall. The rest of the tall plants again gave a three to one proportion of tall and dwarf. Further, when any of these impure talls were crossed with dwarfs (for all dwarfs were evidently pure) half the offspring were tall and half dwarf.

Mendel drew a conclusion from this experiment which is now obvious though it was repugnant to the then prevailing thought; he assumed that the first cross was hybrid for an *element*, as he called it, determining tallness or dwarfness, the genotype of each plant having both the element for tallness (T) and an alternative and dissimilar element for dwarfness (t). These two elements were inherited from its two parents, TT and tt; and further, that these elements separated in the formation of the germ cells so that some had one and some the other in equal numbers. Hence the hybrid Tt gives germ cells T and t and progeny recombining T and t at random as a result of random fertilisation, in the proportions $1\ TT : 2\ Tt : 1\ tt$. Since Tt shows the undiminished tall character, three of this dominant character appear to every one of the recessive.

From this experiment it follows that the product of fertilisation is genetically double, that its genotype is determined by certain particles or arrangements of particles which retain their individuality from one generation to another, and that corresponding particles from opposite parents separate when the germ cells are formed so that they are genetically single. These particles, which we need not define more accurately for the moment, are now known as *genes*. Mendel's observations of their effect enable us to define a hybrid as a zygote derived from the fusion of dissimilar gametes. They enable us to predict likewise that such a hybrid will itself give rise by *segregation* to dissimilar gametes.

From this experiment followed a whole series of others calculated to discover what happens when an organism is hybrid for several of these gene differences, that is, hybrid in respect of several pairs of alternatives or *alleles*. Usually any particular two genes will *recombine* freely, each of the classes for one allele (*A*)—pure dominant, hybrid and pure recessive—consisting of the same proportions (1 : 2 : 1) of the three classes for the other (*B*). Thus a double hybrid *AaBb* gives:

$$1 \; AABB : 2 \; AaBB : 1 \; aaBB$$
$$: 2 \; AABb \; : 4 \; AaBb : 2 \; aaBb$$
$$: 1 \; AAbb \; : 2 \; Aabb \; : 1 \; aabb.$$

Or, taking the externally distinguishable classes:

$$1 \; AABB : 2 \; AaBB : 2 \; AABb : 4 \; AaBb$$
$$1 \; AAbb \; : 2 \; Aabb$$
$$1 \; aaBB \; : 2 \; aaBb$$
$$1 \; aabb,$$

i.e. 9 : 3 : 3 : 1.

By this experiment Mendel established the free segregation of two elements or genes whose variations or differences controlled height and colour. But free recombination meets with exceptions. Where, for other genes, the cross has been made between *AABB* and *aabb*, more of the *AB* and *ab* classes of gametes may be formed by the hybrid than the alternative, or *crossover*, classes *Ab* and *aB*. Evidently there is some restriction on this crossing-over or recombination. Moreover, the restriction is found to be of different degrees between different pairs of genes. Some pairs have crossed over in 30 per cent, of gametes and others in only 1 or 2 per cent.

When hundreds of pairs of genes have been tested for crossing-over in various species of *Drosophila*, *Zea Mays*, *Pisum sativum* and *Pharbitis*, it has been found that those pairs which show a mutual restriction of crossing-over, or linkage as we say, can be arranged in groups, and that within each group the series of genes is a linear one such that, knowing the proportion of crossing-over between *A* and *B* and between *B* and *C*, we can calculate the proportion between *A* and *C* as a little less than the sum of these two. Finally, the number of these groups is found to agree with the number of separate bodies or chromosomes in the nuclei of the germ cells in the particular plant or animal, 10 in *Zea Mays*, 4 in *Drosophila melanogaster* and so on.

Now the third fundamental experiment had been carried out by Mendel on fertilisation. He counted the number of pollen grains placed on the style of *Mirabilis jalapa* and proved that one pollen grain was enough to fertilise one seed. Ten years later the essential process was seen by Oscar Hertwig. He watched a sperm entering an echinoderm egg, and saw the fusion of their two nuclei. He had discovered what mattered in fertilisation.

The full consequences and implications of Mendel's work, even today, are partly overlooked or misunderstood. This is because the rediscoverers in the year 1900 rediscovered only a part of it. They saw it as a solution of many of their own problems; a discovery to be developed by their own experiments. They did not recognise it as a revolution in the whole of thought about living processes. Let us consider a few examples of this misunderstanding.

One of Mendel's rediscoverers, Correns, had the notion that Mendel's discovery could be represented by two 'laws' of heredity, the law of segregation and the law of free recombination. Correns' notion was most successful. These abstract laws became the foundation of teaching in the subject. The consequences were unfortunate. In the first place it was easily forgotten that these laws of heredity have the special property of contradicting the accepted notion of the regularity of scientific law. They make the character of the individual not predictable, but in certain situations, inherently unpredictable. In the second place, it was easily forgotten that these laws of heredity contradicted accepted notions of the term heredity itself. For, according to Mendelian law, heredity is responsible not only for similarities between relatives but also for differences: the kind of differences which the uninstructed observer has always attributed to the environment. Mendel's work thus undermines our interpretation of the reaction of genotype and environment in all natural situations.

B

Finally, and with the most immediate effect, the representation of Mendel's work by laws of segregation and recombination diverted attention from the fundamental questions of which Mendel himself was aware. These were the questions: What is being segregated? What is being recombined? Mendel's answer had been *elements* but Mendel's followers forgot his answer.

For these reasons biologists have never fully assimilated Mendel's teaching on the most general biological problems. For these reasons also the followers of Mendel between 1900 and 1910 failed to come to terms with students of the cell who had already gone far in understanding heredity. They had seen the indispensable character of the nucleus in the cell, its continuity, and its mode of propagation. But only very slowly did the distinction between the two parts of the cell, the cytoplasm and the nucleus, lead to the recognition of what they did. The cytoplasm varied with the short-term changes, those of growth and development. The nucleus was concerned with the long-term changes, those of heredity. Only very slowly did the obvious conclusion follow from this contrast. The distinction between a short-lived *soma* and an immortal *germplasm*, which Weismann had demanded, held good, not for two parts of each organism, but for two parts of each cell.

Breeding experiments and cytological observations agreed in contradicting the common-sense notion that heredity was a direct relationship between parent and offspring. They showed that the relationship was not between their appearances or phenotypes but between their hereditary materials or genotypes. Our next task is therefore to see what these materials are and how they are handed down from generation to generation.

The nuclei which fuse in fertilisation look alike. It is not surprising therefore that the progeny of reciprocal crosses between varieties are similar. Exceptions to this rule are known. Differences are found which are inherited on the female side only, showing that the cytoplasm is carrying specific self-propagating elements like those in the nucleus. We can however attempt to define the part they may play only when we understand the more precise action of the visible determinants in the nucleus. When we have done this we shall return to the cytoplasm.

2

THE SUBSTANCE OF HEREDITY

As a single cell grows into a mature organism it divides into many cells and its nucleus into many nuclei. It is then that we are able to understand the particulate character of its permanent or heredity-making structures. We recognise

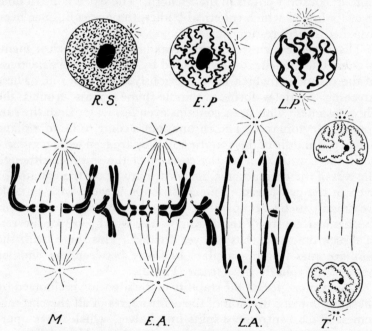

Fig. 1. The cycle of mitosis. *R.S.* Resting stage with large nucleolus. *E.P.* Early prophase with double chromosomes in relic spirals. *L.P.* Late prophase with centrosomes at opposite sides of nucleus. *M.* Metaphase with four chromosomes orientated on plate of spindle. *E.A.* Early anaphase with centromeres divided. *L.A.* Late anaphase. *T.* Telophase with nucleolus being re-formed at the secondary constriction. (Darlington, 1937a.)

nuclei by their having a characteristic method of division, *mitosis*, which provides that the products of division are genetically identical.

The resting nucleus is globular and bounded by an even membrane. The nucleus is sometimes optically homogeneous in life but differential refractivity as well as certain fixations can be made to reveal its structure. It consists of a compactly coiled mass of threads, the chromosomes. The first sign of mitosis is that these threads become separated from a watery substrate or sap. They are then seen to be loosely coiled and lying in closely associated pairs or, as we may say, each chromosome is double. They then begin to shorten and thicken to form double cylinders or rods (Fig. 1). They all show one, or perhaps more, constrictions at constant points in their length. The extra constrictions mark points to which spherical bodies, the nucleoli, have been attached in the resting nuclei.

This *prophase* is ended by the breakdown of the nuclear membrane. The nucleus is then invaded by the less watery particles of the cytoplasm which have previously been kept out. These invading particles form a spindle-shaped mass around the chromosomes. This mass contains even less water than the surrounding cytoplasm. The chromosomes come to lie in a plane across the middle of this spindle and they are seen to lie regularly with one constriction on the equator of the spindle, although the rest of the chromosome, its body, may lie off the equator or even in the cytoplasm. The constriction is seen, with suitable treatment, to be occupied by a small body, the *centromere* or mechanical centre of the chromosome, which, unlike the rest of the chromosome, has not yet divided. This stage, with the chromosomes forming a plate half-way between the ends or poles of the spindle is *metaphase* (Fig. 2).

After a short period the stability of the situation is changed by the simultaneous division of the centromeres of all the chromosomes. Each centromere splits into halves, which move apart from one another towards the opposite poles, pulling their chromatids or half-chromosomes after them. Between the two groups the spindle stretches, pushing them farther apart. This stage of separation is *anaphase*. When the sets of chromatids come near the poles, two new nuclei are built up again and the nucleoli are reorganised at the same points which bore them in the parent nucleus. This last stage is *telophase*.

While the nuclei are returning to their resting condition a fine spiral appears inside each chromosome, and its coils slightly loosen and becoming closely entangled disappear in the optically homogeneous nucleus. The nuclear cycle is complete. If, however, we compare this last view with the first we see that the coils which gradually become fewer and straighten out during the contraction of prophase are a direct continuation of those seen at telophase. They are *relic coils*. And while they are disappearing at prophase we must suppose that a new spiral is developing inside each chromatid for the new mitosis.

It is by developing an *internal* coil that the chromosomes contract lengthwise and become conveniently mobile during mitosis. When the coiling fails (exceptionally in certain Protozoa, and abnormally in higher organisms) the chromosomes remain

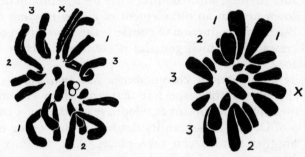

Fig. 2. Metaphase of mitosis in early and late spermatogonia of *Chorthippus* (Orthoptera) showing 3 pairs of chromosomes with median centromeres, 5 pairs with subterminal or terminal centromeres and the single sex chromosome (*X*).

long, so long that the daughter chromatids may fail to separate at anaphase, and a single nucleus is restored with a double number of chromosomes. Such under-coiled chromosomes have more coils than the normal but they are of smaller diameter, so it is clear that the whole nuclear cycle consists in a process of diminishing the number and increasing the diameter of coils in a chromosome. During prophase two successive coiling cycles overlap.

Although the separation of chromatids takes place at anaphase it will be seen that the division of the chromosome into two chromatids takes place earlier. It has evidently been accomplished after the end of telophase when they were single and before the beginning of prophase when they had become double: that is during the previous resting stage, when the threads were dispersed in the nucleus and half uncoiled. How this division must be supposed to work is a molecular problem. It depends on the molecular structure we assume in the chromosome.

What is this structure? It seems that the chromosome is a nucleo-protein (that is a combination of protein and nucleic acid. It is probably based on units consisting of polypeptide chains to which are attached double columns of polymerised nucleotides forming desoxyribose nucleic acid or DNA for short. The cyclical changes in spiralisation of these nucleo-protein units constitute a molecular spiral which must underlie and determine the visible coiling cycle of the chromosome itself. The visible division must be preceded by a reproduction, the laying down next to an old element of a new element exactly like it. Such a reproduction of course is the foundation of those life processes with which genetics is concerned. How does it take place?

The reproduction of chromosomes has two aspects. The chemically measurable aspect is that any given chromosome complement forms a nucleus at telophase containing a constant quantity of DNA. This quantity doubles in the resting nucleus before another mitosis can take place. The microscopically observable aspect consists in the appearance of two threads, two chromatids, where there was one before.

It is an essential property of these essential materials of life that the attraction on which the division of the chromosomes depends is between identical elements and is limited to pairs. Owing to this specificity of attraction, each chromosome divides into two exactly equivalent daughter chromatids, and the two daughter nuclei are also exactly equivalent in chromosome content; they contain the same number of chromosomes of the same sizes and shapes and composed of the same linear arrangements of particles. Hence so long as mitosis regularly continues every nucleus formed has a constant outfit of chromosomes with a constant quantity and constant arrangement of nucleo-protein materials. This constancy applies to the whole of an individual. It ensures the permanence of the genotype, that is of the character of the individual, a character which, as we know in some animals and in many plants, may be propagated vegetatively without any clear limit in time or space.

3

SEXUAL REPRODUCTION

MANY species of Protozoa, Fungi and Algae seem to have no other kind of nuclear division than mitosis. Their propagation or reproduction is then said to be purely asexual or vegetative. But in most of these lower organisms and in nearly all the higher plants and animals (whose life histories we know much better) there occurs another type of reproduction with a distinct and universal character of its own. This depends on two changes in the nucleus—*fertilisation* and *meiosis*. The combination of these two alternating and compensating processes in the life cycle is known as sexual reproduction. What are these two processes?

Fertilisation consists in the union of the nuclei of two gametes in forming a zygote. In view of the self-propagating permanence of the chromosomes the zygote has two sets of the chromosomes of which each gamete has one. And in so far as the gametes are from related parents the two sets are related and therefore correspond in form and structure, so that each type of chromosome is represented in the zygote by two homologues. The zygote is therefore said to be *diploid* (with $2n$ chromosomes) and the gamete *haploid* (with n chromosomes).

Meiosis consists in two divisions of the diploid nucleus of the mother cell accompanied by one division of its chromosomes. Each chromosome pairs with its homologue, so that $2n$ chromosomes form n pairs during the first nuclear division and the chromosomes of each pair pass to opposite poles without separation of their chromatids. These chromatids then separate at the second division. Each of the four nuclei therefore has one of the four chromatids of each pair of chromosomes. They are haploid nuclei once more.

In most of the lower organisms the fusion of the gametes is followed immediately by the compensating meiosis. The diploid phase merely lasts through one resting stage. In the higher organisms the diploid phase is the main part of the cycle and the haploid is reduced to one resting stage in the higher animals.

In man there are some cells which continually multiply; for example those which produce blood and sperm cells. For the rest of his body the diploid phase consists of about 50 mitoses in sequence yielding some 10^{14} cells. The prolongation of the diploid stage is achieved in the Basidiomycetes by a special device. The two gamete nuclei divide side by side in every cell of the plant. As soon as they fuse, meiosis takes place. Until then we have a diploid organism with only haploid nuclei.

The two important factors in permitting sexual reproduction are usually the bringing together of the two gametes from different places and the providing of a food supply for the new diploid individual. These conditions are usually satisfied by *sexual differentiation*, that is by a division of labour between the two gametes. One travels with the minimum burden, the other merely waits with the food supply. The one is the male cell or spermatozoon, the other the female cell or egg. When the same parent individual bears both it is said to be hermaphrodite. When separate individuals bear opposite sex cells the individuals themselves are said to be male and female and the species as a whole is said to be sexually differentiated.

Sexual differentiation of gametes begins with a minimum where there is no difference in size between the gametes, only in movement, as in *Actinophrys* or *Spirogyra*. It ends with the extreme of difference in size between a sperm and a bird's egg, which is many million times larger.

Sexual differentiation of individuals bearing the gametes may apply to the haploid individuals where a haploid generation is retained, as in Protista and Bryophyta. In the higher organisms where the haploid generation is telescoped, the sex of the gametes is determined by the differentiation of the preceding diploid generation. Thus the diploid is a male or a female, a man or a woman, by virtue of producing only one kind of haploid gametes—sperm or eggs. The haploid generation bears, not a sexual character of its own, but that which has been imprinted on it by the parent male, female or hermaphrodite of whose body it forms a part.

Sexual differentiation as between individuals is characteristic of mobile animals; hermaphroditism is characteristic of sessile plants. The two modes of reproduction often occur in the same group however and the change from one to the other is often quite a trivial one. The fundamental problem, the problem that we have to consider first, is therefore that of sexual reproduction as a whole, including the cell processes that underlie it.

4

MEIOSIS: PAIRING AND CROSSING OVER

THE first question about meiosis is of course what makes it
different from an ordinary mitosis. The character of the
division is undecided at the preceding telophase. This is
shown by one of the products of mitosis in certain fungi undergoing meiosis and forming an ascus while the other undergoes
mitosis, e.g. in *Peziza*.[1] It is also shown by the nature of the
division, mitosis or meiosis, being determinable experimentally
during the preceding resting stage in certain diatoms.[2] The
difference has arisen before the beginning of prophase, however.
In mitosis the chromosomes divide, as we saw, during the resting
stage. In meiosis they begin the prophase still undivided. The
difference must be established during the resting stage.

Experiments with breaking the chromosome by X-rays at
different times during the resting stage before a mitosis make
it clear that the chromosomes split into two just before the
prophase begins. Similarly, experiments with tracing the
entrance of radio-active phosphorus into the nucleus (where it
helps to make the nucleic acid of the reproducing chromosome)
show that this new material is completely assembled only at
the end of the resting stage.[3] Evidently, therefore, the prophase
in meiosis begins before the resting stage reproduction of the
chromosomes is complete.

We saw that in mitosis the particles of each chromosome
attract similar ones to themselves during the resting stage, so
that one thread reproduces or becomes two. This reproduction
is described as division and is followed by the association
throughout prophase of the two chromatids which arise from
the division. At the beginning of meiosis, on the other hand,
the chromosomes appear as single threads and the separate
homologues therefore attract one another. In the diploid, unless
it is a hybrid, there are two homologues of each kind of chromosome corresponding in all their parts. These chromosomes come
to lie side by side in pairs.

[1] Wilson, 1937.   [2] Geitler, 1934.   [3] Darlington, 1955.

The chromosomes at this thin thread stage show a granular structure not usually seen during the rapid early prophase of mitosis. They are indeed still engaged in activity; they are reproducing themselves and they show a structure which is apparently concerned with this activity. They look like strings of unequal beads unequally strung together. These beads are the *chromomeres*. In homologous chromosomes they correspond in number, size and position, and each chromomere pairs with a similar partner. The centromere stands out from its neighbouring chromomeres, being further separated from them than they are from one another. So also do the chromomeres responsible for the organisation of the nucleoli of which there are usually two in a diploid complement.

The chromosomes usually begin to pair near the ends, but sometimes near their centromeres. Where the centromere lies near an end the most regular result is attained. This regularity is facilitated in many animals by all the ends which are going to pair first lying close together to one side of the nucleus (perhaps even attached to the nuclear membrane) before pairing actually begins. Once pairing has begun, whether at a centromere or at an end or at both at the same time, it passes along the chromosome like the closing of a zip-fastener.

The process of pairing probably arises from three sources of attraction which act in sequence. First, at a distance, similar chromomeres which usually lie in corresponding order on the pairing chromosomes are producing similar proteins: their products may attract one another. Secondly, when close together, identical chromomeres attract one another specifically in pairs. And, thirdly, the torsion under which each chromosome is held after the attachment of its ends develops a coiling which may assist and can certainly counterfeit, the normal attraction of similar chromomeres. Thus the partner chromosomes become coiled round one another, *relationally* as we say to distinguish this coiling from the internal coiling already referred to.

When pairing is complete the diploid complement of chromosomes is present as the haploid number of *bivalent* chromosomes. In this way the mitotic position of association of similar threads in pairs is restored. The double thread or *pachytene* stage is in a stable condition, which unlike the mating-thread stage may be indefinitely prolonged.

Pachytene is ended by four changes which regularly occur together and together constitute the crisis of meiosis:

First, the partner chromosomes fall apart.

Secondly, each partner is seen to have formed two chromatids which remain closely paired.

Thirdly, the paired chromatids are seen to exchange partners at certain points known as *chiasmata* where pairs of chromatids have evidently broken and have reunited in new combinations; they have thus undergone *crossing over*.

Lastly, the relational coiling of the chromosomes is partly undone by the crossing over and chiasma formation.

When these changes are complete we have the *diplotene* stage (Figs. 3 and 17).

The detailed mechanics of this remarkable series of changes we shall go into later. For the present we must notice two mechanical properties of obvious significance. One is that we might expect the chromosomes to fall apart when they divide if indeed attractions are limited to pairs of threads, whether chromosome or chromatids. The other is that, notwithstanding any such limitation, the chiasmata would hold chromatids together in fours by being exchanges amongst fours. On this view, all association of the partner chromosomes is conditioned by attraction. But after the beginning of diplotene this attraction is between chromatids and not between chromosomes as such: the chromosomes are held together by the chiasmata, that is by the occurrence of crossing over.

Observation bears out this view. At the beginning of diplotene the partners begin to show mutual repulsion. Where only one chiasma is formed between two chromosomes the four arms open at right angles to form a cross. Where there are two chiasmata the loop between them opens to form a flat circle. What remains of the relational coiling is obliterated.

The chromosomes begin to contract into their internal spiral and the effect of their repulsion now becomes more marked. It shows itself in two ways. In closed loops the repulsion is necessarily stronger than in the open arms of the ends adjoining them. their parts being closer together. These loops expand at the cost of the open arms; the chiasmata slip towards the ends. Secondly the associations of the two arms containing the centromeres extend at the cost of the two arms not containing them (Fig. 3).

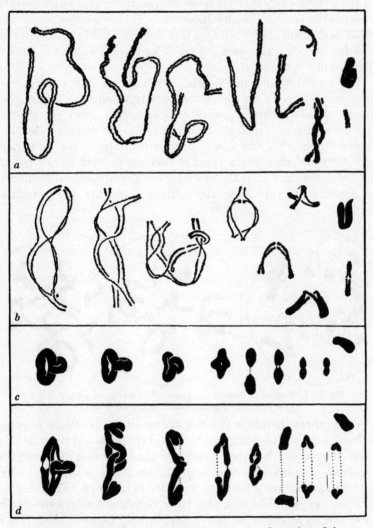

Fig. 3. The first division of meiosis in the sperm-formation of the grasshopper *Chorthippus*. *a.* Pachytene. *b.* Diplotene; 8 bivalents have one to three chiasmata each while *X* is unpaired. *c.* Metaphase. *d.* Anaphase. Each series is shown as though in a Mercator's projection of the cell, *X* to the right. Centromeres not shown. (After Darlington, 1937*a*.)

In both these cases there is more or less movement of chiasmata towards the ends of the chromosomes. This *terminalisation* occurs in all organisms, in greater or less degree, chiefly according to whether the chromosomes are small or large. Again we have a zip-fastener movement.

The most obvious movement, the most obvious evidence of repulsion, is where the chromosomes are smallest: for example, in the smaller chromosomes of *Chorthippus*, and in all the chromosomes of *Lepidoptera* and most Dicotyledons. All the chiasmata move away from the centromeres to the ends and give terminal chiasmata; and if two are formed between one pair of arms they fuse at the ends, the penultimate association of chromatids replacing the ultimate one at the terminal chiasma.

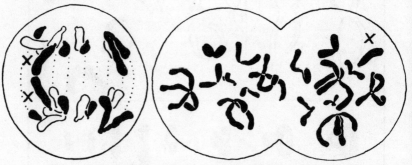

Fig. 4. Left, the two second metaphases in *Chorthippus* with 8 and 9 chromosomes. Right, second anaphase, with *X*.

Thus where the chromosomes are small the bivalents become rods or rings, rods having one terminal chiasma and rings having two. Where, on the other hand, the chromosomes are large the bivalents remain very much the same shape as at diplotene. The chiasmata are separated by more even loops. They are, as we may say, equilibrated and their number remains the same, from one to as many as fifteen but usually two or three. Each pair of chromosomes in any species has a characteristic average frequency of chiasmata under standard conditions.

If the nucleus is small, as in mother cells on the male side, the bivalents become evenly spaced in it, and if they are very short most of them lie on the spherical surface of the nucleus. If the nucleus is large, as in mother cells on the female side, the bivalents are less evenly spaced. The same repulsion which apparently acts between all chromosomes in all prophase nuclei acts also within bivalents, but it is insufficient to secure complete terminalisation in large bivalents. It is also insufficient to secure even spacing in large nuclei. The repulsion is an inverse function of distance. It is, however, insufficient to modify the powerful attraction of homologous threads in pairs at all stages of prophase.

At the last stage of prophase, *diakinesis*, the chromosomes have come to be contracted a little more than at metaphase of mitosis, they are a tenth their pachytene length in *Lilium*, a fifteenth in *Zea*. They are associated in pairs by terminal or interstitial chiasmata, and the members of these pairs no longer attract but repel one another. Since the chiasmata themselves are the result of crossing-over, such as we have already inferred in breeding experiments, we see that crossing-over is a condition of the pairing of the chromosomes being maintained from pachytene to metaphase. Hence also it is a condition of the reduction of the number of chromosomes and of the regular character of meiosis and sexual reproduction. This principle is true of all sexually reproducing species. It governs, as we shall see later, the character of every genetic unit from the gene to the species. It is the central fact of genetics.

5

MEIOSIS: THE PROCESS OF ASSORTMENT

OUTSIDE the chromosomes meiosis continues to follow the same course as mitosis. The chromosomes themselves, on the other hand, follow a course modified in essential respects by their association in pairs, an association which results from the initial difference between the two types of division.

When the spindle breaks into the prophase nucleus the bivalents first come closer together, and then arrange themselves in a metaphase plate half-way between the two poles. But their internal relations are very different from those of simple mitotic chromosomes. The two centromeres of each bivalent lying in the spindle are axially *co-orientated*, that is to say they lie on an arc or axis passing through the two poles of the spindle. One centromere lies on one side of the equatorial plate, its partner a similar distance on the other side. As this is happening they move apart, so that as a rule they are nearly as far from one another as each of them is from the pole on its side. And they may even stretch apart much further. If there is a chiasma close to the centromeres the segments of chromosome between them and this chiasma are drawn out into a finer thread than other segments: they are evidently under tension. The centromeres are repelling one another even more strongly than at diakinesis. Meanwhile, the bivalents adjust themselves laterally, so that seen from the pole they are, as in mitosis, evenly distributed on the plate, while any long free arms of peripheral bivalents lie outside the spindle in the cytoplasm. They remain in this equilibrium position for a short time. Suddenly the attraction between chromatids lapses. The centromeres of partners then move apart and draw their attached chromatids towards the opposite poles (Fig. 5).

The two nuclei that are thus formed at telophase resemble those at a mitotic prophase inasmuch as the bodies of the chromosomes are double, although the centromeres are single. There is therefore the haploid number of chromosomes, but the diploid number of chromatids. They also differ from or-

dinary telophase in the readiness of the centromeres to undergo the division which has been, so to speak, circumvented at
the first anaphase of meiosis. It seems to be this property of the
centromeres which precipitates the second division of meiosis.[1]
For in normal meiosis the second division quickly follows the
first and it does so without any further division of the chromosomes. In some organisms no resting stage intervenes, and at the
second metaphase the chromosomes are still super-contracted
as at the first division. In others there is a short resting stage,
the chromosomes partly uncoil, and at the second division are
coiled only as at mitosis.

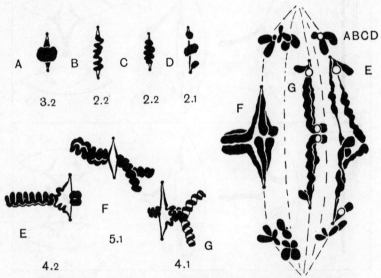

Fig. 5. First metaphase and anaphase in *Uvularia* ($n=7$), showing
how the separation of chromatids distal to the chiasmata in the long
chromosomes (E, F, G) with more numerous chiasmata delays them
relative to A, B, C and D. The numbers of total and terminal
chiasmata are given under each bivalent. The chromatids are
jointly coiled in pairs at metaphase, separately at anaphase.
Centromeres are shown. (After Darlington, 1937*a*.)

At the beginning of the second metaphase the chromatids of
each chromosome lie wide apart, joined only by the still undivided centromere. Only just before anaphase do they somewhat
irregularly come together, touching perhaps only at the ends
or not at all. Anaphase of this division is thus seen to be deter-

[1] Dowrick, 1953.

c

mined directly by the division of the centromeres; contact of the
bodies of the chromosomes is superfluous. This process shows
what is mechanically necessary in mitosis and what is not. The
centromere is the sole internal agent in separating the chromosomes at anaphase (Fig. 4).

The first important consequence of these two divisions is the
reduction of the chromosome number from the diploid to the
haploid, which owing to the segregation of homologues includes
a member of each set. But these chromosomes are no longer the

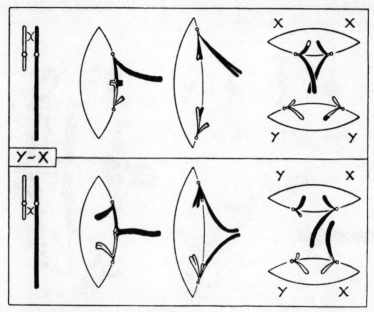

Fig. 6. Meiotic behaviour of a pair of chromosomes, X and Y,
where Y has lost a terminal segment present in X. Above, crossing-
over takes place between the centromeres and the equal ends.
Below, crossing-over takes place between the centromeres and the
inequality so that the first division is 'equational', the second
'reductional'. Note, all four chromosomes produced at second
telophase are different in origin in both cases. Cf. end papers.

unaltered parental chromosomes. They have recombined their
parts by crossing-over. Numerically the reduction is due neither
to the first nor to the second division of the nucleus, but to the
combination of the two with no division of the chromosomes
between them. Qualitatively the 'reduction' or separation of
the corresponding parts of the partner chromosomes occurs at

the first division or the second division according to the position of the segment. Obviously the separation of the parental centromeres takes place at the first division. The same applies to the parts between the centromeres and the chiasmata nearest to them. On the far side of the nearest chiasma the second division is reductional. Beyond a second chiasma the time of reduction depends on the relations of the different crossings-over between chromatids at the two chiasmata (Fig. 5).

In certain fungi spores are produced after meiosis in which the two divisions have spindles in the same axis and are followed by mitoses also in the same axis. The spores are therefore in rows of eight which are in fact four pairs. They sometimes show immediately the action of genes whose alleles segregated at meiosis: for example in *Bombardia* pigmented and colourless spores regularly occur in equal numbers in each set. These may be in the following types of order (using *A* or *a* for the allele in each pair of spores):

1. *AAaa* or *aaAA*
2. *AaAa* or *aAaA*
3. *AaaA* or *aAAa*

It will be seen that the first kinds are such as would arise with first division segregation, the second and third with second division segregation. And the proportions of sets of the two kinds thus tell us how much crossing-over has taken place between the segregating gene and the centromere of its chromosome.

This method is now used in studying the linkage of genes in many fungi[2]: it enables us to map the position of the centromere as the gene which gives 100 per cent segregation at the first division of meiosis.

We have already seen that crossing-over is a condition of chromosome pairing and segregation at the first division. We now also see that it is the means of an even more profound change. For owing to crossing-over the unit of segregation is not the chromosome itself but a part of the chromosome. Owing to crossing-over, meiosis gives rise to four nuclei all different from one another in regard to the parental origin of every member of its haploid set of chromosomes. Furthermore,

[2] Catcheside, 1951.

owing to the positions of crossing-over differing for each bivalent in different mother cells, no two will give the same kinds of result in the recombination of differences between the parental chromosomes, provided of course that there are enough differences to be recombined. Sexual reproduction is thus a mechanism which secures the greatest variety of recombinations of genetic differences. This is its one universal and therefore presumably primary function. All others are optional: they must therefore be secondary and derived.

We must also notice that meiosis occurs in the same way in its mechanical and therefore genetical essentials in all sexually reproducing organisms. It is this cytological uniformity which explains why the principles of heredity, established separately in the reproduction of a few organisms, such as *Pisum* and *Zea Mays*, *Drosophila* and the mouse, confirm one another. And it is this uniformity which assures us that the same principles will equally apply to all sexually reproducing organisms even where, as in men or mules, experimental breeding is inconvenient or impossible.

Finally, we must notice that the invention of meiosis in previously mitotic organisms was the last critical step in the evolution of genetic systems, since it made sexual reproduction possible. Later we shall see from the ways in which it can be reversed how it must originally have come about.

6

CHANGE OF QUANTITY: POLYPLOIDY

CHROMOSOMES may divide without the nucleus dividing. As a rule this happens in the development of certain animal and plant tissues whose cells are not going to undergo any further mitosis. Such cells are in this way provided with double-powered or even higher-powered nuclei to do their work.[1] The same result can however arise in cells of the main reproductive stream, embryonic or meristematic cells which have an indefinite future of mitotic generations. In these later mitoses we then see the result. The diploid nucleus $(2x)$ has given rise to a tetraploid $(4x)$.

The abnormal failure of mitosis arises in nature in various ways from extreme temperatures, physical injury and so on. In experiment it is readily induced by treatment with drugs such as colchicine. These can be seen to stop the action of the centromeres in generating the spindle and in dividing. The metaphase chromosomes thus fail to divide and a single nucleus is re-formed.

The change from diploidy to tetraploidy is permanent and usually irreversible. All the descendants of the new cell are tetraploid and are usually as constant in number as the diploid. They constitute a new line of cells. And if they are in the germ-line they can constitute a new race or new species of plants or animals.

The cells of new tetraploids will under the best conditions be twice as large as corresponding diploid cells and will therefore develop giant tissues and giant organisms. This is generally true of the flowering plants. Organisms however seem to be adapted to a most favourable size, and if this adaptation is inflexible no increase in size but rather a reduction may follow the doubling of the chromosomes; this is true of some mosses and also of insects and amphibia.[2]

Doubling, or more properly a failure of reduction, may likewise occur at one of the two divisions of meiosis, especially where

[1] Geitler, 1953.   [2] Fankhauser, 1941.

pairing of chromosomes has abnormally failed. Instead of haploid gametes or a haploid generation, corresponding diploids appear. When the next fertilisation takes place, diploid and haploid nuclei fusing, a triploid $(3x)$ is produced (Fig. 6).

Triploids and tetraploids arise very frequently in nature and in experiment amongst both plants and animals. The different modes of reproduction in higher animals, usually with male and female individuals, and in higher plants, usually with herma-phroditism, however lead to opposite results. In animals, the general necessity of cross-fertilisation usually prevents an iso-lated tetraploid from leaving progeny, for it is usually sterile with its diploid relatives and a triploid itself is always infertile. New sexually reproducing species do not therefore readily arise from polyploidy in animals and less than a dozen clear ex-amples are known. In flowering plants on the other hand nearly half the species owe their origin to this change of

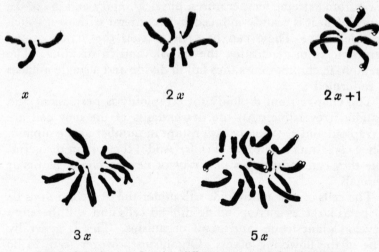

Fig. 7. Complements found in different spontaneously arising plants of *Crepis capillaris* $(x=3)$. Note the nucleolar constriction separating the small 'satellite' of one chromosome. (After Navashin, 1926, and Hollingshead, 1930.)

quantity. Wheat, oats, potatoes, plums and tobacco are poly-ploid in nature and in cultivation. They have four or six times the *basic number* of chromosomes, x, found in the gametes of their diploid relatives.

By making polyploid plants and animals which can be compared with diploid relatives differing only in multiplication of the nuclear contents, nature has given us ready made the largest conceivable experiment. And it is one which we can amplify without limit in controlled experiments. Its importance is twofold: in studying the activity and hence the physiology of the resting nucleus and its constituent genes, and in studying the movements and hence the mechanics of the chromosomes especially at meiosis.

The behaviour of polyploids at meiosis is significant in theory and in practice. Take first the *triploid*. It has three chromosomes of each type instead of two as in the diploid. When they pair during prophase only two chromosomes come together at any one point. The third is left out. As in the hidden reproduction, so also in the visible movement of chromosomes, attraction is limited to twos. Pairing it is, in a strict sense. Yet in another part of the chromosomes a different one of the three may be left out; they may change partners (Fig. 7). If then chiasmata are formed at different places between one chromosome and both the other two, the trivalent is maintained; all three are held together until metaphase. If, however, one has been left out in the original pairing, or having paired has failed to form chiasmata, it is left unpaired, a univalent, at metaphase while the other two behave like a normal bivalent. Since univalents can arise for either of these two reasons they are frequent in nearly all triploids. But they are most frequent where the chromosomes are shortest and have fewest chiasmata. This is particularly obvious where, as in *Hyacinthus*, there are long and short chromosomes in the same triploid complement.[3]

Just as during prophase no regular result can follow from the association of three chromosomes in pairs, so there can be no regular co-orientation of the three centromeres of a trivalent at metaphase or regular segregation of its members at anaphase. They come to lie in various ways according to the positions of their chiasmata in relation to their centromeres and the chance of their first moving under the influence of their repulsions on the spindle. These different ways may be classified as linear, convergent or indifferent. The *linear* arrangement (all in a row) is favoured if all three centromeres have chiasmata very close to

[3] Darlington and Mather, 1933.

them so that all three are held near together. The *convergent* arrangement (one repelling two opposite) is favoured where the centromeres are farther apart and equidistant, especially when the chiasmata are terminal. The *indifferent* arrangement with

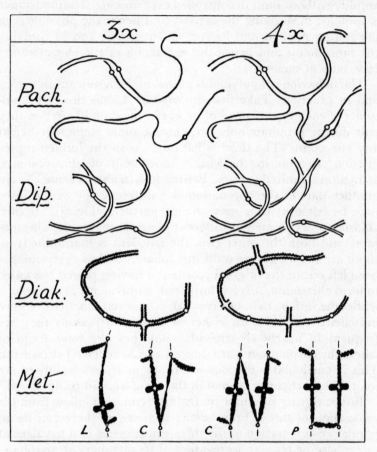

Fig. 8. The first meiotic division in triploids and tetraploids, showing the formation of trivalents and quadrivalents with linear, convergent and parallel co-orientations. The centromeres are represented by rings.

one showing no tension with either of the other two arises when this one is remote and the other two close together (Fig. 8).

Where the centromeres lie convergently, two chromosomes will pass to one pole and one to the other. Where they lie linearly or indifferently the equatorial one will be left on the plate and will behave at anaphase as a univalent. Its origin will still be recognisable, if it is large enough and has had an interstitial chiasma, by its chromatids; unlike those of a true univalent, they lie wide apart distal to this chiasma that is on the far side of the chiasma from the centromere.

Univalents, true or false, lying on the plate, divide after the bivalents have separated. Anaphase comes too early for them. They divide, as mitotic chromosomes do, by the division of their centromeres. But lagging behind the bivalents in this way they may fail to overtake them and be left outside the daughter nuclei. Indeed true univalents characteristically move on to the plate only at the end of metaphase or beginning of anaphase. They may even remain off the plate, on one side of it. They will then be included in the nucleus formed on that side.

At the second division we therefore have in each nucleus the normal double chromosomes together with some single chromosomes if univalents have successfully divided at the first division. Two chromosomes derived from one trivalent no longer show any connection. The normal chromosomes divide normally. The daughter univalents, unable to divide again, may again lag on the plate and are then often lost in the cytoplasm at telophase.

A triploid therefore gives reduced nuclei each containing a haploid set together with a random distribution of the extra set, each chromosome of which has half a chance of getting into one of the four nuclei—or rather less if some are lost. Thus a triploid hyacinth $(3x = 24)$ gives pollen grains with all numbers from 8 to 16. Some being lost, however, the modal frequency is 11 and not 12.

The properties of *tetraploids* can be predicted in some detail from those we have noted in triploids. The chromosomes pair two by two at pachytene. They occasionally change partners, and they then recall the shapes of diplotene bivalents. The same mechanical condition (an attraction in pairs) produces the same result at different stages of prophase in diploids and tetraploids. The nature of the homologous threads, chromatids or chromosomes, makes no difference to the attraction.

According to the possibilities afforded by the exchanges of partner and the formation of chiasmata in a limited frequency

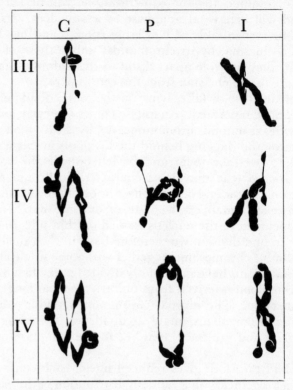

Fig. 9. Forms of trivalent and quadrivalent found in polyploid species of *Tulipa* with convergent, parallel and indifferent co-orientations. (From Upcott, 1939a.)

in different parts of the chromosomes, either one quadrivalent, two bivalents or rarely a trivalent and univalent are formed by any particular group of four chromosomes. Hence as in triploids the associations produced by any particular group are variable. In *Primula sinensis* where each bivalent of the diploid forms two or three chiasmata the tetraploid regularly forms *n* quadrivalents. In the mosquito *Culex* on the other hand where each bivalent has only one chiasma, exceptional tetraploid sperm mother cells rarely show quadrivalents: they simply have two sets of bivalents.

In a locust, *Schistocerca*, with similar tetraploid cells the longer chromosomes with two, three or four chiasmata form quadrivalents, while the shorter chromosomes with never more than one chiasma do not.[4]

Quadrivalents arrange themselves in linear, convergent or indifferent order like trivalents. But apart from these they may also lie with two pairs of centromeres parallel and, relative to one another, like two indifferent bivalents. Again the linear and indifferent configurations leave lagging 'univalents' on the plate: only the convergent and parallel ones have a regular segregation. A tetraploid under the ordinary conditions described is therefore incapable of forming uniform gametes with exactly two chromosome sets.

Where multivalent chromosomes are formed in meiosis, whether in triploids or tetraploids, the products of meiosis have variable numbers of chromosomes. And those which depart from the regular basic number or a multiple of it are at a disadvantage. The gametes and the zygotes they give rise to are said to be unbalanced and they are largely eliminated. The diploid and the tetraploid are therefore less fertile than their diploid parent; their progeny are less able to survive. This is the rule. Later we shall discover means by which the rule may sometimes be evaded.

[4] White, 1954.

7

CHANGE OF POSITION

i. *Structural Change*

THE chromosomes, as we have seen, are linear arrangements of particles which correspond with the linear arrangements of genes inferred from breeding experiments and, like them, are constant and permanent. This is the material and structural basis of heredity. We now have to consider the material and structural basis of variation.

All chromosomes are liable to undergo changes in their potentially permanent linear structure. Crossing-over is of course such a change. But it is recurrent and predictable. It recombines what is there already; it produces nothing beyond this. But the mechanism is significant. Two threads break, and their broken ends rejoin in a new combination.

The chromosomes of all plants and animals in nature suffer accidents from time to time which change their linear structure. These accidents are known as structural changes. They take place by breakage followed by reunion of the broken ends in a different way. The breakages however are not in pairs at corresponding places in homologous chromosomes paired at pachytene. On the contrary they are usually in the resting nucleus and hence at random in number and position. The reunions are also at random and hence altogether new chromosomes are formed with new linear arrangements of their materials.

Structural changes can be induced to take place much more frequently by X-ray treatment. Comparison of the results shows what happens when the chromosomes break. During the resting stage the chromosomes, except at their free ends, are still under a coiling stress. If one breaks the ends must fly apart and are not likely to rejoin again. If two break, or one breaks at two places, the different ends are therefore able to rejoin in a new combination.

A single break without rejoining divides the chromosome into

32

two parts and leads to the loss or *deficiency* of the broken part without a centromere, the *acentric* fragment. A double break and rejoining within a chromosome leads either to *inversion* of the segment between the breaks or its *deletion* from the chromosome, again as an acentric fragment (or ring if its ends join up).

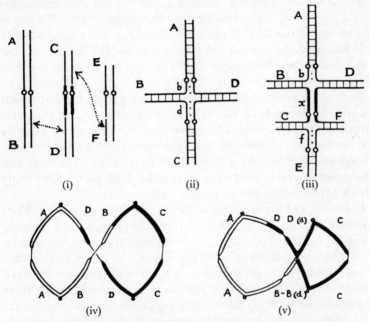

Fig. 10. The results of interchange hybridity. (i) Three pairs of chromosomes between which two interchanges occur. (ii) and (iii) The pachytene configurations of four and six chromosomes produced by one and two interchanges: *x*, differential segment; *b*, *d*, and *f*, interstitial segments. The cross-lines show the parts of the chromosomes between which crossing-over can take place without giving inviable combinations (i.e. not *b*, *d*, *f*, or *x*). (iv) Convergent co-orientation in a ring of four produced by terminalisation of four chiasmata from (ii). (v) Formation of a chiasma in the *d* segment in addition. (After Darlington, 1937*a*.)

Two breaks in different chromosomes, with rejoining, lead to *interchange*, which may give two new normally constructed chromosomes or, if the rejoining is the wrong way round, to one *dicentric* chromosome and one acentric chromosome. The two chromosomes concerned may be homologous or not, the breakages and recombinations taking place, it seems, largely according to the chances of position (Fig. 10).

The effects of these changes at the following mitosis have been seen chiefly in plants and animals treated with X-rays or by other special agents, since only then do they occur with measurable frequency. We then find that they may take place either before or after the chromosomes have divided during the resting stage. If before, then the changes apply to both the chromatids of each affected chromosome in the same way. We have 'chromosome breaks'. If after division, then the changes apply only to single chromatids. We have 'chromatid breaks'. These occur only when treatment has been applied towards the end of the resting stage.[1]

Another consequence of structural changes that is important genetically depends on the behaviour of acentric and dicentric chromosomes. Acentric chromosomes, like univalents at early first metaphase of meiosis, are entirely passive and are nearly always lost at anaphase. They never develop new centromeres. The centromere is evidently a specific and permanent body which cannot arise from anything else.

Dicentric chromosomes also have something to tell us. They divide in various ways. Their two centromeres, unlike the non-dividing centromeres of a bivalent, orientate independently. Evidently there is an *auto*-orientation of the centromere which is correlated with preparation for division and prevents *co*-orientation in pairs. Now, if the two chromatids between them lie parallel no harm is done. The two centromeres pass to each pole with a loop chromatid between them. If, on the other hand, the chromatids make half a coil between the centromeres they are pulled out diagonally to make a cross, and unless they are very long they are likely to break under the anaphase tension. What happens to the broken ends? Two of them pass into each daughter nucleus. Invariably, or almost invariably, these ends find one another at telophase and reunite to re-form the dicentric. In this way dicentrics have been known to perpetuate themselves, slightly varying in the length of the intercalary segment, year after year.[2]

When they come to meiosis however a new obstacle arises which dicentrics cannot easily overcome. Their two centromeres are then liable at first metaphase to become co-orientated and therefore break the chromosome at anaphase: non-homo-

[1] Darlington and La Cour, 1945.   [2] Hair, 1953.

logous arms go to opposite poles and that is the end of the dicentric chromosome.

It follows that the majority of structural changes damage the chromosomes that suffer them and are not therefore likely to survive. Those we find in nature are the ones that have survived and they correspond with types expected from experiment: inversion, interchange and one more complicated type, removal or *translocation* of an interstitial segment from one position and its insertion in another position in the same or a different chromosome. This last change is less common because it requires three breaks. But, by recombination, translocation will give secondary changes, duplications and deficiencies, which have the important effect of changing the balance of the whole chromosome set.

ii. *Polytene Evidence*

Apart from a large translocation or a grossly asymmetrical interchange, the results of structural changes cannot be seen from the shapes of the ordinary mitotic chromosomes. They are, however, characteristically shown by the chromosomes at pachytene in organisms that are hybrid for them—containing unchanged chromosomes and their changed homologues paired in their homologous parts. We then have a fold formed for a deletion, a loop for an inversion, a cross for an interchange, and more complicated configurations for more complicated changes (Figs. 10 and 11).

These arrangements are exactly mimicked in salivary and other gland cells in the dipteran flies.

The nuclei of these cells are polyploid and of the kind that will never divide again. They have multiplied many times and the chromosome threads which are said to be *polytene* are stretched out to an exaggerated extent to reveal a pattern of chromomeres like that in the pachytene stage of meiosis. Each chromomere being represented 16, 32 or more times forms a band in a ribbon which may be 250 μ or a quarter of a milli-metre long. Attraction like reproduction is without limit: homologous bundles pair as single threads do in meiosis. In hybrids the polytene nuclei with their paired chromosomes reveal configurations of the same kinds as at pachytene. And although the cells have no genetic future, they provide the key to what is happening at meiosis in flies where the actual pachytene stages are beyond the reach of vision. They provide also the means by which gene arrangement can be compared in

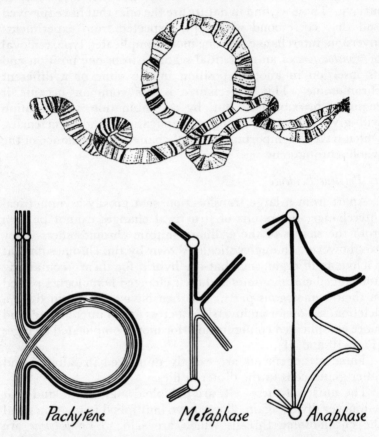

Fig. 11. Above, formation of a loop by pairing of two relatively inverted segments in the salivary gland cells of the cross of *Drosophila melanogaster* and *D. simulans* (Pätau, 1935). Below, the consequences of single crossing-over at meiosis in such an inversion hybrid with the formation of a dicentric bridge and an acentric fragment.

related individuals or species. The chromomere bands are so large that every group of them is characteristic and recognisable. The whole natural conditions of variation in chromosome structure are diagrammatically exposed to view (Fig. 11).

iii. *Interchange Hybrids*

Let us now return to consider the consequences of these systems of pairing at meiosis in the hybrid. An interchange hybrid will have an association of four at pachytene (*AB–BC–CD–DA*, Fig. 10). When crossing-over takes place in all four pairs of segments of the interchange hybrid an association of four chromosomes is formed at diplotene which gives, with complete terminalisation, a ring at metaphase. If crossing-over takes place between three of them a chain of four is formed. These associations behave just like mechanically similar associations in a tetraploid. The difference in genetic content and in the genetic consequences of their movements has no effect on the movements themselves. We find the same linear, convergent, indifferent and parallel co-orientations. With complete terminalisation the convergent arrangement is the commonest. It alone can give genetically complete haploid combinations (*AB* and *CD* or *BC* and *DA*). These alone can survive; the others are defective and come to nothing. If crossing-over fails between the interchanged segments, as it does when they are short, two bivalents, *AB–BC* and *CD–DA*, will be formed. Segregating at random they will give the *competent* combinations in half the cells and incompetent ones (*AB* and *DA* or *BC* and *CD*) in the other half.

There is a third method by which interchange hybrids give defective gametes. If crossing-over takes place between the centromeres and the point of interchange (*b* and *d* in Fig. 10 (ii)) any orientation gives a regular separation and a competent combination for only two of the four chromatids at the chiasma. Half the effects of crossing-over in these interstitial segments are done away with: half the spores or gametes die.

Moreover if another interchange takes place to give a ring of six at meiosis another kind of segment is created (*x* in Fig. 10 (iii)). Crossing-over in this *differential* segment will also reduce the competent combinations to half. But those that survive are found to have suffered reverse interchange and the selfed progeny arising in this way have a ring of four instead of a ring of six.

Abnormalities thus result from three causes: from the interchanged segments being too short to have crossing-over, from

D

the segments proximal to them being long enough to have crossing-over, and from the chiasmata resulting from crossing-over not being terminalised. Such are the causes of sterility in interchange hybrids such as those in *Pisum sativum*.[3]

iv. *Inversion Hybrids*

The inversion hybrid tells an altogether different story. Crossing-over between the relatively inverted segments (if they do not include the centromere) produces two new chromatids, one dicentric, the other acentric. At first anaphase the dicentric chromatid is stretched across the spindle, forming a bridge between the two groups of separating chromosomes, and the acentric chromatid is left passive on the plate. In a grasshopper, where the telophase nuclei are widely separated, the bridge is usually broken near the middle; in a plant, unless the bridge is short, it survives and can still be seen joining the second division metaphase plates. When, as in the eggs of *Drosophila* or the embryo-sac mother cells of a plant, the four nuclei that are formed at meiosis lie in a row instead of in a square, the two free arms joined to the dicentric chromatid pass to the inside two of the four cells. Since the end nucleus alone usually functions as the egg or spore nucleus, these do not show the results of crossing-over in an inversion so readily as the male nuclei, which are taken from all four products of meiosis.[4]

One crossing-over prevents another near it but two crossings-over can take place in a long inversion. The results depend on whether the same or a different pair of chromatids are concerned in the two. If the same, one will compensate for the other: their chiasmata will be reciprocal, normal chromatids will be restored and no abnormality will be visible at anaphase. If a new pair cross over, complementary chiasmata will be formed. A double bridge and two fragments will be seen at anaphase. It can also happen that one chromatid crosses over with two different chromatids to give two disparate chiasmata. These will again leave a single bridge and fragment.

When in addition the dicentric chromatid crosses over proximal to the inversion, that is, between it and the centromere, a loop chromatid can be formed returning to the centromere from which it came. This leaves a fragment at the first anaphase and

[3] Sansome, 1933.   [4] Darlington and La Cour, 1941.

forms a bridge at the second.[5] The statistical study of the frequencies of these different kinds of bridge formation therefore enables us to say what relationships exist between the successive crossings over. Sometimes the chromatids that have crossed over at one chiasma are more likely, sometimes less likely, to cross over at the next chiasma. The same properties are indicated by linkage studies in *Drosophila* and in the fungus *Neurospora*.

It will be seen that crossing-over in short inversions is likely to be disastrous to the chromatids that have crossed over. They inevitably lose their ends in the acentric fragment, and they may lose more in the breakage of the bridge. We must therefore make a distinction between real and *effective* crossing-over. Crossing-over may occur very frequently in inversions, but since its effect is so drastic its product will be either a drastic hereditary change or more usually it will come to nothing; the changed cells will die. With inversion hybrids, as with interchange hybrids, crossing-over is effectively suppressed not in whole chromosomes but in certain regions of the chromosomes. It is suppressed *within* an inversion but *proximal* to an interchange. And an index of its suppression in both cases is usually the reduction in fertility of the products of meiosis.

A larger issue than crossing over *within* chromosomes, namely recombination *between* chromosomes, is affected by structural hybridity. The chromosomes within a ring-of-four or ring-of-six can no longer be independently re-assorted like the partners in separate bivalents.

How this restriction is exploited in nature we shall later be able to consider. Meanwhile let us note that all structural changes from the moment of their origin are liable to be eliminated. Some survive mitosis; others do not. Some survive meiosis; others do not. Some survive in hybrids; others do not. The difference between those that succeed and contribute to evolutionary change and those that fail and disappear depends on the character of the changes. They are thus subject to *natural selection*. As we observe in turn the different elements of variation we shall also be observing the different ways in which natural selection works.

[5] Richardson, 1936.

8

HYBRIDS: DIPLOID AND POLYPLOID

i. *Meiosis in Hybrids*

SPECIFIC kinds of hybridity we now know have specific effects at meiosis. Can we use this knowledge to find out how the parents of hybrids are related? In the simplest cases we can. Most plants and animals that are not strictly inbred are hybrid for several structural changes, usually inversions or interchanges. Crosses between species are usually even more hybrid. In extreme cases their behaviour leads to a new kind of result.

Occasionally two relatively inverted homologous segments, especially if they are short, instead of pairing in a loop, pair the wrong way round so as to continue the straight double thread on either side of them. Non-homologous genes therefore lie side by side and no crossing-over takes place within the inversion. In a similar way pairing may slip past a point of interchange where the exchange of partners should take place, the *AA* and *CC* systems of pairing extending at the expense of the *BB* and *DD* (Fig. 10 (ii)). Again non-homologous genes associate. This kind of aberration demonstrates an important principle. We saw that the partner chromosomes coiled round one another at pachytene. To do so they must develop a torsion. A piece of string under torsion will, if its ends are brought together, pair with itself. The association is due to torsion, not attraction. In a non-hybrid both forces work together to the same end. In a hybrid they are alternative, and where obstacles lie in the way of satisfying the homologous attraction the non-specific torsion draws dissimilar parts of the chromosomes together.

It is clear that the obstacles to correct pairing become greater where the differences are most numerous. This is shown most clearly, although indirectly, by the chromosome behaviour in the salivary glands of some *Drosophila* species. In *D. melanogaster* × *D. simulans* the differences are few and simple (Fig. 11). In *D. miranda* × *D. pseudo-obscura*, on the other hand, so many

40

changes in arrangement have taken place that corresponding segments are scattered in different chromosomes and sometimes cannot be traced. The chromosomes in many cells entirely fail to pair. At pachytene they would probably pair at certain points and non-homologous torsion pairing would extend from these points. However this might be, very little crossing-over could take place; the chromosomes forming no chiasmata would be unpaired at metaphase. These crosses are highly sterile in both sexes.[1]

Such indeed is the characteristic behaviour in crosses between species. The pairing of the chromosomes is more or less incomplete at metaphase. It is also variable from cell to cell on account of variations both in the amount of true pachytene pairing and in the frequency of crossing-over in the paired parts. Thus while the chromosomes of *Allium fistulosum* or *A. Cepa* form one, two or three chiasmata, those of their hybrid range from none to three; about a quarter of the chromosomes form no chiasmata and are therefore univalent at metaphase (Fig. 21). At one extreme, in the cross between *Brassica oleracea* and *Raphanus sativus*, bivalents are rarely formed, while at the other, in the cross between *Festuca pratensis* and *Lolium perenne*, the chiasma frequency is scarcely reduced and the failure of pairing is as rare as it is in the parent species. These contrasts in crosses between pairs of species with the same chromosome number show that the genetic differences underlying the distinctions between these pairs are different in kind, in degree, or in their distribution relative to chiasma formation.

When crosses between species having an intermediate degree of abnormality are examined in detail the cause of the contrast is made clear. In *Lilium* hybrids the frequency of chiasma formation is reduced. And such chiasmata as are formed are largely between inversions. Inversions are known to impair the association at pachytene just as they do in the salivary glands. It is they therefore that reduce the frequency of chiasmata. The extent to which pairing fails is a measure of structural hybridity. Evidently the genetic differentiation between *Brassica* and *Raphanus* has been accompanied by structural changes in the chromosomes, that between *Festuca* and *Lolium* has not.

Since crossing-over is a condition of metaphase pairing the

[1] Dobzhansky, 1938.

numbers of chiasmata in the bivalents are always greater, in different individuals or different cells of the same individual, where there is a larger proportion of bivalents formed (e.g. in *Triticum* crosses and in a maize mutant with defective pairing).[2] Where the chiasma frequency and metaphase pairing are greatly reduced, the distribution of chiasmata shows the effects of torsion pairing. Pairing begins in one part of the chromosomes, usually the ends, between homologous parts, and is continued by torsion elsewhere. Chiasmata are thus restricted to the ends in many hybrids such as those between *Triticum* and *Aegilops*. Any restriction of pairing also (for a reason we shall see later) causes a localisation of pairing and of crossing-over (cf. Fig. 21).

ii. *Polyploidy and Fertility*

In these ways the behaviour of the chromosomes at meiosis in hybrids helps us to understand the normal course of meiosis. But it also helps us to understand the special properties of the hybrids.

Where almost all the chromosomes appear at metaphase as univalents the normal course of meiosis is entirely upset in one of three general ways. The simplest is that found only in certain moth hybrids (e.g. *Pygaera pigra* × *P. curtula*) where two effectively mitotic divisions replace meiosis. The chromosomes, all univalent, divide at both. A second type is that where all the univalents divide at the first division and two nuclei are formed which fail to divide again. A third type is that where the first division instead of the second fails. The chromosomes fail to come on to the first division plate. The spindle stretches as it would at a normal anaphase but instead of separating two equal groups it merely disperses one scattered group. Consequently one or several nuclei may be reconstituted. If one, then it divides to produce two equal nuclei at the second division. If several, then many nuclei with different and defective numbers of chromosomes are formed.

All intergrades occur between these last two types in plants, and they show that the difference between them is a simple one. Where the change in the centromeres of the univalents which enables them to orientate and divide takes place early enough

[2] Beadle, 1933*a*.

in relation to the development of the first division spindle this first division is successful and the second is suppressed. Where the centromeres are too late the first division is suppressed. This difference between different organisms in the timing of the centromeres of univalents is found when there are only a few of them. When nearly all the chromosomes are univalent it dominates the conduct of division.

When most of the chromosomes are unpaired a regular result of meiosis can thus ensue from its failure as a process of reduction and its replacement by one or two mitoses. This *non-reduction* is a characteristic consequence of non-pairing in hybrids. Non-reduction results in the formation of diploid gametes. These are fertile and yield polyploid offspring, triploid if in one gamete, tetraploid if in both. Hence hybrid or *allo-polyploids* are produced, as opposed to the *auto-polyploids* arising from non-hybrid diploids. The same result will follow failure of mitosis in a hybrid. Take the simplest instance, that of the *Raphano-Brassica* hybrid ($x=9$). The whole 18 chromosomes usually appear as univalents at meiosis, and the effective pollen grains and egg cells have this whole complement. Thus the diploid hybrid with two sets of chromosomes, *RB*, produces gametes *RB* from which offspring *RRBB* ($4x$) arise. At meiosis the *Raphanus* chromosomes pair with their identical mates and likewise the *Brassica*. Eighteen bivalents are formed, meiosis is regular and its products numerically and genetically uniform. The hybrid is giant; it is also fertile and true breeding as we should expect. It is functionally diploid (Fig. 28).

The behaviour of *Primula kewensis* is different and specially significant. The diploid hybrid is a cross between two species, *P. floribunda* and *P. verticillata*, each with 9 bivalents. The hybrid likewise has regular pairing, but if the members of each pair are different in only one segment the chance of recovering a complete and perfect set of one species amongst the gametes of the hybrid would be $1/2^8$. And this recovery would be necessary if translocations had taken place between all the chromosomes since their common origin.

An important distinction arises at this point. Both these hybrids are sterile. But the sterility of diploid *Raphano-Brassica* is due to the irregular distribution of whole chromosomes while that of diploid *Primula kewensis* is due to the irregular distribution of their parts entailed by the perfectly regular distribution of the whole chromosomes themselves.

P. kewensis however produces tetraploid shoots by failure of mitosis, and like the tetraploid seedlings of *Raphano-Brassica* these are giant and fertile. But they are not absolutely true breeding. As we should expect, the chromosomes of opposite diploid parents occasionally pair as well as the identical mates from the same species. Cells sometimes have one, two or even three quadrivalents. Thus while usually the tetraploid *FFVV* gives gametes *FV*, occasionally it gives gametes *FF* or *VV* in regard to one or two of the nine chromosomes in the set; or, if we take crossing-over into consideration, in regard to parts of one or two chromosomes. Thus an allopolyploid like *Primula kewensis* with imperfect differentiation of its chromosome sets characteristically shows a new type of variation arising from the segregation of differences between the chromosomes of its original diploid ancestors. And the diploid ancestors of an allopolyploid species may be very remote.[3]

Now, it may be asked, how can the chromosomes of *verticillata* so generally fail to pair with those of *floribunda* in the tetraploid although they pair regularly in the diploid? We saw that in many diploid hybrids the chromosomes pair regularly at metaphase in spite of obstacles to complete pairing at pachytene. We also saw that pachytene pairing must be much more rapid where there are no such obstacles. When therefore there are four chromosomes of each kind capable of pairing, two somewhat different in structure from the other two, we should expect the similar pairs to be so quickly associated that the dissimilar pairs would come together only occasionally. When chiasmata come to be formed the discrepancy is likely to be exaggerated, very small segments falling apart without chiasma formation. Thus *competition* in pairing will give rise to what may be described as *differential affinity*. Dissimilar pairs of chromosomes that are capable of association in a diploid, where there is no competition, will fail to associate in a tetraploid, where each has an identical mate.

The consequences of competition are shown in the analysis of polyploids as well as in their synthesis. Most flowering plants can give rise occasionally to seedlings by 'haploid' partheno-

[3] Upcott, 1939a.

genesis. That is to say the egg cell with a reduced number of chromosomes develops directly without fertilisation. An allo-tetraploid *Nicotiana Tabacum* which regularly forms $2x$ bivalents and no quadrivalents gives rise in this way to a diploid which has several bivalents. Chromosomes pair in this diploid in the absence of competition although they never pair in the tetraploid. The hexaploid *Solanum nigrum* $(6x = 72)$ with no multivalents gives by parthenogenesis a triploid $(3x = 36)$ which has complete pairing of two sets of chromosomes. Similarly it often happens that two species, hexaploid and diploid, like *Prunus cerasifera* $(2x = 16)$ and *P. domestica* $(6x = 48)$ crossed give a hybrid which behaves like a regular allotetraploid species, forming the diploid number of bivalents.

It is not surprising therefore that allopolyploid species are liable to occasional lapses from their excellent diploid behaviour. Chromosomes of different sets pair and cross over, secondary segregation of ancestral diploid character takes place and a new kind of variation appears. This is most frequent in relatively new polyploids like *Nicotiana Tabacum* and *Triticum vulgare* and leads to a different variation system from that of diploid species.

iii. *Evolution of Polyploids: Polynemy*

The kinds of polyploid species of plants illustrate in several ways the processes of natural selection to which their variations have been subject. Most such species are allopolyploid. A few are autopolyploids, and they often occur side by side with their diploid ancestors. These autopolyploids are of two kinds. They may depend largely on vegetative reproduction, in which case the lower fertility of the original autopolyploid is of little account. This is true in moderate degree of tetraploids like *Tradescantia virginiana* and in an extreme degree of triploids like *Lilium tigrinum* which exist purely as vegetative clones. Alternatively they may change the pairing habit of their chromosomes. The number of chiasmata may be reduced to one for each chromosome so that no quadrivalents can be formed. This happens to a varying extent with the tetraploid species of *Tulipa*.[4] The same result can be attained in another way. The specias *Dahlia variabilis* $(8x = 64)$ is functionally an autotetra-

[4] Upcott, 1939*b*.

ploid. That is to say it has random segregation of genes in fours and forms frequent quadrivalents. Nevertheless meiosis regularly yields 32-chromosome gametes. This is made possible by the regular formation of one chiasma in every chromosome arm and its regular terminalisation. The quadrivalents are therefore always rings and these co-orientate convergently to give even segregation.[5] Thus reproduction from seed means inevitably selection for fertility and this is achieved in an autopolyploid by abolishing or controlling multiple pairing. How common this type of selection may be in plants with smaller chromosomes we do not yet know.

Both in auto- and allopolyploid forms selection also apparently acts to remove the original gigantism, partly or entirely, polyploid species may be even smaller than their diploid ancestors. In *Silene ciliata* two similar types exist in different localities, one with 24, the other with 192 chromosomes. In such species important genetic changes must be necessary for the behaviour in polyploid cells to be adapted to the reproductive needs of the plant. The absence of polyploidy in certain groups of plants, such as *Ribes*, is less likely to be due to a failure to produce polyploid shoots or to a regular perfection of meiosis than to the failure of these genetic adaptations.

One kind of adaptation which can occur and, in organisms with large chromosomes evidently has to occur, is a reduction of chromosome size. All species of plants and animals have a standard size of chromosome in each tissue and this standard size is usually maintained through most or even the whole of development. In polyploid plants and animals this standard size is often smaller than it is in their diploid relatives. Whether it is smaller than it was in their immediate diploid ancestors does not matter. The point is that polyploidy has been possible only in those species or races of *Narcissus* or *Tulipa* or *Mantis* which have the smaller chromosomes.

How does this reduction of chromosome size come about? By X-ray treatment of root-tips it has been possible to induce mitoses showing chromosomes of a reduced size. Among seedlings of the same parent plant of *Lolium perenne* evidence of an even greater change has been found: a range of size of perhaps 1 : 16 (Fig. 12). In the course of differentiation of one

[5] Lawrence, 1931.

individual changes in chromosome size may also occur. This is true of normal differentiation in many plants. In the regeneration of rat liver a fivefold halving (to 1/32) seems to be possible. Evidently prophase can be brought on before the chromosomes have reproduced: chromatids are then formed with half the proper number of nucleo-protein units in their structure.

These changes show us one of many adaptations that must be supposed to underlie and condition the evolution of polyploidy. They also show us something of the physico-chemical

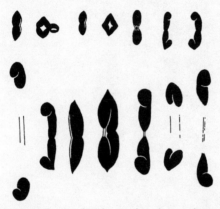

Fig. 12. First metaphase and early anaphase in two sister seedlings of *Lolium perenne* ($n=7$) to show the size difference. $\times 1700$. (Thomas, 1936.)

properties of the materials underlying all chromosome structure. The ultimate nucleoprotein thread of which the chromosome consists must often, or always, be a multiple thread: the chromosome is *polynemic*. And a halving of the polynemic thread may compensate physiologically and mechanically for a doubling of the complement in polyploidy. Several interesting physiological questions arise with regard to the relations of polyploidy and polynemy, one of which may be mentioned.

Consider the relative sizes of growth of haploids, diploids and polyploids. Where a haploid or polyploid arises from diploid ancestors, through an error in reproduction, it is different from the diploid, smaller or larger. But where it is a regular part of the sexual cycle it can be adjusted to precisely the same size.

Haploidy and diploidy then have no differential effect on growth. In some red and brown algae the two phases can have the same type of growth. They are said to be isomorphic. Similarly in the Hymenoptera the males which are normally haploid need be no smaller than the diploid females. And when a male turns out to be diploid (owing to a breakdown in its system of sex determination) it is no bigger than a haploid. The genes can be adjusted or *compensated* to produce the same effect in double dose as in single dose. Is this done by a change of polynemy? We do not know.

9

CHANGE OF PROPORTION

i. *Differentiation and Specificity*

FAILURE of pairing of two chromosomes is found at meiosis in most diploid plants and animals from time to time owing to one or more of several conditions such as senility, abnormal temperature, hybridity and even a mutant genotype. Hence germ cells arise with one chromosome too many or too few. In the higher plants where the haploid generation goes through several cell divisions those cells with a chromosome missing from the haploid set never go any further. They die. Those with the extra chromosome live, and often provide functional gametes, especially on the female side where the haploid generation is less important. This difference of behaviour may be seen most readily in species of *Oenothera*, where $x + 1$ and $x - 1$ germ cells are regularly produced. They give rise to many trisomic offspring $(2x + 1)$ but to no *monosomics* $(2x - 1)$.

This natural selection tells us that the whole haploid set is necessary for life and development in any diploid organism. It is necessary in a double dose or at least in a balanced dose. Accordingly the haploid set may be defined as that group of chromosomes which is necessary for the full development of the haploid generation or when added to another similar set is necessary for the full development of the diploid generation. Clearly this is almost bound to be so, for any chromosomes that can be lost without disadvantage from the haploid set are bound to be lost by chance irregularities sooner or later. The haploid set is an adaptive unit. And selection works at once on the newly formed pollen grains. Only twice has an $x - 1$ pollen grain been seen to go through its first mitosis and in one of these (in *Uvularia*) it was still exceptionally attached to a complementary $x + 1$ pollen grain.

We should expect, in view of this defect of the $x - 1$ germ cells, to find that $2x - 1$ zygotes are never produced. This is true except where the missing chromosome is extremely small, as happens in some species of *Drosophila*; or where competition is eliminated, as by killing the normal germ cells with X-rays in *Zea Mays*. Nor is it surprising to find that such zygotes are of feebler growth than the straightforward diploids. It is, however, something new and significant when we find that the complementary type of trisomic plants and animals are also of feebler growth; and further that each of the different chromosomes of the haploid set when it is present in excess gives a different type of abnormality. In the tomato (*Solanum Lycopersicum*) with twelve pairs of chromosomes, twelve kinds of trisomic occur, recognisably different in the shape of their leaves.[1]

When we recall chromosome behaviour at meiosis we see however that this specific and different physiological action of each chromosome is not in fact an isolated property: every member of the haploid set has a specific and therefore a different property of attracting a mate at meiosis. The physiological differentiation of the chromosomes could have arisen in a sexually reproducing organism only if it was coupled with a mechanism securing the segregation of similar chromosomes to opposite poles in meiosis. And both must depend on the specific and different properties of the individual particles which make up the chromosome thread and which associate independently at pachytene in polyploids, as the changes of partner they undergo most clearly demonstrate.

These considerations lead us further. If the differences between the chromosomes depend on differences between the chromomeres which make them up, perhaps losses and gains of single chromomeres will also produce a physiological effect. There are now a large number of observations bearing on this question in *Drosophila*. We find that losses of certain chromomeres are almost as injurious to the organism as losses of whole chromosomes. When the deficient zygote produced is hybrid for the loss (corresponding to $2x - 1$) it is of poorer and abnormal growth. When it is pure for the loss (corresponding to $2x - 2$) it dies at any early stage. The condition is lethal. In plants such deficiencies affect the haploid generation as well. In *Zea* they kill the pollen and injure the eggs.[2]

Now it will be seen that loss of a chromomere or a small seg-

---

[1] Rick and Barton, 1954.   [2] Rhoades and McClintock, 1935.

ment of chromosome, which we earlier referred to as deletion, will behave in inheritance like one of Mendel's alternative elements. The pure form is lethal while the hybrid crossed with the normal will give a 1 : 1 proportion of the hybrid and pure types in the progeny. Several different mutations of *Drosophila*, such as 'notch' wings, are known to be due to this kind of change. The gap can be seen in one of the pairing chromosomes in the salivary glands of the hybrid just as it can be seen in the pachytene chromosomes of *Zea* at the place expected from study of the gene linkages in breeding experiments.

ii. *Heterochromatin*

But all the different chromomeres are not equally indispensable. They are different in their work and also different in their importance. There are even some whose loss has no observable effect on the organism.

This dispensability can be most easily shown in such chromomeres when they occur in large blocks which may be recognised in the cell. They are then distinguished as *heterochromatin* by their different behaviour in resting nuclei from the normal segments which are known as *euchromatin*. Heterochromatic segments remain condensed and heavily staining in resting nuclei.[3]

In plants and animals with large chromosomes heterochromatin can often be distinguished not only in the resting nucleus but also at metaphase. To do so we have to bring cells into mitosis at freezing point. They are then starved of nucleic acid at metaphase and thinner than the euchromatic segments.[4] In polytene nuclei of *Drosophila* the segments of heterochromatin show yet a third special kind of behaviour. They are dispersed into very small chromomeres which fail to stick together in bands, and become almost invisible.

Not only have the heterochromatic segments in *Drosophila* little observable effect on the character of the fly. They contain no genes that reveal striking or major mutations. They have for this reason been described as *inert*. The term is convenient provided that we remember it refers only to the absence of violent and therefore specific effects. It is better to assume that they are active but less specific in their activities than those

[3] Heitz, 1935.   [4] Darlington and La Cour, 1940; Callan, 1942.

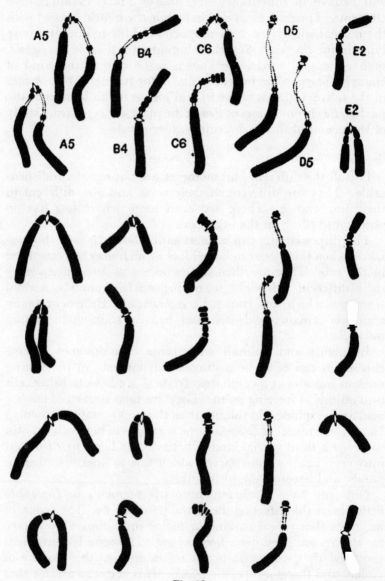

Fig. 13.

genes forming large chromomeres in the euchromatic segments.

Heterochromatin therefore seems to differ from euchromatin in its chemical structure, in its physiological activity and hence in its capacity for visible mutation. The distinction is genuine evidence of the qualitative differences between parts of chromosomes. In several plant genera, such as *Fritillaria*, there are however species with corresponding chromosomes, some of them with and some without heterochromatin. It is therefore evident that euchromatin can change into heterochromatin (or *vice versa*) in the course of evolution. How can this happen? There must be some collective control which can affect all the different properties of heterochromatin together in blocks. But we have as yet little experimental evidence of how this control takes effect.[5]

iii. *Inert Chromosomes*

Another kind of evidence of the nature and occurrence of relatively inert genes arises from the study of supernumeraries or B chromosomes as they are called in plants. These supernumeraries, which are often entirely heterochromatic chromosomes, have been found in many species of Hemiptera and Orthoptera as well as of flowering plants. They are not held to be members of the haploid set since they vary in number in different individuals, one, two, three or even 20 of a kind. They are usually smaller than any members of the normal complement. Such supernumerary chromosomes, occur in as many as five or ten per cent of species of flowering plants. We often find that they vary in number in different mitoses. The reason is that the centromeres of these chromosomes are not accurately

[5] La Cour, 1951; Darlington, 1957.

Fig. 13. Chromosomes of *Trillium hagae* at metaphase of mitosis in the root tip following nucleic acid starvation of the heterochromatin segments at a low temperature. The species is hexaploid with a set of five chromosomes labelled A to E $(x=5; 6x=30)$. It is derived from doubling in a cross between parents whose chromosomes are recognisable in the hybrid, *T. kamtschaticum* $(2n=10)$ in the top two rows and *T. tschonoskii* $(2n=20)$, in the bottom four rows. The plant is structurally homozygous, i.e. all chromosomes have identical mates. The numbers represent types of chromosomes in respect of which *T. kamtschaticum* is variable. Centromeres represented by diamonds, heterochromatin by constrictions or dotted threads. *Note:* there is as usual more heterochromatin in the diploid than in the tetraploid species.

× 1500   (from Haga, 1956.)

E

synchronised with those of the ordinary complement. They may divide too early or too late.

At meiosis supernumerary chromosomes do not pair or form chiasmata with the standard chromosomes. If they did they would reveal their relations and their origin. Moreover a moment's thought will show that crossing-over between the two types of chromosomes would in fact destroy the distinction between them.

How do these supernumeraries arise? Breakage of bridges following crossing-over in inversions is continually taking place in most organisms. If the centric fragment passes to the same pole as its unbroken sister and happens to be inert it will be capable of surviving as a supernumerary. Breakage of the centromere itself by *misdivision* at meiosis has been found to give rise to extra fragments in pollen of *Gasteria*, and this origin would account at the same time for the abnormal centromeres of supernumeraries.[6]

The plants with this enormous excess of non-specific chromosomes show no external abnormality and the freedom with which they vary in number shows that no selection is working against them. On the contrary selection of some kind must be working for them. But clearly it is of a kind which escapes the definition we gave of a haploid complement. Here are chromosomes which confer no unconditional advantage or disadvantage on any specific organism. What then do they do? We may suppose that they confer an advantage not on the individual but on the species, the advantage of variability.[7] Although they are sometimes euchromatic, sometimes heterochromatic, they always have the character of inertness. Or rather let us again say they are non-specific in their activities. This is a question to which we shall return.

iv. *Selection and the Complement*

Quite otherwise is the condition with extra active chromosomes. Often trisomic plants of poor growth will sport a shoot of normal and vigorous diploid tissue. Such a sport will soon dominate the situation and overwhelm the abnormal plant from which it was derived. Trisomic shoots appearing on diploid plants on the other hand are almost unknown, mono-

[6] Darlington and Keffalinou, 1957.   [7] Darlington, 1956a, b.

somic ones entirely so. The change is always in the reverse direction. Any irregularity in cell division is controlled by the regularity of *cell selection*.

Since somatic changes in number arise from widespread mechanical defects at mitosis it is evident that the different types of cells which arise from them compete in their growth. The normal is then nearly always selected at the expense of the abnormal by a departure from the strict rules of development expected in a genetically uniform tissue. The result of this is shown most strikingly by high polyploid mosses and flowering plants with odd chromosomes beyond a multiple of the basic set. These odd chromosomes are lost in development: the combination of mitotic errors and cell selection produces a genetic regulation of the plant.

If we set aside supernumerary or non-specific chromosomes we can lay down certain clear rules about the standard complement of specific chromosomes.

Thus a normal type of growth in all groups of organisms is produced by a modal chromosome constitution which is what we call haploid in the gamete and diploid in the zygote. Further this modal constitution is adaptive; it is actively maintained by selection and must therefore be continually modified and continually sustained by selection of variable combinations. This modal adaptation or adjustment is known as *balance*.

v. *Balance and Interaction*

The kind of physiological processes underlying the attainment of balance can be shown by considering the actions of particular genes having a definable chemical effect. *Dahlia variabilis* behaves as an autotetraploid in inheritance. Each gene can be present in none, one, two, three or four doses, none being the pure recessive, four the pure dominant. Take the combinations of two genes affecting pigment production, B and I, in plants which are recessive for the other variable pigment genes. The pigments concerned are the anthocyanins, pelargonin and cyanin, and a mixture of flavones. We have the combinations shown in Table 1.

We see that B and I, which separately or together in low dosage produce cyanin, in increased dosage produce pelargonin and at a certain threshold suppress the cyanin production altogether.

The reason for the relationship in this case is indicated by other evidence to be the development of the anthocyanins and flavones from sugars through a common antecedent, and the greater divergence of pelargonin than cyanin from this com-

GENE DOSAGE	i_4	I_2i_2	I_3i
b_4	— WHITE	*flavonal* + IVORY	*flavonal* + + IVORY
$B\ b_3$	cyanin — CHOCOLATE	cyanin *flavonal* + PURPLE	pelargonin and cyanin *flavonal* + + PALE PURPLE
B_2b_2	pelargonin — RED-CHOC.	pelargonin *flavonal* + CARMINE	pelargonin *flavonal* + + PURPLE

Table 1. Significant tetraploid combinations of two genes B and I in their five dosage states in *Dahlia variabilis* showing (above) the chief anthocyanins and the quantities of flavones produced and (below) the resultant colours of the petals under the best conditions of growth (from Lawrence and Scott Moncrieff, 1935, modified by Bate-Smith *et al.*, 1955).

Note: The extreme dosage states B_2, B_3 and B_4 are indistinguishable, likewise I_3 and I_4 and even i_3 and i_4. The bottom recessive combinations are, as often happens, of reduced viability.

For a new illuminating analysis of such reactions in *Antirrhinum* see Jorgensen and Geissman, 1955.

mon antecedent.[8] A change of quantity as well as a change of proportion leads to a change of quality in the product. Balance therefore depends on quantities of individual genes relative to other specific genes and also relative to the totality of genes.

Combined chemical and genetic studies of variations in the synthesis of plant pigments are supported by profound studies of variations in the nutrition of fungi, which also of course depends on synthesis. They show that synthesis proceeds in sequences which converge and diverge. Where one molecular step has two antecedents or precursors two genes may cooperate in producing one effect. Where two successors follow one precursor two genes may compete for this one precursor, or for the enzymatic activity of one gene.

[8] Robinson, 1936.

These varied actions are thus likely to condition one another subject also to variations in development and in the environment. The more detailed the variation at our disposal for experiment, the more complex the interactions, the more intricate the balance, we are able to infer.[9]

vi. *Change of Balance*

Most changes of balance due to gains or losses of whole chromosomes, or of small parts which behave as Mendelian changes, are deleterious simply because they have usually occurred before and would themselves have become the mode if they had not been deleterious. They have been tried in the past and found wanting. But changes in balance nevertheless have occurred in the past which were tried and found good. They have happened in the two possible ways, by structural change and by polyploidy.

When a small segment x is translocated from a chromosome A to a chromosome B a hybrid nucleus is produced with four chromosomes which we may call A^xB. AB^x. This will produce gametes A^xB^x as well as AB from which pure zygotes with four x segments will arise, $A^xA^xB^xB^x$. In a word the x segment has been *reduplicated*. The type is unbalanced in regard to a single segment. Such new types have arisen in *Drosophila melanogaster* where reduplication of a particular segment produces a narrow 'Bar' eye and a double reduplication a type of lower vigour with an even narrower eye known as 'Super-bar'. When the structure of the salivary gland chromosomes in different *Drosophila* species is examined, small *repeats* of similar sections are found, indicating that this kind of change has taken place freely in the past. Thus we cannot suppose that the haploid set contains one gene of every kind. It must contain only one gene of some kinds, but of others two, three, four, or more. On the other hand, since all genes are, as we believe, liable to mutate, two identical genes in different parts of the chromosomes are not likely to remain identical. They will evolve. They will diverge. They will become two slightly different genes. The evidence of this happening in diploids we shall see later. In polyploids corresponding genes of different sets will also evolve and diverge. The difference between diploid and

[9] *cf*. Beadle, 1945; Wagner & Mitchell, 1955.

polyploid species in regard to the numbers of chromosomes of each kind need not therefore be reflected in the numbers of genes of each kind.

The existence of reduplications and replacements within the haploid set of genes warns us of the dangers of two other apparently obvious assumptions. Many identical pairs of genes need not be Mendelian alternatives and many alternatives need not be identical or even closely related in origin. Alternative inheritance of genes depends physiologically on a property of mutual replaceability in the genotype. Mechanically however it depends not on the identity of the genes whose inheritance is being studied but on their linear sequence or, as we may say, on the identities of their neighbours. It is a function of position in the chromosome.

The consequences of reduplication are seen at meiosis in the flowering plants, where it often happens that two reduplicated segments within the same set cross over and form a chiasma. In haploid plants which often arise by the development of an egg without fertilisation it happens that two chromosomes or more often form chiasmata.[10] Again we see the definition of a haploid set is not a matter of absolute analysis but of functional convenience.

This leads us to consider whether changes in balance of chromosomes of the basic haploid set are not possible. Related species like *Crepis capillaris* ($n=3$) and *C. tectorum* ($n=4$) often have different basic numbers. But it is not necessary to suppose that any serious change of balance is involved in the change of number. Four chromosomes can be derived from three by a change akin to simple breakage. The fourth chromosome may begin as an inert supernumerary which afterwards by translocation of an active segment becomes a necessary part of the haploid complement. Since so many species are known with such supernumeraries, this method of changing the chromosome number of the basic set is probably the usual one.

vii. *Secondary Polyploidy*

A second method of change involves a change of balance and consists in the mere reduplication of whole extra chromosomes. In *Datura Stramonium* ($n=12$) trisomic plants produce among

[10] Catcheside, 1932.

their seedlings tetrasomics which have two extra chromosomes both of the same type. This happens only with a few of the smallest extra chromosomes. They can have 11 bivalents and one quadrivalent, or 13 bivalents. These plants being much more seriously unbalanced than the corresponding trisomics are of poor vitality and scarcely set seed. However when we begin with a tetraploid the unbalance produced by two extra chromosomes is not so violent. The proportional upset corresponds with that in a trisomic diploid. It is not surprising therefore that it has been possible to derive a new type in this way from an allotetraploid species, *Nicotiana Tabacum* $(4x=48)$. This new form is hexasomic, having an extra pair of chromosomes derived from crossing with *N. sylvestris*. One type of chromosome is represented six times and the other eleven four times. Its complete constitutional formula may be represented as $2n = 4x + 2 = 50$. It has a new or secondary basic number of 25, and its external appearance diverges from that of species with the old primary number of 12. Such a plant may be described as a *secondary polyploid*.

This type of change, which has been carried out with several species in experiment, has no doubt played an essential part in the origin of many species. It will often determine an important change of form at the same time as intersterility with the old type. When there appears in a group a new basic number which is not a direct multiple of a lower one we may therefore suspect this kind of change. But other changes can be responsible. Mere fragmentation without change of balance (Fig. 23), may give new basic numbers. And combination of diploid species with different basic numbers may give dibasic polyploidy, as in *Saccharum* and *Narcissus*. We have therefore to apply several tests, of which two may be mentioned.

In the first place the change must be a change in a polyploid, and in a group in which changes in the basic numbers of diploid species occur rarely, if at all. This is true of many groups of flowering plants, such as the Rosaceae.

In the second place a special relationship of the chromosomes must be seen at meiosis. In allopolyploids where the chromosomes are small and contracted to a spherical shape the homologous bivalents do not form multivalents but come to lie next to one another on the metaphase plate and closer together than do the non-homologous chromosomes. Groups of three or four bivalents may appear in this way in hexaploids or octoploids, but the associations are variable, depending on the chances of the right pairs lying near one another during the preparatory stages of metaphase when the bivalents all come close together. Evidently a specific attraction, like that which brings similar chromosomes together at prophase, is acting at a distance to modify the even equilibrium on the metaphase plate. It does not show itself so readily at mitosis, or at meiosis when the chromosomes remain long, because presumably they offer more resistance to movement.

In a secondary polyploid we can recognise the numbers of chromosomes of each type by their association in this way. Thus in *Dahlia* all the species have a basic number of eight[11] except one, *D. Merckii*, which has 36 chromosomes. Its haploid complement of 18 is not derived from one of 16 by fragmentation, because there are two associations of three equal bivalents together with six associations of two bivalents. Its formula is:

$$2n = 4x + 4 = 36.$$

This species stands alone in the genus in its morphological character. It is evidently a secondary polyploid.

Taking even larger groups we can acquire not less certainty but more where the secondary polyploid type is absolutely constant. This is the case with the Pomoideae. The rose group of the Rosaceae show a constant basic number of 7, the apple group, embracing hundreds of species, show an equally constant basic number of 17. Chromosome behaviour makes it clear that the formula of the apple is

$$2n = 4x + 6 = 34.$$

It is to this change in balance from 7 to 17 that we must suppose the apple and the hawthorn owe their distinctive fruits.

The secondary polyploid therefore has a secondary balance. The original balance has no absolute validity. It merely represents a tested combination, a tested proportion. Just as the wild type of genes work better under wild conditions than the mutant types usually do, so the wild type of balance works better than a new type of balance. If the wild type did not do so it would

[11] Lawrence, 1931.

soon cease to be the wild type. The inefficiency of most mutants is a corollary of the efficiency of natural selection. When the mutant gene or secondary balance appears which is not inferior it survives and a new step in evolution is made.

Naturally we cannot expect that the evolutionary story will often be as simple as this, and no great interest attaches to the tracing of phylogenies which are more conjectural. No doubt many are intermediate between the simple types we have chosen for demonstration. It is merely necessary to establish the principle that evolutionary changes can take place by large as well as by small changes of balance and that alteration of the basic number of chromosomes may occur with or without such changes.

IO

THE MANAGEMENT OF THE CELL

i. *The Work of the Nucleus*

IF a cell is cut in two, whether it is free-living *Amoeba* or a nerve-cell in man, the part with the nucleus survives, grows and regenerates, the part without the nucleus dies. This has long been known. But now we know that even if a small part of the nucleus is missing, a single chromosome or piece of chromosome, the whole cell suffers and sooner or later, according to the needs of growth or the severity of competition, it fails to survive.

A very neat experiment has been performed with the egg of *Drosophila*, by Ulrich,[1] which shows the contrast in organisation and control between nucleus and cytoplasm. Of eggs X-rayed in the cytoplasmic end a dose of 100,000 roentgen units will kill half; and it will kill them slowly. Of eggs X-rayed at the nuclear end a dose of 500 roentgen units will kill half; and it will kill them during the first few cleavage divisions. They die because some of the chromosomes in the egg nucleus have been broken and the fragments without a centromere have been lost at mitosis.

After meiosis in plants we see in every anther a vast experiment laid out before us which demonstrates the action of this principle. In pure lines of plants every pollen grain may grow, divide, differentiate and mature. In hybrids a proportion of grains fail to develop. They stop growing at one stage or another before maturity. Why? Segregation of differences at meiosis leads to the formation of nuclei some of which are defective in their gene outfit. And these defects are expressed in a slowing down of the rate of production of proteins in the grain. Doubling of chromosomes, as we have seen, stops this segregation. It stops the breakdown of the pollen and restores fertility.

Some genes act within a few minutes, others do not take

[1] Ulrich, 1957.

effect until a whole life cycle had elapsed. They all have their different modes and times of action because they all work together in adjusted or adapted sequences. All co-operate to produce the complete system, the good genotype.

How do they co-operate? It is clear that the nucleus is a system cut off from the cytoplasm by its semi-permeable membrane. But within this membrane the nucleus is no simple chemical system. It contains in a permanent although partly hidden state the linear arrangements of genes. These are concerned in two tasks; one, we may say, is physiological, the other genetic. The one is that they organise materials which will pass into the cytoplasm. The other is that they organise materials in their own likeness for their own reproduction. How do we recognise these two types of activity?

ii. *The Chemical Hierarchy*

Our first approach may be chemical. The chromosomes memselves, as we saw, consist of nucleoprotein fibres. These fibres arise by the joint polymerisation of protein and desoxyribose nucleic acid or DNA. The DNA is recognisable and also measurable by the Feulgen reaction used for staining chromosomes. Each species of organism so far as it has a constant complement of chromosomes has also a constant quantity of DNA in these chromosomes. This quantity doubles in the resting nucleus when the chromosomes reproduce.

This DNA is fixed for the species not only in quantity but also in quality. The evidence of this fixed quality is that the proportions of the four kinds of nucleotides whose linear polymerisation constitutes DNA are fixed for each chromosome complement; but they differ from species to species. Now the linear arrangement of the materials of all chromosomes is fixed. The fixed proportions are therefore assumed to be due to a fixed order of nucleotides in each chromosome.[2] In this way the DNA columns are able to carry what has been called the genetic code, the permanent instructions which are transmitted from one nucleus to another at mitosis. The reproduction of the chromosomes provides for the exact replication of this code.

The activity of the cell outside the nucleus does not however

[2] *cf.* Darlington, 1955.

depend on DNA but on ribose nucleic acid. This RNA is similarly composed of four nucleotides but they are not capable of forming columns of indefinite length. Protein production in the cell, as Caspersson and Brachet first found, is correlated with the amount of RNA in the nucleolus and in the cytoplasm. For this reason it seemed that the nucleus, in directing the activity of the cell, depended on the production of RNA by the genes. This RNA was collected in the nucleolus and diffused into the cytoplasm. This view, which we owe to Caspersson,[3] has now been confirmed by many experimental tests. But especially we must notice that the proportions of nucleotides in the RNA of the cell vary characteristically from tissue to tissue. It is as though different pieces of the chromosome were acting to produce different kinds of RNA which are released into the cytoplasm to propagate themselves there, and to propagate different kinds of protein characteristic of each stage of development and of each tissue.

The picture that chemistry gives us is one of a hierarchy of particles. The nucleus is the seat of the highest determination and, so far as mitotic reproduction is concerned, the highest rigidity. The cytoplasm is subordinate but flexible. It also has its means of limited genetic continuity. To these notions we shall have to return later with new evidence. Now let us go back to consider what the visible structures and movements have to tell us.

iii. *Gene Cooperation*

The materials produced by the activity of the genes partly diffuse away from them without leaving visible evidence of their character. Partly however they collect in association with particular genes.

This is true of the nucleolar organisers; it is also true of heterochromatin; and during mitosis it is true of the centromeres which keep the spindle fibres attached to them. Other physiological materials perhaps diffuse freely in the nucleus. But between these extremes it seems that there are products and processes which are canalised: they pass along the chromosomes. In this way, the spiralisation of chromosomes is often seen to begin at the centromere and is evidently controlled from

[3] Caspersson, 1941.

it. Similarly nucleoli in many plants are not formed at specific organisers but flow along the chromosomes to the ends. And position effects are all recognisable as interactions between genes mapped on the same chromosome by linkage experiments. Other examples of canalisation will appear later.[4]

Thus internally the structure of the nucleus is organised out of materials which work in many different ways. This work however is done partly through the cytoplasm and entirely in response to the action of the cytoplasm. The evidence of how the nucleus works through the cytoplasm arises from experiments in which we break a working nucleus into two parts. Each of these is unworkable alone but the two cooperate if they remain in the same cell. The cooperation is of two kinds and may be shown in two ways. Chromosomes can be broken with chemical reagents. Maleic hydrazide, an isomer of an RNA nucleotide, uracil, specifically breaks heterochromatin in *Vicia faba*. The nucleolar organisers in the acentric fragments then pass into a small nucleus while the main nucleus contains no organisers. The small nucleus then burrows into the side of the large one without their membranes touching. Evidently the two nuclei are directly exchanging essential materials and this makes them move together and mutually adjust their shapes.[5]

A second kind of nuclear relation is indirect. Complementary nuclei (with 6 and 8 instead of 7 and 7 chromosomes) can be formed by a heat shock at meiosis in *Uvularia*. In these circumstances nucleolar organisers are not apparently or usually concerned and no such direct exchange occurs. What happens is that both nuclei are exchanging with the cytoplasm.[6] As in *Vicia* the two nuclei are synchronised in reaching mitosis, that is, in chromosome reproduction. But each seems to have its own essential nucleolar service and the two do not move together.

Synchronisation of nuclei coming into mitosis tells us some of the things we most need to know about the working of the nucleus and the cell. We know that in normal mitosis a nucleus cannot enter prophase until the chromosomes have doubled and until the protein and DNA of which the chromosomes are composed have doubled. Synchronisation means that two cells or two nuclei in the same cell are working equally well or are

[4] Darlington, 1957.   [5] McLeish, 1953, 1954.   [6] Barber, 1941.

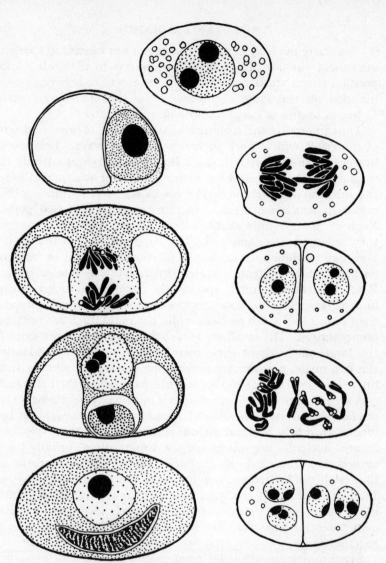

Fig. 14. Development of normal and rogue pollen grains in a special clone of *Tradescantia bracteata*. Right, normal type with vacuoles ensuring a transverse spindle and differentiation of the products of mitosis into mitotic and non-mitotic cells. Left, rogue type without vacuoles, with a lengthwise spindle and no differentiation of the products: both usually fail to divide again but a second mitosis may be induced in both by a temperature shock as shown in the figure. *Note:* the chromosomes are then half-size and there has presumably been no doubling of DNA before mitosis. Stippling indicates protein and RNA in cytoplasm, protein and DNA in nucleus.

× 1500 (from La Cour, 1949.)

equally necessary to one another. We are not surprised to find that groups of meiotic cells with identical nuclei are synchronised in anther and testis. And when synchronisation breaks down in the pollen grains we regard this as a symptom of the differences that have arisen between the pollen grains by segregation at meiosis. But when we follow the pollen grains through their mitosis we find it gives rise to two nuclei in two cells which are not synchronised (Fig. 14). The axis of this mitosis is radial with respect to the old mother cell. The daughter nucleus which is central with respect to the old mother cell undergoes another mitosis, the one which is peripheral does not. If the axis of the first mitosis is not radial but tangential this differentiation does not arise. The daughter nuclei both divide; indeed they are synchronised. Evidently the position in the cytoplasm affects the rate at which the materials for reproduction, DNA and protein, are pumped into the nucleus and thus make nuclear division and cell division possible.[7]

iv. *Nucleus and Cytoplasm*

Synchronisation and the upsetting of synchronisation are the key properties underlying all differentiation of cells in plants and animals. They show that the rates of growth and development and mitosis in cells are affected in two ways. They are affected by differences in the composition of the nucleus such as arise at meiosis or by irradiation. They are also affected by differences in the composition of the cytoplasm such as arise within one cell whether it is a pollen grain or an animal egg. Since nuclei are usually constant in character throughout vegetative development it is on differences in the cytoplasm that differentiation of tissues during development primarily depends.

Is then the whole pattern of development determined or laid down in the single cell, spore or egg, from which a plant or animal develops? We might say that it is determined but we ought not to say that it is laid down. The reason is this. The nucleus although uniform in structure throughout development is not uniform in action. It is constantly reacting with the cytoplasm and setting going series of activities which react on itself. The first primitive steps in differentiation lead therefore

[7] La Cour, 1949.

to more complex results which are not determined by the character of either the cytoplasm or the nucleus alone but by their interactions.

A few diverse kinds of evidence of these interactions are worth noting at this stage of our work.

In many animal hybrids as well as in mutant or unbalanced types development begins quite satisfactorily. At a certain stage where new kinds of process might be expected to begin, such as gastrulation or pupation, development breaks down.[8] It might be said that it is merely an absolute defect of the nucleus that is to blame. The nucleus is timed to go so long and then stops. But experiments with the Evening Primrose, *Oenothera*, rule out this explanation. Here, as we shall see later, one nucleus may flourish and multiply in the cytoplasm of the egg while an identical nucleus dies in the pollen grain and *vice versa*. Similarly one nucleus may flourish and multiply to make the embryo while in the endosperm (which in *Oenothera* is diploid like the embryo) an identical sister dies, and *vice versa*.[9] Thus it is a defect in interaction of nucleus and cytoplasm that is concerned. The two are mutually adapted at each successive stage of healthy development.

If this interaction means anything it means that the nucleus is acting differently at different stages. It is not merely that it can multiply at different rates for this is something which affects every gene in precisely equal measure. On the contrary different genes must be working at different rates in different stages of growth and different parts of the body or even in different parts of the nuclear cycle. We may notice that all the visible genes in the nucleus provide evidence of these differences. The centromere works quite differently in response to changes arising in the cytoplasm during the successive stages of mitosis. A nucleolar organiser in *Vicia* does work proportionate to the number of chromosomes it is working for and varying with the state of the cell in which it is working. The heterochromatin which remains condensed and stores DNA in mitotic resting nuclei of *Drosophila* is dispersed and its products unattached in polytene nuclei. These nuclei by their contrast in structure with ordinary resting nuclei provide the extreme

[8] Hadorn, 1937, 1955; Staiger *et al.*, 1952.
[9] Hiorth, 1926; Darlington and La Cour, 1941.

example of a new mode of activity developed in response to a changed cytoplasm.

Recently, excellent studies of development of polytene nuclei have revealed a more detailed differentiation of activity. They have shown that the organisation of chromomeres changes during development. In different tissues and in different stages of development the same materials in the linear structure of the chromosomes can exist as one large compound particle and as several small separate particles (Fig. 15). Such changes in

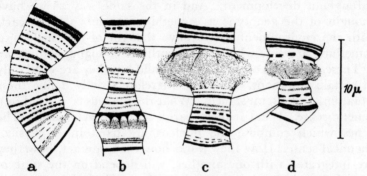

Fig. 15. A short segment (region 9) of the third chromosome of the fly *Chironomus tentans* showing the genes in the polytene chromosomes in different degrees of activity. Malpighian tube cells (*a, c*) and rectum cells (*b, d*) from larva (*a, b*) and pupa (*c, d*). *Note:* the *X* bands are condensed in the larva; they are dispersed in the pupa. But at both stages the genes differ in behaviour in the two tissues.

× 3000   (from Beermann, 1952; *cf.* Breuer, 1955; Pavan, 1955.)

integration are reversible and they are independent in different chromomeres. In other words each chromomere has its individual genetically determined type of development or series of reactions. These reactions are of course reactions amongst all the genes which are working at the time and also reactions between all these genes and the cytoplasm.

Differences in the kinds of activity of genes at different stages of development help us to understand the differences in be-haviour of chromosome segments which are heterochromatic in one species of *Fritillaria* and not in another. In both cases we are dealing with differences in reaction of the nucleus and the cytoplasm.[10]

Taking together all the evidence of what we see in the cell we notice that it explains, it provides the framework for under-

[10] La Cour, 1944, 1951, 1956.

standing, many diverse problems of the working, reproduction, growth and heredity of organisms. It also removes some conflicts that seemed to exist between traditional ways of representing the importance of the nucleus and the cytoplasm. But at the same time naturally it does not exactly fit all the traditional or classical points of view on the subject.

Thus in classical genetics we have thought of the genotype as the sum of the genes. We have thought of both the sum and the parts as something fixed and absolute for the individual throughout development. And in the same way as we have thought of the genotype as something absolute which reacts with the environment so we have thought of the nucleus as something absolute which reacts with the changing cytoplasm.

These old points of view are still valid but they are valid only in certain situations. We must therefore strictly define these situations and circumstances. What the nucleus is, is fixed in a genetic sense. What it does, varies with the cytoplasm. The genes which compose the nucleus are fixed in a physico-chemical sense. How they work, how they interact, how they are integrated with one another, will depend on the state of the whole cell for the time being. As a rule in experimental breeding we catch the difference in activity between a gene and its alternative or allelomorph at one point in development. We cannot expect to see the evidence of changes in organisation and activity at successive stages. This is more especially so since specific activity is likely to be the least frequent state of any gene, the most frequent state being non-specific activity or no activity at all. The gene of physiology is a fluctuating entity.

To put the matter in another way, we have two methods of studying the relation of heredity and development. One is by experimental breeding, the other by cell study. Experiments in heredity chiefly depend on separating unitary differences and using them to demonstrate very long-range effects. Study of the cell chiefly depends on using very large and complex differences to demonstrate immediate effects. The two overlap and where they overlap they agree. But our means of describing them will not agree unless we base our terms and notions on both kinds of study. With this caution we may turn in the following three chapters to consider the genes and the genotype and their modes of interaction from other points of view.

11

THE ATOM OF GENETICS

i. *Kinds of Change*

WE are now in a position to discover more exactly what some of the hereditary differences that are subjected to breeding tests mean in terms of the chromosomes whose changes are responsible for them.

An interchange hybrid $(AB+CD)$ $(BC+DA)$ produces two kinds of regular gametes, the same as those from whose fusion it arises, $AB+CD$, and $BC+DA$ (Fig. 10). It consequently produces offspring of three kinds $(AB+CD)$ $(AB+CD)$ (pure), $(AB+CD)$ $(BC+DA)$ (hybrid) and $(BC+DA)$ $(BC+DA)$ (pure). It produces them in the proportion 1 : 2 : 1, the Mendelian proportion for an F_2. But it also produces unworkable combinations by what is called *non-disjunction* of the pairing segments when the co-orientation of the ring of four is parallel instead of convergent. These combinations are defective and sterile. The interchange hybrid is therefore recognisable by its partial sterility and we might ascribe the inheritance of this sterility as due to a gene difference S-s which in the hybrid condition gave sterility although SS and ss were fertile. In fact this kind of explanation was used before the meaning of the chromosome behaviour was understood.

A more widely known type of Mendelian difference is that produced as we saw by a deletion (or duplication) of a small segment. Such deletions were at first described as gene mutations before closer linkage studies showed them to be due to loss of a small segment, a conclusion whose rightness was finally demonstrated by direct study of the salivary gland super-chromosomes.[1]

But cytological study has gone much further than this in revealing the material basis of variation. The inversion of a segment of the X chromosome of *Drosophila melanogaster* (arising from X-ray treatment) produces in the true-breeding condition

[1] Muller and Prokofyeva, 1935.

a roughness of the eye surface. This may be regarded as a recessive mutation located at one of the points of the breakage which led to the inversion. But it happened that, in a stock of flies hybrid for this inversion, a reversal of the inversion took place; the new change was the exact reciprocal of the original structural change. At the same time the mutation disappeared. Evidently the genetic change was directly determined by the change in the linear order of the particles at the break. It could be due only to the physiological action of one gene depending on the proximity of another.[2]

ii. *Position and Interaction*

How important this principle of the *position effect* may be we do not know, but it applies to many pairs of genes in linear proximity in the chromosomes in *Drosophila* and presumably therefore elsewhere. When an interchange takes place a genetic difference appears and the pure interchange type may even be lethal. The behaviour of the Bar gene already referred to illustrates the point in another way. As we saw, Bar is due to the reduplication of a segment. Two segments immediately adjoining repeat one another, like *abcdcdef*. When the fly is pure for Bar it sometimes happens that crossing-over takes place between the right *cd* of one chromosome and the left *cd* of the other, so that a new chromosome is produced with three *cd* segments. A fly hybrid for normal and this 'Super-bar' then has four *cd* segments like a simple pure Bar fly. But it shows the Bar character more strongly. It has fewer eye facets. The relative position of the *cd* segments affects their action.

Certain properties of the position effect are worth noting for future reference. The first is that it may occur between like elements or between unlike elements. The Bar reduplication concerns like elements. Sometimes however it is a question of a reaction between a gene in a euchromatic segment and a block of heterochromatin. Here unlike elements are concerned. With like elements proximity reinforces action. With unlike elements it evidently can do the same. How can this come about? Only, it seems, if the products of gene action are conveyed along the

---

[2] Grüneberg, 1937; *cf.* Stern, 1948.

chromosome thread; only if their movements are linearly directed. Or to use the expression that we derived from the direct study of the chromosomes, canalised.

We have already seen that the individual particles or genes making up the chromosome, although units of inheritance separable by crossing-over, are not units in regard to physiological action. They interact throughout development. We now see that they interact even inside the nucleus. They are balanced or adjusted therefore in 'normal' or 'wild-type' members of the species, not only in their proportions but also in their positions on the chromosomes. Even more important, we see that Mendelian differences may be determined in three recognisable ways: by mechanical defects in segregation; by proportion changes; by position changes. All these three are determined by changes in the linear order of the particles, by *intergenic* change.

It might indeed be thought that such changes between genes were important enough in their action to account for the whole range of variation observed now and inferred in evolution. But this cannot be true. Changes of arrangement and balance can effect genetic changes only by virtue of differences between the particles that are rearranged or rebalanced. The specific properties of mutation known in many genes justify this conclusion. The specific attractions between homologous particles in the chromosomes bear it out. Specificity implies diversity.

The genes making up the chromosomes must therefore be different. They must also be capable of giving rise to one another by their specific and limited steps of mutation unless we assume a special creation of each gene. There must therefore be a process of *intragenic* change, change at the level of the nucleotide, as well as one of intergenic change which is grossly structural and visible.

This distinction is strict and indisputable in theory, although in practice it only separates the known from the unknown. We know which mutations are undoubtedly intergenic; we do not know which are undoubtedly intragenic. There is no means of distinction by physiological effect and we cannot see whether a single gene may have been turned the other way round or have lost an attached radical.

iii. *Inferences of the Gene*

Let us now consider how the gene is inferred. Mendel ascribed the cause of the discontinuities which he studied to unspecified but none the less material *elements*. As soon as it became possible and necessary to relate these factors to particular cells it also became possible and necessary to allow them a material character. This Johannsen did (without quite realising how far he was going) by giving them the name of genes. These Mendel genes were obviously units of recombination and mutation. Their position and structure Johannsen did not define. But he went so far as to suggest that the genotype was 'the sum total of all the genes'. He was assuming implicitly that the whole hereditary substance consisted of particles analogous to those whose differences made the direct inference of genes possible. He was also assuming, and again implicitly, that there were units of mutation which corresponded one-to-one with the units of heredity.[3]

These implications of the Mendel gene were partly made clear by Morgan.[4] The chromosome was shown to be the vehicle of heredity. The chromomere of cytology showed particulate inheritance; the segregation of differences showed particulate variation. The two were consistent and provided a theoretical model on which nearly all predictions could be based in experimental practice. The gene became the unit of crossing-over.

Later work has entirely vindicated the concept of the Morgan gene as a unit of inheritance. But it has equally invalidated this particle, or indeed any particle, as a unit of variation, for the reason we have already seen: any one particle can cause variation in several different ways, by changes in quantity, in quality and in position. Further the co-existence of these three types of variation affects the practical use of crossing-over as a means of determining the unit of inheritance, in this way: an inversion may cause a mutation and at the same time suppress crossing-over within the inverted segment in any organism hybrid for the inversion. What does this mean? It means in any organism in which the effects of crossing-over could be detected. If there is another mutation within this

[3] Darlington, 1953*b*.   [4] Morgan, 1926.

segment the two will appear as a single unit of crossing-over.

Where then are we to look for a reliable criterion of a genetic particle? Crossing-over is useless if it can be suppressed by structural hybridity. Mutation is useless if it can be simulated by structural change. The chromomere is useless if it varies during development. Moreover, when a chromosome, or part of one, seems to be inert and shows no variation within the species, how are we to represent its structure in terms of genes? When a differential segment in an interchange hybrid (Fig. 10) never crosses over with its homologous segment although they may differ in genetic action, again, how are we to represent its structure?

These questions can be answered only if we can control the mutations of the gene and relate them to the observable structure of the chromosome, and thus make its diagnosis independent of the tests of crossing-over and undefined mutation. Even then the answer relates only to a special situation.

This has been done by Muller's introduction of the technique of X-ray treatment. The distal end of the X chromosome in D. melanogaster contains a group of chromomeres, changes in which affect the type of bristles on the thorax, producing the so-called 'scute' mutations. The number of bands in this region may be determined most exactly by ultra-violet photographs. This number will be a minimum estimate, since some bands may be too small for resolution. The number of breaks which can occur in the same region under the influence of X-rays can be determined by examining the chromosomes of all flies affected by treatment, and by testing the viability of derivatives with different recombinations of breakages. The number of different points of breakage shown by specific physiological effects is not less than the number of chromomeres seen in photographs.[5]

iv. *Allelism*

The breakage-cum-viability test tells us something definite about the linear structure and the cooperative activity of the genetic materials. But it leaves important physiological questions to be answered. Position effects and canalised interactions warn us that parts of the chromosomes which can be separated by breakage or crossing-over may nevertheless com-

[5] Muller and Prokofyeva, 1935.

bine to act as units. That is the physiological unit may be larger than the recombination unit. Now multiple alleles are classified both by physiological and by recombination tests. How do they behave?

Multiple allele series show a wide range of behaviours. At one extreme two mutant alleles when heterozygous reconstitute the wild type as though each carried a normal allele of the other. Thus with a and α mutants of A the two chromosomes of the heterozygote might be represented as $a+/+\alpha$. Or where no dominance arises, as in the Rhoesus blood group gene in man, the heterozygote for two mutants produces both the mutant antigens without any interaction. In such cases we have no hesitation in assuming a multiple structure in the gene. But at the other extreme we find no interaction. The albino-Himalayan heterozygote in the rabbit although both genes are allelic to the wild agouti do not add up to give more pigmentation than Himalayan. How are we to understand their structural relations?

The practical solution of a number of such problems has come from the study of very rare crossing-over by the use of very large progenies in *Drosophila* and micro-organisms.[6] In certain multiple allele series like 'bithorax' in *Drosophila* the heterozygote for two mutants showed no interaction beyond dominance of one over the other. But rare crossing-over has produced a recombination, $a+/+\alpha$ has given $a\alpha/++$. One chromosome then has both mutations and one has neither mutation, i.e. it is wild type and being dominant the fly is wild type. These cross-overs occur with a frequency of the order of one in 10,000 or even 30,000 flies.

The question now arises as to how a and α are interfering with the activity of their chromosomes. Is the lack of cooperation between the two chromosomes due to strict canalisation of processes along each of them? If an inversion is put into one of the two chromosomes in the $a+/+\alpha$ heterozygote such as will prevent the two chromosomes lying parallel (as homologous chromosomes do in the resting mitotic nuclei of flies) it in fact causes stronger expression of the mutation. The size of the physiological gene therefore depends on the canalisation of processes along the chromosome just as the size of the re-

[6] E. B. Lewis, 1954.

combination gene depends on the frequency and distribution of crossing-over—and on the efficiency of our means of discovering it.

Such crossing-over occurs between two changes in what appeared to be one gene. Mutations in different parts of the complex are then said to be pseudo-allelic. The term is intended to suggest something spurious. It was in fact the previous notion of allelism which was spuriously simple. The discovery of all kinds of complex genes has revealed many contradictions between the physiological units and the mechanical units which different experimental methods can reveal in the same piece of chromosome. The size of the unit that we shall describe as a gene must always depend on practical convenience, convenience in relation to the conditions of experiment and observation. Finer breeding methods will continually reveal smaller units. But there is another mode of inference with its own independent validity.

Since genes correspond with chromomeres or parts of chromomeres wherever it has been possible to test them; and since all chromomeres share with all genes the same essential properties of attraction, reproduction, linear arrangement and crossing-over; we can say that all chromomeres or parts of chromosomes, irrespective of the possibility of testing their recombination by mutation and crossing-over and irrespective of their having any specific physiological action, are composed of genes. The genes are units into which the linear structure of the chromosomes can be conveniently divided.

In this sense the nucleolar organiser and also the centromere are genes. They are genes whose character is defined by their visible activities in the cell and by their changes in structure inferred from breeding experiments. And since their products, nucleoli or spindle fibres, remain attached to them we may describe them as *organellar* genes. These organellar genes sometimes break into fragments which, as we shall see later, have the same activities as the unbroken genes, although weaker. They must therefore be multiple. They must consist of small supplementary parts, and have arisen by reduplication of single small genes.[7]

We thus have two radically opposed methods of inferring the

[7] McClintock, 1934; Darlington, 1939a, 1957.

existence of genetic particles in the nucleus. There is however yet a third method which depends on breeding experiments but dispenses with the mendelian situation.

v. *Polygenes*

So far we have been discussing the kinds of genes whose changes have been the basis of mendelian experiments. These genes are so powerful in their effects that their mutations are recognisable at least in the homozygous state. Every individual can be recorded according to whether it is *AA* or *Aa* on the one hand or *aa* on the other. But are there not genes whose changes are too slight to recognise? Are there not genes whose whole effect is too minute to allow of any differences in them to be traced in ordinary breeding experiments? We have already seen that there are apparently or relatively inert chromosomes and segments of chromosomes which are not quite inert but merely less specific in their effects. Are there genes which merely act in modifying the action of specific genes without themselves being wholly specific, that is quantitatively rather than qualitatively?

For the examination of these questions Mather has carried out experiments on quantitative inheritance. He has, for example, studied the inheritance of variation in bristle number in *Drosophila*. The variation is always greatly modified by environmental conditions within the same culture. But when selection is continued over many generations using the records of large progenies with appropriate statistical safeguards the result is significant. It shows that the genotype is controlling this variation. Moreover, it shows that many genes are at work. The appearance of mutation in these genes is probably often the result of crossing-over between compensating or balanced groups of such genes.

Thus genes of small, similar, and supplementary effect have to be inferred in the chromosomes. These genes have no necessary connection with the large specific major genes. Mather calls them *polygenes*.[8]

There is evidently some connection between these polygenes and the kinds of genes we find in supernumerary chromosomes, in heterochromatin, and in the organellar type of gene.

[8] Mather, 1954.

But heterochromatin can change into euchromatin and supernumeraries may be either heterochromatic or euchromatic.
Moreover one gene may affect the kind of action of another.
We must evidently therefore not yet attempt any strict classification. We can however be quite confident in splitting up our
old classes. We can be quite confident in saying that genes are
of many kinds. These different kinds are not merely the symptoms of the different techniques we use in identifying them; for
each technique reveals the three main classes of gene. Seen
under the microscope we have the small gene of heterochromatin, the larger particle of euchromatin, the inversion or
interchange complex, and the organellar gene. Inferred from
breeding we have the polygene, the major gene, the multiple
gene or super-gene.

These comparisons and classifications are of course pro-
visional. We are only at the beginning of our understanding
of what they mean. But we cannot overlook the fact that they
imply evolution. We are accustomed to supposing that evolution takes place from the simpler to the more complex. For the
gene this seems also to be true. But we must be prepared for
unexpected kinds of change to appear when we attempt to put
polygenes, complex genes, super-genes and organellar genes
into their diverse evolutionary sequences.

One word about the size of the gene. In the largest chromosomes, as we have seen, the unitary nucleo-protein threads are
probably multiplied 256 or 512 times: they are polynemic. In
consequence the amount of DNA in the resting nucleus can
be thousands of times greater than that in the nuclei with
very small chromosomes, as in many fungi or sponges.[9] In
consequence, if we choose to reckon it as multiplied along with
the chromosome, the gene must be proportionately larger. If
we reckon it as the ultimate nucleo-protein unit then its minimum value will be of the order of 100 Angstrom units in each
dimension: something comparable to the smaller plant viruses.

vi. *Conflict of Definitions*

Recapitulating, we can now resolve certain difficulties which
beset the early development of genetics. It was earlier assumed
(very properly, on Occam's principle) that the same unit might

[9] Darlington, 1955.

be used to cover all the aspects of genetic analysis. Mutation, or variation, was one aspect. Transmission or recombination or crossing-over was another; activity was a third. We now know these do not correspond. Mutation includes two contradictory types of process. The unit of crossing-over is elastic depending on the types of mutation that are being recombined. Activity is variously organised and the relations of the different parts of chromosomes vary in the same nucleus; any one part may vary in the course of development. And all parts certainly vary in the course of evolution.

That all these units exist and the term gene is indispensable to describe them is clear. But it is also clear that the term cannot be extended from one situation to another without reservation. Recombination, mutation and activity are not interchangeable situations. Different stages of development are not interchangeable. Different species of organisms are not interchangeable. Above all development depends on the interlocking reactions of genes. They begin within the nucleus with the position effect; they continue in the interactions of nucleus and cytoplasm, of cells and of tissues; they are made visible in the development of polytene chromosomes; they are represented and expressed in the general principle of balance. The great achievement of genetics has been to separate for analysis the studies of heredity and development. And having done so, to reconcile the contradiction in the properties of genes between their independence in heredity and their combination in development.

12

CHROMOSOME MECHANICS

i. *Changes of Shape*

NUCLEAR division, whether mitosis or meiosis, consists of a series of co-ordinated changes and movements in the chromosomes or bound up with the chromosomes. As we watch them in life or in a phase-contrast film, these movements resemble the well-disciplined evolutions of athletes or soldiers. Yet the structures we observe are not organisms. They are molecules of immense size. And their versatile physiological capacities are contained within a mechanical framework of highly regular construction. Furthermore, their movements, which are elaborate and diverse to an incomparable degree, are not directly adaptable. On the contrary, as the movement of molecules should be, they are determined and predictable. Any error is irremediable: it leads to a succession of other errors usually culminating in disaster for a cell or an organism. A study of the regularities as well as of the errors and breakdowns, combined as they are with a great array of known structural and genotypic conditions and with certain physical experiments, enables us to infer the agencies at work.

Changes in shape of the chromosomes are, as we have seen, due to internal movements in the chromosome thread—the spiralisation cycle. This cycle consists in mitosis of the assumption in each chromatid of a regular system of coils whose diameter increases and whose number decreases, both before the metaphase rod shape is assumed and while it is disintegrating as a *relic coil* at telophase and the following prophase. Why, it may be asked, should this uncoiling of the chromosomes of one mitosis be postponed to the next? The rate of uncoiling of different parts of the same chromosome is unequal. This shows that it depends on the chances of spatial distribution. It shows that uncoiling is indeed limited by the confinement of the chromosomes in a restricted space, the resting nucleus. They are not free to move in response to their changing internal

81

stresses as though they were *in vacuo*. They show a lag therefore in their adjustments to these stresses which may be compared to the hysteresis of non-living systems.

At meiosis each chromatid similarly assumes an internal coil, but here we can see in the larger chromosomes that within the *major spiral* another *minor spiral* is developed, a spiral of smaller diameter which no doubt begins to be formed when the major spiral has reached a certain diameter. Whether the slenderer mitotic chromosomes also include both orders of spiral formation we cannot yet say.

In spite of the different amounts of coiling to be done, large and small chromosomes spiralise at the same rate. It is clear therefore that this coiling is not conditioned externally by a rotation of the ends. It must be directly due to an internal change which compensates for it spatially, rendering a rotation of the ends unnecessary. This argument is clinched by the fact that ring chromosomes without any ends (resulting from crossing-over between translocated segments) are capable of coiling and uncoiling as freely as rod chromosomes. Such a compensating system of coiling we may describe as a *molecular spiral*[1] whose torsion must change subject to changes in the substrate. The chemical and physical evidence suggests that the polynucleotide columns of DNA which constitute the fibrous framework of the chromosomes are polymerised in a double helix, the Watson-Crick model. This model would require uncoiling for separation and reproduction of the paired columns. Such uncoiling would provide the spatial conditions for the molecular spiral. Four groups of observations and inferences are thus brought into relation with one another:

(i) Coiling and uncoiling of the chromosomes in the mitotic cycle.

(ii) Reproduction of the chromosomes and separation of their products, the chromatids.

(iii) Relational coiling of chromosomes at meiosis.

(iv) Structure of DNA *in vitro* inferred at the molecular level.

These observations and inferences are consistent on the assumption of cyclical variations in the amplitude of the helix. Such variations would determine the visible coiling and com-

[1] Darlington, 1935*a*, *b*, 1955.

pensate for it. They would also at one stage in their variation permit separation of the paired columns of nucleotides a necessary condition of their separate reproduction.

ii. *Changes of Position*

What changes take place in the substrate are shown by the external movements of the chromosomes. In treating these movements we shall find it useful at first to take all comings together as signs of *attraction* and all goings apart as signs of *repulsion*. Later we can enquire what these terms may mean and what they may lead to.

The first of these movements is the pairing of the chromosomes as threads at the early prophase of meiosis. This is by our definition a movement of attraction. Four properties strike us in regard to this attraction. First, it is not between threads for the threads can change partners in polyploids. It is an attraction between particles—genes or chromomeres. Secondly, it exists only between pairs of particles. Thirdly, it is directionally specific: it does not allow of slipping for it is not before the pairing but after it that the chromosomes are compelled by their internal torsion to twist round one another. Fourthly there is a *time-limit* to the attraction: the pairing often comes to a standstill before it is complete.[2]

These principles show that there is a specific structural basis in the individual gene for the pairing attraction. Further this structural basis depends on the lack of reproduction of the chromosome for it ends when the chromosomes have reproduced and their DNA content has doubled. Normally this is after pairing; but it is before pairing if the time-limit interrupts pairing.

From the evolutionary point of view other interests attach to these comparisons. The attraction between pairs of genes is satisfied at mitosis by the previous division of each chromosome into two chromatids. At meiosis, prophase begins before the chromosomes divide. When corresponding chromosomes come together therefore in pairs they restore an equilibrium like that found at mitosis.

When later the chromomeres divide, the chromosomes fall apart. The same attraction works therefore at all stages in the

[2] Darlington, 1940*a*.

prophase nuclei of mitosis and meiosis, and meiosis is distinguished from mitosis by the *precocity* of the beginning of prophase in relation to the division of the chromosomes. That is a change in the timing relation of two processes. These are an external or cellular process, the initiation of cell-division, and an internal or nuclear process, the reproduction of the chromosomes. This initial precocity has its effects on all the subsequent stages of meiosis and later we shall see how their variations provide us with a test of the theory with its assumption of the two processes and the change of timing.

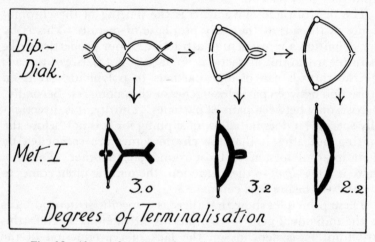

Fig. 16. Above, the stages of terminalisation in a bivalent with three chiasmata. Below, the metaphase configurations produced when terminalisation is interrupted at early or late stages. The three types are *Fritillaria, Tulipa* and *Campanula* in plants, or *Chrysochraon, Chorthippus* and *Acridium* in animals.

It need not be supposed that the primary specific attraction between genes acts at any great distance, since the chromosomes are brought together in pairing by their proximity at one or two points of contact from which the pairing spreads. The residual attraction which is responsible for secondary pairing and is also specific to like pairs of bivalents on the other hand seems to be exerted at a considerable distance. But it may be derived from an earlier close association of heterochromatic blocks.[3]

Between the pairs of threads, chromosomes or chromatids,

[3] Thomas and Revell, 1946.

associated by the primary attractions there exist at all stages repulsions of varying strengths. Now the attractions are always specific. They discriminate between homologous and non-homologous particles. But the repulsions are always non-specific. They do not discriminate. They are however of two kinds, distributed and localised. The distributed repulsions express themselves not by violent changes, since they are always acting, but rather by the maintenance of uniform spacing of the chromosomes in the prophase nucleus, on the metaphase plate and on the anaphase spindle. This repulsion is to be expected from the surface charge (or double electric layer) on the particles of an amphoteric electrolyte in a substrate not at its isoelectric point. It is analogous to the repulsion which preserves the suspension of colloidal particles. Its variation is to be expected from variations in the pH of the substrate. If, as we know, the chromosome is a chain molecule, then pH variation might also be expected to produce the changes of shape we have seen in the spiralisation cycle by changing the equilibrium between successive side chains.

iii. *Reactions of the Cytoplasm*

The localised repulsions are those between centromeres. They make themselves felt first during prophase of meiosis by causing the movement of chiasmata away from them, that is towards the ends of the chromosomes. The force leading to terminalisation of chiasmata seems to be slight and variable. Moreover, it is not associated with any change in the structure of the substrate. Provisionally it may be regarded as a manifestation of the activity which develops its full strength after the dissolution of the nuclear membrane and the development of the spindle.

The greatest advantage is to be had from comparing the behaviour of bivalent chromosomes at meiosis inside the prophase nucleus with that on the metaphase spindle. Inside the nucleus the bivalents show no orientation. On the spindle all their pairs of centromeres are co-orientated axially. When an orientated structure is obvious in the spindle before the chromosomes come on to it we must suppose that the co-orientation of the centromeres depends on that of the spindle.

Co-orientation also depends on a reaction between centro-

G

meres. It is strongest between centromeres which are held
closest together by the configuration of the chromosomes in
which they are lying. Bivalents are formed exceptionally (as
in hybrid lilies and grasshoppers) in which only one chiasma is
formed instead of three or four, and the centromeres are therefore much farther apart than usual, so that their mutual repulsions become insignificant. They fail to show tension between
their centromeres. Such bivalents fail to co-orientate themselves. Again when a bivalent is late in arriving on the plate
and cannot twist itself into an axial position in the restricted
space left to it on one side of the plate, its unorientated centromeres produce no special stretching of the parts of chromosome
between them.

Thus repulsions in the spindle are enhanced in an axial
direction. Now it is in this direction that the fibrous constituents
of the spindle are orientated. This may be shown by the effect
of hypertonic solutions on the spindle. It contracts sideways
and not lengthways.[4] The enhancement of repulsions therefore
is evidently correlated with the orientation of molecules in the
spindle. It works in the axis of orientation. This orientation
takes place in various ways.

The simplest method of origin of the spindle is seen in animals
and lower plants where it develops under the influence of particular bodies, the *centrosomes*. These bodies have the permanence, individuality and methods of division of the centromeres,
but they lie free in the cytoplasm outside the nucleus and
unattached to the chromosomes. One is associated with each
nucleus. It divides at telophase, and the daughter halves
separate at the end of prophase. A radial orientation of the
cytoplasm develops round each, which extends into the nucleus.
It forms the spindle by union of the two sides which seem to
stimulate one another by what we may call a polarity reaction.

In some Protista the centrosomes may develop the spindle
inside the nuclear membrane, which breaks down only at anaphase. In others the spindle may develop without any centrosomes either inside or outside the nucleus. The two sides of the
spindle are then less convergent and no clear pole can be distinguished. Such is also the position in the higher plants, and
here it has often been shown that there are no individual spindle

[4] Belar, 1929.

organisers, since single chromosomes lost in the cytoplasm can set up little spindles of their own. This last condition is established in some aberrant plants and regularly in the coccid bugs where the joint spindle arises from the fusion of separate centromere spindles.[5]

In some Protista also the centrosome, or kinetosome, is concerned in making the fibres, cilia or flagella, which are the cell's organs of locomotion. In these cases the kind of activity in which these fibre-forming particles engage depends on the zone of cytoplasm in which they happen to lie.[6] The particle thus reacts with its substrate to produce one or other kind of fibre. So it is with the centrosomes and centromeres whose activities are co-ordinated in producing a different kind of fibre during mitosis.

Owing to these reactions the organisation of the spindle shows a greater mechanical range in the course of evolution than that of the chromosomes. Its evolution is conditioned by the compartment, cell or nucleus, in which it works. The co-operation of the centrosomes, for example, is dispensed with in the higher plants, where the cell is usually contained within a rigid wall and the centrosome is in ordinary tissues unnecessary.

iv. *The Centromere Cycle*

At metaphase we have two kinds of system to compare in all organisms: those at mitosis and at meiosis. At mitosis the centromeres of all the chromosomes are pushed into the single plane of the equator equidistant between the two poles. At meiosis the pairs of centromeres lie on either side of this equatorial plane. But in both the centromeres are orientated. Both produce a *congression* on the plate. In place of co-orientation of the centromeres of bivalents there is a self-orientation of the single centromeres of chromosomes at mitosis. This self-orientation which is correlated with congression is not developed in the centromeres of univalents at meiosis until after the bivalents are co-orientated. It thus seems that three activities of mitotic centromeres go together.

First, congression shows the development of a reaction of the centromeres with the spindle as a whole on the fusion of its

[5] Darlington and Thomas, 1937.   [6] Lwoff, 1952.

separate components developed by the centromeres. Secondly, there is a reaction between paired elements within the centromere which is analogous to that in co-orientated centromeres but constitutes an internal polarity. And thirdly, there is a readiness to divide into two.

In all these reactions, congression, polarisation and division, the centromere at meiosis is delayed relative to that at mitosis. The precocity of metaphase catches it too soon.

The timing relation of mitosis and meiosis thus enables us to understand the spindle mechanics as well as the prophase mechanics. It leaves one important situation at meiosis without strict analogy. The co-orientated centromeres at meiosis lie congressed on the metaphase spindle in a state of equilibrium. In position it corresponds with mid-anaphase at mitosis which is the stage of most rapid movement.

As the metaphase forms, the spindle widens in the equatorial region both in meiosis and mitosis. It does so owing to the fusion of the separate centromere spindles. Thus when pairing happens to fail at meiosis and the univalents do not congress on the plate, the spindle does not expand in the middle; on the contrary it stretches lengthwise.

This is a sign of extremely slow centromere activity, rather than of its complete absence, for such spindles occur in plants with purely centromere spindles as well as in animals with centrosome spindles.

Another aspect of the centromere spindle is shown by the convergent co-orientation of the centromeres in multiple configurations. Evidently one centromere can generate two convergent spindles in its reaction with two others. This happens regularly in the co-orientation of multiple rings. The successive converging little spindles then adjust themselves to form the whole joint metaphase plate and metaphase spindle.

The formation of the metaphase plate shows that the centromeres, or rather the spindles they have made, are repelled by the centrosomes or the poles. They lie half-way between the centrosomes in mitosis because their repulsion is equal. They are not pushed off the spindle, they cohere to form the whole spindle.

The nature of the spindle is now beginning to be clear. It depends on the organisation in the cell of fibres. These fibres are organised either by the localised enzymes of centrosomes or centromeres or by both in co-ordination. They tend to arrange themselves in spindle-shaped bundles. They have the character of a liquid crystal which depends on a parallel and axial arrangement both of the fibres themselves and of the water attached to them and gives them the physical properties of what is known as a tactoid.[7] The fibres are unstable and short-lived. But they have the habit of growing, the growth being balanced in normal cell division, unbalanced where, for example, pairing fails in meiosis. Further the fibre-organisers depend for their activity on a polarity, either between pairs of centrosomes, pairs of centromeres, or poles of a dividing centromere. All these polarity reactions which encourage fibre-formation also encourage movement apart along the fibres which are formed, a movement which seems to be due to a property of stretching inherent in the fibres themselves.

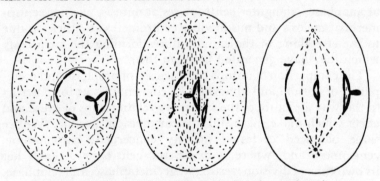

Fig. 17. The relation of spindle orientation to the co-orientation of bivalents at first metaphase. (After Darlington, 1936a.)

This metaphase system is a system of balanced activities. It is ended by the anaphase movement. The chromosomes move apart a short distance under the centric repulsions. These repulsions are due no doubt to the growth of little spindles between the daughter centromeres at mitosis or between the co-orientated centromeres of the bivalents at meiosis. As they grow they constitute what Belar described as the stem-body, the part of the anaphase spindle between the separating bodies of chromosomes and distinct from the centrosome spindle in its optical properties.

[7] Bernal, 1940, cit. Barber and Callan, 1943.

The switch to anaphase takes effect differently in bivalents at meiosis and in unpaired chromosomes at meiosis or mitosis. In bivalents there is no change at the centromeres, which do not divide; metaphase comes too early. The change of equilibrium is brought about by a lapse of chromatid attractions. In unpaired chromosomes the centromeres divide as in mitosis, and the daughter centromeres move apart. In all cases the change to anaphase is helped by a decay of the old spindle between the centromeres and the poles.

As the centromeres move apart the spindle between them, the stem-body, changes shape. It stretches, and this stretching, this growth of the centromere spindles, seems to be what is pushing the centromeres apart. Here it is an effective stretching of attached spindle fibres but it is analogous to the ineffective stretching of apparently unattached spindle fibres where pairing has failed at meiosis. Thus the movement of the centromeres at anaphase—daughter centromeres at mitosis, partner centromeres at meiosis and misdividing centromeres at either—is due to the stretching of the spindle fibres forming the stem-body which they have generated between them.

The comparison of mitosis and meiosis, of prophase and metaphase, of normal and abnormal pairing enables us to construct in this way a picture of the successive relationships of cause and effect which make successful nuclear division possible. We see three balanced cycles of activity concerned: chromosome, centromere and, where it exists, the centrosome. Each has its own time of division: resting stage, metaphase, and telophase. Each has its own cycle and kind of activities. The chromosome cycle is correlated with a cycle of spiralisation and of hydration, and the first two must be related to changes in the properties of the same substrate. Furthermore the contrast between the behaviour of the chromosomes inside the nucleus and outside it suggests that the observed fluidity of the nuclear sap is due to the exclusion of spindle-forming materials and must be conditioned by a semi-permeability of the nuclear membrane.

Finally we notice that the centromeres of meiotic metaphase bivalents must be less advanced than those of mitotic metaphase chromosomes, for two reasons. They are capable of co-orientation although dicentric chromosomes at mitosis are not. And they are not capable of self-orientation and division unless they are delayed. Apparently the precocity of the prophase, in meiosis in extending to metaphase and providing a new balance, works satisfactorily. It does so because co-orientation replaces division of the centromeres at the later stage, just as pairing replaces division of the chromosomes at the earlier stage.

v. *Genetics of the Centromere*

In all chromosome movement the most clearly identifiable structure is of course the centromere simply because it takes the leading part. Fortunately we now have experimental evidence bearing on its structure, its reproduction and its activity.

The first kind of evidence is derived from errors which may befall the dividing centromeres at meiosis. These errors occur spontaneously but may be aggravated by X-ray and other treatments. The centromere fails to divide correctly in the normal plane: it misdivides. *Misdivision* is seen in its simplest form when the centromere divides crosswise instead of lengthwise. This may happen to a normally paired bivalent or to a univalent at the first anaphase or again to a daughter univalent at the second anaphase. The result is to produce two chromosome arms with terminal centromeres. Each of these new *telocentrics* may make a working chromosome and supernumerary chromosomes no doubt often arise in this way (Fig. 18). But misdivision may be unequal. It then gives a strong fraction which survives and a weak fraction which is lost.

This behaviour leads to several conclusions. It shows, in the first place, that the centromere is a multiple gene composed of similar and supplementary parts like polygenes.[8] It also shows that the centromere is capable of evolution and must be adapted for size and strength to its work. The fate of these telocentrics is also significant in other respects. If there are several they may join in pairs to produce the effect of interchange.[9] If there is only one, its two chromatids may unite within the centromere to give an *iso-chromosome* with identical arms, a double half-chromosome. Such a chromosome is known to form part of the regular gametic set in a flowering plant *Nicandra physaloides*.[10]

Thus the centromere is a genic structure. It is composed of a group of identical complementary units; centrogenes we may

---

[8] Darlington, 1939a.   [9] Morrison, 1953.
[10] Darlington and Janaki Ammal, 1945.

call them. It has the same properties of reproduction as the ordinary genes of the chromosome but its timing is shifted in a characteristic way which fits its special functions. Its enzymatic activities are probably like those of other genes but it alone acts in the metaphase as well as in the resting nucleus. And of course it acts differently at different stages in the cycle. It controls pairing and spiralisation and terminalisation in prophase and fibre-formation at metaphase. Moreover its products may be localised or they may move along the chromosome.

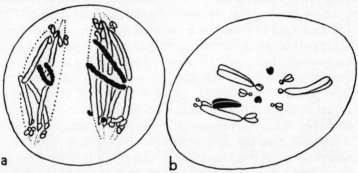

a   b

Fig. 18. Misdivision at meiosis and its consequences in the pollen grains of *Gasteria* ($n=7$). *a*. Second anaphase after misdivision of the centromere in one long chromosome at first anaphase. The two chromatids of the long arm of the misdivided chromosome have formed a lagging iso-chromosome in the left-hand cell. In the right-hand cell the two chromatids of the partner chromosome are now misdividing to give four telocentrics. *b*. Mitosis in the pollen grain after misdivision in two long chromosomes: one long arm and two short arms all telocentric are included in place of one whole long chromosome ($n=9$).
× 1600   (from Darlington and Kefallinou, 1957.)

The localisation is characteristic of metaphase. The movement is characteristic of resting stage or prophase. The same difference, as we have seen, is found in the resting nucleus between ordinary genes in heterochromatin and euchromatin.[11]

The centromere can thus vary in quantity. It can vary in size and strength. Can it vary in quality, in its mode of activity? In certain groups of plants and animals, in the *Cyperaceae*, the rushes and sedges such as *Luzula*, in the scorpions, coccids and butterflies,[12] no localised centromere can be identified. The movements of the chromosomes seem to be initiated at the ends, at both ends. And if the chromosome is broken into

[11] Darlington, 1957.   [12] Godward, 1954; Suomalainen, 1953.

two by X-rays both fragments are capable of independent movement.[13] The same kind of situation arises in the nematode *Ascaris* where the chromosomes break up into numerous fragments during development. But here the chromosomes are long, the centromeres are few and their positions are still recognisable since they and not the ends still take the lead in anaphase. In *Ascaris* the chromosomes are clearly polycentric.[14] Are they similarly organised in the organisms with end-repulsions?

The answer to this question is provided by a number of mutant plants with normal mitosis, but having abnormal centromere activity at meiosis. They are best known in *Zea* and in *Secale*. In these plants at the second metaphase the chromosomes are held together as usual by their centromeres. But the ends of some of the chromatids show a marked repulsion for their own centromeres. The chromatids are thus stretched in the axis of the spindle like the segments between centromeres and chiasmata at first metaphase. Later the chromosomes are able to separate normally when the centromeres divide (*cf.* Fig. 31b).[15]

What has happened seems to be that the action of the centromere in organising the spindle which is normally localised here diffuses along the chromatids to their ends. A fibre-forming enzyme produced by the centromere which is normally fixed shows canalised movement, and the fluid centromere develops co-orientation with a fixed centromere at the second division of meiosis where no co-orientation ordinarily occurs at all.[16]

By analogy with these other experimental situations the difference between the diffuse multiple centromere and the single, powerful, localised centromere becomes partly intelligible. At the same time it shows us a mode of evolution which secondarily governs the evolution of chromosome numbers.

vi. *Mechanics and Physiology*

This analysis of the structures, activities and movements of chromosomes shows that, contrary to all appearances, there is a common character in the forces generated by chromosomes and acting on chromosomes at different times, at prophase and

---

[13] La Cour, 1953*a*; De Castro, 1954.   [14] White, 1937.
[15] Rhoades, 1952.   [16] Darlington, 1957.

metaphase, at metaphase and anaphase and, above all, at mitosis and meiosis.

The differences between these stages and processes depend on changes in the relations of two systems. On the one hand are the constant bodies, the centromeres responsible for repulsions and the rest of the chromosomes responsible for attractions as well. On the other hand are the substrates which are cyclically changing.

The reactions of the constant bodies with the changing substrates, reactions whose effects are sometimes localised, sometimes canalised and sometimes diffused, are responsible for the different movements which we have ascribed to repulsions and attractions.

Such a constancy and simplicity were inevitable at some level of analysis. Two things are remarkable about it. One is that the constancy of chromosome mechanics extends throughout multi-cellular organisms. It is a constancy which is broken only by the diversity of mitosis in the protista and, as we shall see, of meiosis in one sex in some animals. The other is that this simplicity of chromosome mechanics in the dividing cell is compatible with the prodigious elaboration of gene activity which we have reason to assume inside the resting nucleus and the resting cell.

Chromosome movements are indeed a uniform and limited demonstration of what genes can do by adaptation and co-ordination to fulfil a uniform and limited function, that of their own propagation and distribution. And whether we describe this demonstration as mechanics, physiology or genetics no longer matters for this is where the three meet.

13

THE MECHANISM OF CROSSING OVER

i. *A Protein Model*

STRUCTURAL changes in the chromosomes take place by the breakage of the threads in one or more places. This is followed by reunion of the broken ends in new combinations. Such a reunion does not always follow; but, unless the break is in the middle of a centromere, reunion is always necessary for keeping the whole complement of genes intact and therefore for the survival of a balanced cell. Crossing-over likewise depends on breakage and reunion, but it occurs regularly at the pachytene stage of meiosis and at no other stage. Moreover, it consists in an exact recombination of the parts of chromosomes, which are regularly and closely paired at this stage and no other. We ought therefore to be in a position to say what it is in the mechanical conditions of the paired chromosomes that allows of this regular consequence of their association. What are these conditions?

During pachytene the paired chromosomes develop relational coiling. How they do this may best be seen by placing two twisted woollen threads close together. When they are released they untwist themselves individually and in doing so, since they stick together laterally; they twist round one another. They are, however, now found to be only half untwisted. Their *internal* torsion has come into equilibrium with an equal and opposite *relational* torsion. This equilibrium is the basis of all spinning operations. The internal torsion of the wool corresponds to a strain set up in the molecular spiral of the chromosome. The same change in the absence of lateral attraction produces an internal instead of a relational coil.

The pachytene equilibrium must be of the same kind essentially as the spinning equilibrium, since the forces responsible for both are known on other grounds and are analogous. The wool threads stick together by friction, the chromosomes by specific attraction. Their not slipping round one another shows that this attraction is specific in direction as well as in choice of partner. The wool and the chromosomes coil equally because they resist torsion. They both have longitudinal cohesion. Both these properties are likewise necessary if the chromosome is to reproduce to give a regular and coherent daughter thread. From which it follows that when the two chromosomes are internally twisted at the end of pachytene they will each divide to give two daughter threads coiled round one another. And this coiling will presumably be in the opposite direction to that of the relational coiling between chromosomes (see end-paper diagrams).

The proportion of the internal torsion which is released to give relational coiling varies in the wool model according to the amount of torsion. So also it must be with the chromosomes. Not only this. The size and strength of the threads, and thus any external conditions affecting these properties, will modify the pachytene equilibrium. One special circumstance must be remembered. Where the ends of the chromosomes, or of certain segments, are fixed, no relational coiling at all will be developed between chromosomes. This will necessarily occur within inversion loops. It is also likely to occur when the pachytene stage is short and equilibrium is never reached. The state of strain under these conditions will not be diminished. Rather will it be increased. And the conditions of crossing-over will be the same. The difference will be in the result. At diplotene more chromatid coiling and less chromosome coiling will be seen. How far the variations actually found at diplotene depend on such differences in the normal pachytene equilibrium and how far on partial failure of pairing at pachytene we do not yet know.

Such must be the varying conditions at the end of pachytene. What relation have they to the action of crossing-over? It will be recalled that in *Fritillaria* the pachytene pairing is often confined to two regions, centric and distal, with an unpaired region in between. This type of association is of critical importance, for in the unpaired middle region the same torsion arises and, since the ends are held together in the paired regions on either side of it, the same coiling will develop as in the paired regions. It will merely develop more slowly in a middle part than in an end part since the twisting has to be conveyed to the ends which it will cause to rotate. No crossing-over can, however, take place in an unpaired region.

What do we find at diplotene? In the paired regions chiasmata are formed and little coiling is left, while between them in the formerly unpaired regions coiling still survives. Apparently therefore chiasmata replace coiling in the paired parts at the end of pachytene. They must then be determined by the coiling strain which they themselves remove (Fig. 19).

ii. *Experimental Evidence*

The comparison of diploid and triploid forms of plants with centric localisation of pairing affords a crucial test of this assumption. The comparison has been made in *Fritillaria latifolia*.[1] In the triploid, as is usually the case, the chiasma frequency is increased in proportion to the number of chromosomes. But pachytene pairing, as inferred from chiasma formation, spreads further along the chromosome than in the diploid. Moreover, the maximum number of chiasmata, which is four for a bivalent in the diploid, rises as high as nine in a trivalent of the triploid. The maximum is reached in bivalents with numerous changes of partner; and this happens only in bivalents of the type where the centromere is close to an end. It is thus evident that the numerous points of contact in such cases prevent the uncoiling of intercalary pieces of chromosome. They thus store the torsion or, as we may say, the crossing-over potential of the chromosomes. This potential is much higher per unit of length in an organism with localised pairing than in one with complete pairing since only thus can it have regular chiasma formation.

In many organisms such as a garden tulip, a lily or the grasshopper *Chorthippus*, a small proportion of the pachytene coiling still survives at the earliest diplotene stage, although pairing has presumably been complete at pachytene. At diplotene, relational coiling can then be seen in three distinct forms. There is a coiling of the chromosomes round one another between chiasmata; a coiling of the chromatids of each chromosome also between chiasmata; and finally a coiling, or rather a mere crossing, of two of the four chromatids at each chiasma which is a relic of the earlier chromosome coiling (Fig. 3). All these

[1] Darlington, 1940*a*.

types of coiling disappear in free arms before diakinesis. In closed loops the other two kinds are both translated into

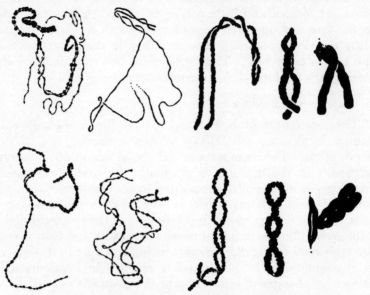

Fig. 19. Pachytene to first metaphase in *Fritillaria*. Above, in a species with moderate proximal localisation giving intermittent pachytene pairing and consequent survival of relational coiling. Below, in a species with complete pachytene pairing and consequent replacement of relational coiling by chiasma formation throughout the length of the chromosomes. Subterminal centromeres in both bivalents. (After Darlington, 1935.)

chromatid coiling: each loop flattens in one plane and successive loops come to lie at right angles, making each chiasma symmetrical.[2]

iii. *Breakage and Reunion*

It remains to explain how the strain of relational coiling can determine crossing-over when the pachytene equilibrium is brought to an end. It will be seen at once that this situation is unique in the history of the nucleus. Two chromosomes in a state of strain are split into four chromatids. At the same time the attraction between the chromosomes lapses. Each chromosome has to support separately its internal strains. Equilibrium

[2] Darlington, 1936*b*.

can only be re-established by the abolition of all relational coiling but, as observations of the diplotene stage show us, even the coiling of free arms does not disappear for some time. There is a lag in the adjustment of external form to internal stresses, the same hysteresis indeed which we noted in regard to relic coiling. It is this combination of a sudden strain with a delayed adjustment in a system, the elements of which have been weakened by division, that must be supposed to lead to a breakage of chromatids.

The diplotene change begins near the centromere in *Fritillaria*. Elsewhere it may begin near the ends. It is not likely to be simultaneous throughout each chromosome. Nor can the breakage of two chromatids at one chiasma be simultaneous. When a chromatid breaks between two genes the strain on its partner will be reduced by the release of their mutual coiling. The two broken ends will (if our model is a valid representation) revolve round their unbroken sister in opposite directions. At the same time the strain will be increased on the chromatids of the partner chromosome, for the coiling of the two chromosomes has been in equilibrium with that within each. When the strain on one is removed by breakage, that on the other is increased. On account of the specificity of the attractions between genes, this increase of strain will be greatest at a point opposite the first break. The first break will therefore immediately determine a corresponding one in a chromatid of the partner chromosome. Its two broken ends will uncoil and in doing so will meet the ends of the others before they meet one another again. They will rejoin just as the broken ends do when structural changes occur.[3]

One of the remarkable properties of crossing-over is that the two breaks occur at exactly corresponding points in the partner chromosomes. There are exceptions which give rise to well-known instances of adjoining duplications such as the Bar gene in *Drosophila* and Rhoesus in man; but they are rare. The reason for this rarity is undoubtedly the discontinuity of the chromosome. The number of places at which it can be broken are limited by the number of units of crossing-over, which are probably the chromomeres. Where chromomeres are large crossing-over will be most even. Where chromomeres are small,

[3] Darlington, 1935a, b.

as with polygenes, unequal crossing-over will be more frequent and may even be largely responsible for polygenic 'mutation'.

iv. *Interference*

Now since the ends of the chromosomes are free and the centromeres are single and show no specific attractions, both the ends and the centromeres are likely to be points of zero torsion. Only at a certain distance from them will the critical strain for crossing-over develop. Crossing-over will be suppressed in certain regions.[4] Similarly when crossing-over has occurred, reducing the strain in its neighbourhood, the chance of another cross-over near the first will be reduced. In fact crossing-over will be impossible within a certain distance, which will depend on the amount of coiling that has been undone by the crossing-over. Hence if the distributions of cross-overs are measured from the centromere we should expect zones of high and low crossing-over to be spread along the chromosome, gradually disappearing beyond the second or third chiasma. This is approximately what is observed in species of *Drosophila*. Especially it must be noticed that very close to the centromere there is no crossing-over. There will also be *interference* between successive cross-overs. Such interference has been measured from linkage by Muller and from the frequency distributions of chiasmata by Haldane. The frequency of double crossings-over within short distances is less than randomness requires. The curve of chiasma frequency per bivalent is narrower than a Poisson distribution will allow. Finally there should be no interference across the centromere: this is shown to be true both from chiasmata in *Fritillaria* and from linkage experiments in *Drosophila*.[5]

Summing up: precocity, chromomere formation, pairing, torsion, reproduction and repulsion may be seen as a natural sequence of events. And if repulsion is the immediate agent both of crossing-over and of chiasma formation we may say, not that crossing-over determines chiasma formation, but that they are indeed two aspects of the same thing.

We are only at the beginning of our understanding of crossing-over. In special circumstances it has special properties.

[4] Mather, 1938.
[5] Mather, 1938; Bennett, 1938; *cf.* Callan *et al.*, 1947.

Some of these will be dealt with later. Moreover in bacteria and viruses processes of recombination are now known which, as we shall see, have the same long-term effects, and have the same biological rôle, as crossing-over. But they have not the same closely knit relations with meiosis and with the elaboration of genetic systems which we are now going to discuss.

14

GENOTYPIC CONTROL

i. *The Twin Errors of Mitosis*

M ITOSIS in the indispensable tissues of animals and plants and under ordinary conditions follows a very regular course. We find differences in the organisation of mitosis in different groups of organisms, especially Protista, but we do not find the variations from which these differences might have been selected. The reason is clear. Any abnormality of mitosis in an indispensable tissue either kills the cell, or kills its progeny or kills the organism itself. There are however expendable tissues in which these consequences matter very little. Such are the pollen grains.

Following inbreeding in different cereals genotypes have been found with a variety of abnormalities of mitosis in the pollen. They usually show mendelian inheritance when crossed with the normal. Most of them are entirely lethal. They are significant therefore not for evolution but only for the theory of evolution. Two contrasted types of *polymitosis* are to be noted. In the first the nucleus comes into mitosis again and again. Divisions follow one another in rapid succession just as in a tumour. The mitoses are regular but they exhaust and kill the cell.[1] Thus the onset of mitosis which is usually adapted to the needs of the cell can be separated from these needs. The normal habit is an adaptation which is maintained by selection.

The second type of polymitosis is quite different. The nucleus comes into mitosis too soon and indeed reaches metaphase without the chromosomes having reproduced.[2] Thus the change in the cytoplasm which determines the beginning of mitosis and is usually correlated with reproduction of the chromosomes can be separated from this nuclear change. It can be separated, as we suppose it to be in meiosis, and indeed separated more widely.

[1] Darlington and Thomas, 1941.
[2] Beadle, 1933*b*.

ii. *The Time-Limit at Meiosis*

The genotypic abnormalities of meiosis are not less instructive. For the most part they lead to an irregular narrowing of the difference between mitosis and meiosis.

The most interesting genotypic abnormalities are the modifications of meiosis in the direction of mitosis by a reduction in the precocity of the prophase. The simplest of these modifications is found very generally but in various degrees amongst plants and animals with large chromosomes. It might indeed be regarded as an original property of chromosomes beyond a certain size, the mechanism of meiosis being only afterwards adjusted to allow for the size. For it is clear that the longer the chromosomes the longer it will take them to pair. At a critical time unpaired chromosomes evidently divide for they can no longer pair by attraction. The third unpaired chromosome in a triploid is divided already at pachytene. Perhaps the threshold for division, or more properly reproduction, is, as we might expect, lower in an unpaired chromosome than in a paired one. The attraction for a partner reduces the attraction for substrate materials, which must therefore reach a higher concentration before it results in reproduction.

However this may be, the imposition of a time limit restricts the pairing to the regions where it begins; consequently it restricts the crossing-over also. Then the location of chiasmata at metaphase (relatively little movement of chiasmata taking place in these large chromosomes) shows the *contact points*, the places where pairing has begun in these species. The chiasmata, we find, are *localised* either near the ends (terminally) or near the centromeres (centrically) or near both (Figs. 19, 20[3, 4]).

Species of *Fritillaria* show us the meaning of this distinction because they have different chromosomes with centromeres near the ends and near the middles of the chromosomes. In both types chiasmata are localised near the centromeres, never near the ends which are not adjoining a centromere. The grasshopper *Mecostethus* has all its chromosomes with subterminal centromeres and the chiasmata localised near the ends which have the centromeres. These are examples of extreme localisation. Some species of both *Fritillaria* and *Mecostethus* however are intermediate. Chiasmata are occasionally formed at the

[3] Frankel *et al.*, 1940.   [4] Darlington, 1940*b*.

distal ends of chromosomes as well. Now in species of *Fritillaria* with extreme localisation we find more chiasmata, indicating more pairing, in chromosomes where the centromere is near the end than where it is in the middle. Evidently an end has an inherent advantage in pairing in any organism because it can move freely; the middle parts are tethered.

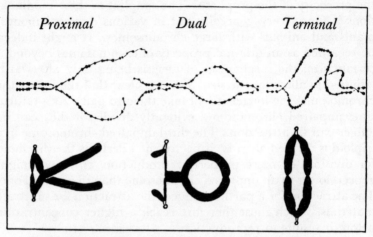

Fig. 20. Three types of localisation of pairing in long chromosomes with little terminalisation. Above, the arrested pachytene; below, first metaphase. The centromeres are submedian in the terminal type. Types: *Fritillaria, Chrysochraon* and *Tradescantia* (4x).

The contrast in the results of centric localisation helps us to understand the opposite type of terminal localisation. In the tetraploid species of *Tradescantia*, pairing and chiasma formation are restricted to the ends while the centric regions which are remote from the ends rarely form chiasmata. Dual localisation is found in another grasshopper *Chrysochraon* where chiasmata at metaphase are all either terminal or very close to the centromere.[5]

The degree of localisation of pairing at meiosis always varies from bivalent to bivalent and also from cell to cell. Consider first the bivalent variation. We always find that bivalents with single chiasmata have their chiasma nearest to the contact point, nearest that is to the end or the centromere as the case may be. Bivalents with a second chiasma form it next to the

[5] Darlington, 1940a.

first and so on in succession. This is equally true when the contact point is at the end as in *Secale* (Fig. 21) or at the centromere as in *Fritillaria* or *Paris*.[6]

It is clear in these cases that pairing in the prophase has begun at the contact point, has proceeded along the chromosome but has been interrupted at different stages allowing of the formation of increasing numbers of chiasmata the further it has been allowed to go.

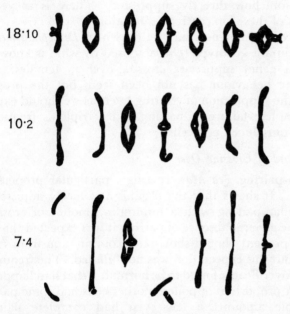

18·10

10·2

7·4

Fig. 21. First metaphase in normal and semi-precocious meiosis in forms of *Secale cereale*. Left: The numbers of total and terminal chiasmata in each cell. Four univalents in the bottom cell. (Lamm, 1936.) Reduced precocity entails reduced pachytene pairing and hence fewer and more localised chiasmata.

The comparison of cells carries this explanation a step further. In inbred types of *Secale* where chiasma-formation partly fails the cells with fewest bivalents and fewest chiasmata have these chiasmata most strictly localised near the ends. Moreover these cells show a reduced spiralisation. They are half-way between a mitotic and a meiotic degree of contraction: the cells are semi-precocious (Fig. 21).

[6] Darlington, 1941.

Some more extreme mutants have their chiasma formation and metaphase pairing largely suppressed. In *Zea Mays*[7] and *Crepis capillaris* strains of this kind occur, but these show neither the failure of pachytene nor the reduced metaphase spiralisation that goes with it. It may be that the pachytene pairing seen in these cases to be complete is not true attraction pairing but largely a torsion pairing of already divided chromosomes. Alternatively it may be that attraction is normal but that torsion is somehow directly suppressed. There is as yet no critical test of these alternative assumptions.

The converse inference may be drawn in *Drosophila melanogaster*. A mutant genotype (characterised by what is known as the Gowen gene) suppresses crossing-over in females. The chromosome behaviour has not been seen, but the progeny show that the suppression of crossing-over, as we should expect, entails complete failure of pairing, since triploids frequently arise from unreduced egg cells.

iii. *Adjustment of Crossing Over*

The non-pairing *Zea Mays* reveals a particular property of adaptation. It shows that the organism is nicely adjusted to secure regular pairing with a minimum amount of crossing-over. In the general absence of pairing it was expected that the occasional progeny should show no recombination from crossing-over. But this expectation was not fulfilled. The frequency of crossing-over Beadle found to be normal. What had happened was this. A proportion of pollen mother cells had some pairing —a variable amount; a few even had complete pairing. Mutant genotypes are not buffered against environmental variations. Cells which gave progeny were solely those rare ones with ten bivalents. These cells must have had a chiasma frequency between the normal and the minimum compatible with complete pairing. The experiment proves that the normal and the minimum are the same.

The same exact adaptation and buffering of the meiotic mechanism are revealed by the variety of disordered types that are produced not by inbreeding but by outbreeding. They arise in the second generation when two differently adjusted species are crossed.

[7] Beadle, 1933*a*

The best example is the cross between the two species of onion, *Allium fistulosum* with centric localisation and *A. cepa* with terminal localisation (Fig. 22). In the F_1 there is evidence of inversion and interchange hybridity, a corresponding slight reduction of chiasma-frequency, and some univalents. The

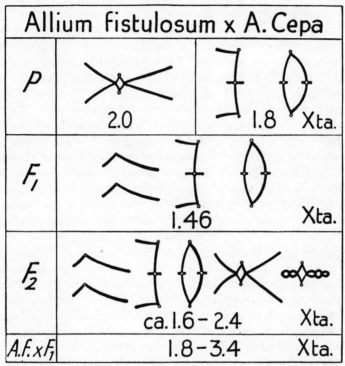

FIG. 22. Chiasma frequency and distribution in two species of *Allium* and in their cross and its derivatives. Numbers are average frequencies for individuals. There is also evidence of inversion and interchange hybridity in the F_1. (After Levan, 1936, 1941; Maeda, 1937, 1942; Emsweller and Jones, 1945.)

localisation is still terminal as in the male parent. Among individuals in the F_2 there is a wide range in mean chiasma-frequencies indicating the effects of mendelian recombination. The highest mean values are above those of either parent and this is due to a reduced localisation. The maximum number of chiasmata formed in a bivalent rises from three in the species to seven in the F_2. Thus the pairing of the chromosomes, although it is more variable, can also be much fuller in the hybrid derivatives than in the pure species.

These recombinations in the *Allium* F_2 thus show a genotypic control of a number of variations in the character of meiosis. The first of these variations is in the *time-limit*, the amount of time available for pairing. Thus the degree of localisation varies and perhaps also the number of chiasmata formed per unit of length paired at prophase. The second variation is in the *contact point* in which the parental species differ. Thus some plants have centric and some have terminal localisation. And, what is more, some have mixed localisation, due perhaps to an irregular arrangement of chromosomes in the pre-meiotic nucleus, of a kind that never occurs in the meiosis of any species.

What do these variations mean? They mean that in species we have well-ordered genetic systems with such control of meiosis as to give regular contact points and regular chromosome pairing. Further such systems are achieved by the elimination of certain kinds of genotype which would occur without selection; genotypes which indeed do occur when an outbreeding species is subjected to a change of breeding system by exceptionally close inbreeding as in maize or rye or by exceptionally wide crossing as in *Allium*.

We thus see that directly or indirectly genotypic conditions may modify the distribution of crossing-over in the chromosomes or may suppress it altogether. And in suppressing it, unless some special secondary mechanism is introduced, they also suppress segregation, reduction, and the ordinary course of sexual reproduction. These genetic variations, as we shall see, provide the materials for important changes in the genetic system when such changes happen to have selective value.

iv. *Chromosome Breakage and Mutation*

A third type of chromosome behaviour which is subject to genotypic variation and genotypic control is the ability of the chromosome to maintain itself; or conversely the occurrence of what is usually called spontaneous chromosome breakage. Again in most stable genetic systems the frequency of such breakage like the frequency of undefined gene mutations is low. It is probably close to or asymptotic to the minimum value that adaptation of the whole system can achieve. But again when inbreeding or crossing disturb the system, or in extreme external conditions, the regularity of reproduction breaks down. Sometimes it breaks down for the chromosomes in general and in the resting nucleus; and sometimes only for their centromeres on the spindle. Recessive types appear like 'sticky' maize which generate hybridity by chromosome breakage during the life of one plant. Usually however the breakage of the chromosomes is concentrated in tissues where it does not affect vegetative life. At meiosis in inbred *Secale*[8] again and also in outcrossed *Chorthippus*.[9] In pollen grain mitoses in many species of *Tulipa*[10] and in nutritive tissues such as the tapetal cells of anthers we may take spontaneous breakage for granted.

What we do not take for granted however is one kind of spontaneous breakage which can be discovered only by experimental treatment. If differentiated cells are stimulated to resume mitosis in roots by growth hormones or by irradiation damage it is sometimes found that the chromosomes have broken in the resting nuclei from which they would never normally have emerged.[11]

This condition shows the reciprocal of the non-breakability of chromosomes in cells with a mitotic future. Where the action of selection on the genotype has no effect the chromosomes become breakable.

Once again we see that normal chromosome behaviour is preserved only by continuous selection working through the mechanism of genotypic control. It breaks down wherever breakdown does not matter. And the potentiality for breakdown is continually made available by genetic variation arising from changes in the breeding system.

Conditions on the periphery of a habitat will often compel a change in the breeding system. And a change towards closer inbreeding or towards wider crossing is equally capable of leading to a sudden explosion of variation affecting secondarily the behaviour of the chromosomes and even their stability.

Closely related to this aspect of genotypic control is its effect on mutation rates. Frequency of mutation, as we shall see later, is controlled by the genotype. In view of the enormously different requirements of asexual micro-organisms without gene

[8] Rees, 1955*a* and *b*.   [9] Klingstedt, 1938.
[10] Darlington and Upcott, 1941.   [11] La Cour, 1953*b*.

recombination, of flies with frequent sexual generations and of trees with vastly infrequent generations, we are bound to expect some degree of adaptation in the genotypically controlled mutation of these forms. We are equally bound to expect, however, that this adaptation will lag behind the changing needs of the organism, particularly when the need is for an increase of mutation. That is in part why we find that large organisms lag behind small organisms in evolution.[12]

v. *Nuclear Self Control*

The cellular aspect of the genotypic control of chromosome behaviour is in effect the physiology of self-control. Like all other kinds of genotypic activity it depends on the interaction of nucleus and cytoplasm. At one extreme, such an interaction is known to take effect at once in the formation of the telophase nucleus in which a gene-deficiency is first segregated at the second meiotic division. A single nucleus is replaced by several fragments of nucleus in the cells with a particular deficiency following non-disjunction in an interchange ring in *Allium*.[13] At the other extreme, in the abnormal pollen grain mitoses described in maize which are determined by recessive mutations, the abnormalities show themselves only in the pollen grains produced by the homozygous diploid plant; they do not show themselves at the mitosis in segregating pollen grains of the heterozygous diploid plant. The abnormal gene has to be there, reacting or failing to react with the cytoplasm, for more than one mitotic cycle, perhaps for a whole life cycle, in advance.

The various types of genotypic control make it possible for genes to be inherited independently, while the genetic system is selected as an integrated whole. The genes are like the members of a legislature in being subject as individuals to the laws they enact as a body. It is through this subjection that the co-ordination of the whole of the hereditary and reproductive mechanisms, the adaptation and evolution of the genetic system, has been possible.

This physiological control evidently works to maintain a uniform action of genes in a changing environment where such a uniform action is desirable. The genes are buffered against such changes as are likely to upset their co-ordinated action in

---

[12] Darlington, 1955.   [13] Levan, 1939.

the system. Single gene mutations represent the minimum change and the minimum unbalance. Buffering by selection of modifying polygenes is probably responsible for the general dominance of wild-type genes in old established species over their mutant alternatives, most mutants depending on the suppression of an old activity rather than on the invention of a new one.[14]

The opposition between genotype and environment is fundamental for all other genetic analysis. How far does it carry us in the study of the chromosomes themselves? We have to attempt to assign all variations in the behaviour of chromosomes to internal or to external causes. But we have found it convenient to distinguish as genotypic those properties of the nucleus in which it acts indirectly on itself, through the cytoplasm. This is to distinguish them from certain properties which depend directly on the internal structure of the chromosomes. These properties are of two kinds: those due to polynemy and those due to hybridity.

Polynemy produces its most striking result at meiosis in hybrids. When species with large and small chromosomes are crossed the dissimilar chromosomes differing presumably in polynemy meet at meiosis in the hybrid.[15] But since few fertile hybrids of this kind are known the consequences have not yet been seen and they are clearly not of great practical importance.

Structural hybridity, on the other hand, is of the greatest practical importance. It produces effects at meiosis which resemble as we know, those of genotypic abnormalities. The two can be distinguished as we saw in *Allium*. And we have to distinguish them on account of the utter contrast in their modes of heredity, their effects on reproduction, and hence their evolutionary consequences.

Indeed, the separation of what is structural and what is genotypic in the variation of chromosome behaviour, and the discovery of how the two interact, are the most persistent problems in our study of the evolution of chromosome behaviour.

[14] Fisher, 1929; Muller, 1932b; Harland, 1936.
[15] Hakansson, 1943; Levan, 1944.

15

THE BIOLOGY OF RECOMBINATION

i. *Processes of Recombination*

MEIOSIS in its characteristic form shows us the two functions of crossing-over. They are complementary. For crossing-over inherently constitutes the recombination of parts of chromosomes. But crossing-over is a condition of the pairing of chromosomes at the first metaphase of meiosis. It therefore also determines the recombination of whole chromosomes and their reduction in number. Thus crossing-over is the key to half the business of sexual reproduction; the other half, of course, being the fertilisation which brings together the differences that are available for recombination. Meiosis thus does something more than compensate for the doubling of fertilisation: it completes the recombining of fertilisation.

In this way, we are led to the first understanding of meiosis, that which we owe to Weismann.

The importance of sexual reproduction, as Weismann pointed out, lies in its effecting a recombination of the parts of the hereditary materials which exposes them to the most efficient natural selection. This recombination we now see is more profound than Weismann imagined. It extends beyond the chromosomes to the genes. The number of units capable of recombination is not five or even fifty, but five thousand or fifty thousand. These units are units of heredity by virtue of crossing-over. If crossing-over ceases to occur they cease to be units: the chromosome is frozen into a single unadaptable block.

It is clear that for any particular inter-mating group there must at any particular time be an optimum amount of recombination and therefore an optimum number of chromosomes and an optimum amount of crossing-over between them. We might consider these together by taking the sum of the haploid number of chromosomes and of the average chiasma frequency of all the chromosomes in a meiotic cell as a *recombination index*.

112

Too high an index would be deleterious by breaking up advantageous combinations; too low an index would never achieve the most advantageous combinations.

One would suppose on grounds of recombination alone that one chromosome would always be better than several, since genes in different chromosomes cannot be kept together. But in fact the matter is not so simple as this. Genes in different chromosomes, as we have seen, can by special means be kept together. Rather it is genes at opposite ends of one long chromosome which cannot be kept together. Moreover, as a consideration of the mechanics both of mitosis and meiosis shows, a single long chromosome, or more especially a single centromere, will not give the easiest separation. The only organism with a single pair of chromosomes, the threadworm *Ascaris*, has several co-ordinated centromeres lying close together in them.

ii. *The First Adaptive Compromise*

The optimum recombination index will depend on the number and concentration of gene variations to be recombined within the breeding group. And hence it will depend on the size of the group and its freedom of mating. Have we reason to suppose that such an optimum—whatever it may be—is generally attained? We certainly have not.

Chromosome number is often one of the most conservative properties of the genetic system. The same number is found constantly in large sections of the Orthoptera, the Gramineae and the Rosaceae.[1] On the other hand, unrelated species having similar genetic systems in other respects have entirely different numbers. It is moreover easier to increase the chromosome number than to reduce it. Both mean a change in the number of centromeres by misdivision or by their loss or reduplication together with that of the adjoining parts of the chromosome. And unless these parts are inert their reduplication will have a less dangerous effect on the balance of the organism than their loss. In a word it seems that increase of chromosome number is an evolutionary step that cannot easily be retraced. It offers immediate advantages at the expense of ultimate survival (Fig. 23).

[1] Darlington, 1956*a*.

Chiasma frequency, on the other hand, has to meet the requirements of regular pairing and reduction before it can meet those of crossing-over. It is indeed readily variable. Within the species *Fritillaria imperialis* clones exist with an average chiasma frequency per bivalent differing as much as 2·6 and 5·0. In short-lived species however where sexual reproduction recurs at short intervals (as we saw in *Zea*) the chiasma frequency is the minimum compatible with regular pairing in the shorter members of the complement.

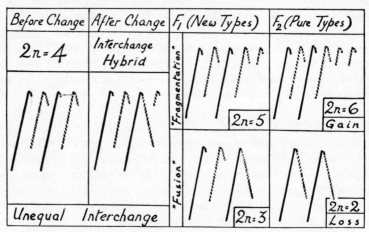

Fig. 23. Diagram showing how two pairs of chromosomes can become one or three in evolution following interchange in a diploid. The first requires loss of a part of a chromosome near its centromere and this part must therefore be inert or non-specific. The second requires gain of a similar part which need not be inert or non-specific. (After Darlington, 1937a.)

Supernumerary or B chromosomes do not always form a chiasma when they are smaller than any of the rest of the complement. Chiasma frequency is proportional to length. This shows that the species is adapted to have regular chiasma formation and metaphase pairing for its ordinary complement. But it is not adapted to provide for shorter members. Statistical comparison in *Secale* shows that the ordinary bivalents have 2·42 chiasmata on the average, while an extra short pair (one-third their length) has 0·83 chiasmata and therefore sometimes fails to pair.[2] The same lack of pairing is found in

[2] Darlington, 1933a.

small extra chromosomes in *Fritillaria*, *Matthiola*, and *Solanum*.

The condition in species with a wide range of size in their normal complement is radically different. The small chromosomes regularly pair with a single chiasma, the longer ones have several chiasmata but their frequency is usually less than proportional to their length. In *Chorthippus* (Fig. 3), where the long chromosomes are more than five times as long as the short ones, they have only 3·3 chiasmata on the average. The same discrepancy is found in many Liliaceae. Evidently these species are adapted to economise in the number of chiasmata formed. Lower crossing-over has, as we might expect, a selective value.[3]

The mechanism which equalises the number of chiasmata formed amongst chromosomes of different lengths is probably of various kinds. There is evidence of two methods that might be effective. It might be due to the pachytene pairing of the chromosomes beginning simultaneously and the last parts of the long ones to pair being already partly uncoiled when they pair, so that the coiling strain developed in them will not be proportional to their length. In the grasshopper *Mecostethus* it is in fact achieved by centric localisation of pairing.

Another means by which crossing-over is reduced in the system is its abolition in one sex, as in the male *Drosophila*[4] and *Callimantis*.[5] The male genotype determines a special type of meiosis in which crossing-over and chiasma formation are dispensed with, and the chromosomes pair by an extension of the usual primary attraction from two threads to four. This device has the effect of reducing the average recombination index of the species. Now chiasmata are formed at meiosis (in one sex or both) in all sexually reproducing species. *Drosophila* shows that the original conditions of meiosis can be removed. It is not now chiasmata which are necessary for the chromosome pairing in the individual, but crossing-over which is necessary for gene recombination in the species: the occurrence of crossing-over remains indispensable for the genetic system but its frequency is halved.

iii. *Breakdown of Control*

Both in chromosome number and in chiasma frequency, however, we must suppose that species are very imperfectly

---

[3] Fisher, 1929.   [4] Darlington, 1934.   [5] White, 1938.

adapted to their needs of recombination. The lag in adjustment will be even greater than in other properties of the genetic system because their adaptation is a compromise. Both of them have other effects unrelated to their function of recombination and these effects will react on the species more rapidly than errors of recombination. Let us now consider some of these.

Simple inversion of a segment of chromosome, unless it produces a position effect, has no significance apart from its effect on crossing-over in the hybrid. When single crossing-over occurs between the dislocated segments in an inversion hybrid, and the dicentric chromatid breaks into two, two new chromatids are formed. They are deficient for the end segment, and one of them may have a reduplication of a proximal segment if the chromatid breaks unequally. Such chromosomes are not likely to survive unless they are supernumerary to the ordinary haploid set. They should be particularly important therefore in polyploids. In fact they arise frequently owing to special circumstances in all triploids and in many tetraploids.

In triploids there is the equivalent of a whole extra set made up of parts of chromosomes unprovided with partners at pachytene. Short segments, such as we saw were frequently repeated within the haploid set, are thus in a position to pair with one another as they never could in a diploid. We therefore often find pairing within this third set. A triploid *Triticum* or *Fragaria* with 21 chromosomes, instead of forming a maximum of seven associations (trivalents or bivalents and univalents), may form eight or nine pairs at meiosis. Some of these extra pairings are due to interchange hybridity. Others are due to reduplications. Some of these again are between inverted segments, some of them between straight segments; even these will of course give rise to new chromosome types, longer or shorter than the original ones and with a different linear order of genes. In addition to all these there is misdivision in univalents. Triploids therefore in *Solanum*, *Tradescantia* and elsewhere constantly give new chromosome types in their progeny. These are usually small chromosomes, and probably supernumerary chromosomes can arise in this way.

In new allopolyploids where the different sets, as in *Primula kewensis*, are imperfectly differentiated, chromosomes from different sets occasionally pair and cross over. Sometimes the result is merely a recombination of genes. Frequently however a structural rearrangement takes place, owing to the chromosomes which have crossed over being structurally different. Such changes have often been found in hexaploid wheats and oats. They give rise to important mutants and demand the constant selection of the varieties in which they occur.[6]

Such changes are *secondary structural changes*, and they must be clearly distinguished from primary structural changes of which they are, as we may say, the illegitimate and casual progeny. Primary changes occur at all stages of development equally in pure and hybrid organisms. Secondary changes occur only at meiosis in organisms which in a broad sense are hybrids—structural or numerical. They occur only through crossing-over between differently placed segments and are therefore liable to be of particular types, each occurring with a particular frequency in a given hybrid. Formerly their effects, like those of primary changes, were ascribed to undefined mutations.

The diploid progeny in which secondary structural changes have occurred usually die, so that crossing-over is, as we have seen, effectively suppressed between the segments in which it will give rise to such changes—within inversions and proximal to interchanges. Recombination is stopped, and in special cases we shall see what effect this may have. The same condition however applies in general to all chromosomes near their centromeres and perhaps also near their ends. We find in fact that near the centromeres of all the chromosomes in *Drosophila* the genes have become inert or non-specific. Thus genes are likely in general to be arranged on chromosomes subject to selection for two kinds of advantage: their physiological interaction and consequent efficiency, and their needs for recombination which are perhaps more important for more specific big genes than for less specific little genes.

In this light the frequency and distribution of crossing-over must have an important effect on the genetic structure of the species. What this effect is we shall see most clearly from the behaviour and evolution of permanent hybrids.

[6] Frankel, 1949.

I

16

THE PURSUIT OF HYBRIDITY

i. *The Breeding Group*

NATURAL selection depends for its scope and effectiveness on the availability and potential permanence of the largest possible number of workable combinations of hereditary differences. These properties depend in turn on the existence of differences between corresponding chromosomes which pair at meiosis and on the occurrence of recombination between such differences as lie in various parts of the chromosome complement. In other words they depend on hybridity and on crossing-over. We have seen that crossing-over is regulated and has a certain optimum value which may or may not be attained. Let us now examine the regulation of hybridity.

The first factor determining hybridity is obviously variation, for if there is no change in the genes and the chromosomes there can be no hybridity. We find that both intragenic and intergenic mutation are controlled by the genotype. A gene in one species of *Gossypium* when transferred to another species by crossing has a higher mutation rate.[1] The particular unstable genes whose frequent mutation is responsible for white flowered plants becoming flaked with colour are always found to vary in frequency of mutation subject to varying genotypes. And they vary also in the time and place of most frequent mutation. The same is true of structural changes. Any change in the breeding system, towards wider crossing or narrower inbreeding, as we saw, causes an enhanced rate of structural change. We must suppose therefore that particular species or at least breeding groups have genotypic properties in this respect more or less adapted to their needs, although no doubt lagging behind these needs as the genetic system changes.

The second factor of importance in determining hybridity will be the system of mating, which in turn will depend on two independently variable conditions: first, the size of the breeding

---

[1] Harland, 1936; Sturtevant, 1937; Rhoades, 1938.

group, the continually varying collection of individuals amongst which mating can take place, and secondly, the biological and spatial freedom of this mating.

The size of the breeding group may be limited by factors of different kinds. On the one hand geographical isolation may separate two parts of a species which would otherwise be capable of crossing freely. And the means by which geographical isolation will arise must depend in turn on *genetic mobility*, that is, on the individual movements or local conservatism of an animal species, and on the pollen or seed distribution in a plant species. On the other hand, a slight differentiation of sexual habits or time of flowering, or a few structural changes in the chromosomes, or a gene mutation for cross-sterility, or even a gene-mutation for self-fertility, or co-ordinated changes in the rate of growth of pollen and the length of the style, may any of them separate the changed individuals from the rest of the breeding group. In doing this these internal or genetic changes break up the breeding group into two parts just as external or geographical changes may do, and equally without any visible sign in the form of the organism to show what has happened. They establish a *genetic isolation* which is to be distinguished from Darwin's geographical isolation or its corollary of ecological isolation.

In explaining this distinction originally[2] I did not make it clear that it is something more than a descriptive distinction. Later genetical writers consequently failed to grasp its strict use and missed its full value. They even allowed themselves to blur the distinction under the common heading of 'isolating mechanisms' descriptively divided into geographical and reproductive elements.[3] Now the distinction turns out to be an antithesis. It has the same kind of axiomatic status for the discussion of evolution that the antithesis between genotype and environment has for the discussion of heredity. It is the antithesis, which we can never afford to drop in our enquiry after causes, between what is internal and what is external in determining the properties of living organisms.

Genetic isolation, as we shall see, is a more frequent and a vastly more varied cause of the origin of races and species than the external modes of isolation. So much so that it is possible

[2] Darlington, 1933*b*, 1940*c*.   [3] e.g. Dobzhansky, 1938.

to predict from the breeding systems of plant species what obstacles will be found to exist to crossing them. Inbreeding species as in *Triticum* or *Oenothera* have needed no genetic isolation to separate them since inbreeding itself constitutes a genetic isolation. In fact they cross experimentally with the greatest freedom.[4]

Freedom of mating within a breeding group depends in the first instance on the restriction of self-fertilisation. In most groups of animals this is achieved of course by sexual differentiation of individuals, or dioecism as it is conveniently called in plants. In plants the methods are less obvious, less severe and more readily changed. For example, an almost regular habit of self-fertilisation is found in many cultivated plants like peas, beans, tomatoes and barley. But crossing was the habit of their wild ancestors. It is merely that in cultivation, crossing being no longer advantageous, the obstacles to selfing have been removed by the natural selection of individuals lacking these obstacles.[5]

ii. *The Genetic Promotion of Crossing*

Amongst the flowering plants an enormous number of devices are known for promoting cross-pollination. The morphological devices were explored in great detail by Sprengel and Darwin; the genetic devices have also long been known but only recently understood.

The most obvious genetic device preventing self-fertilisation is the incompatibility or self-sterility gene system.[6] This system is found in its simplest form in those fungi where two haploid nuclei will fuse only if they differ in respect of a particular gene or genes. In flowering plants the case is similar: the pollen of a self-sterile plant will not fertilise the same plant or any other plant having a particular gene in the same state as itself. The gene concerned exists in the species in a multiple series of alleles which may be called S_1, S_2, S_3 and so on. S_1 pollen will not grow on an S_1S_2 style or an S_1S_3 style, only on one, like S_2S_3, which has no S_1 allele. Hence self-fertilisation cannot occur and pure S_1S_1 individuals cannot be produced. A majority of diploid species of flowering plants probably have

[4] Darlington and Mather, 1949, p. 309.
[5] Darlington, 1956a.   [6] D. Lewis, 1954.

such a differential gene system of self-sterility in some stage of development from a sporadic origin to a universal distribution.

The physiological mechanism varies. Sometimes the pollen will germinate but die in the style. Sometimes the pollen tube will enter the ovule but die without procuring fertilisation.[7] However they work, these contraceptive genes prevent self-fertilisation. They also prevent crossing with other individuals having the same allele. They will not however ensure any cumulative hybridity except in the parts of the chromosome so close to the S gene that very little crossing-over takes place with it.

This lack of crossing-over however is the crux of a large question. The accumulation of differences in association with an S allele, means in juxtaposition with it in the chromosome. It means having no crossing-over between them. And this will make the two into a compound structure. We might expect that its efficiency could be increased in this way and evidence of association of two segments, a primer and a specifier, has in fact been found by Lewis. The most complex organisation however probably develops where the system is confined to two or three alleles. This happens where a difference in length of the style and the stamens, known as *heterostyly*, is combined with an incompatibility reaction.

In *Primula sinensis* the two alternative types of plant are produced in equal numbers and their flowers are contrasted in six respects, as follows:

	PIN	THRUM
genotype	homozygous (*ss*)	heterozygous (*Ss*)
style	long	short
stamen	short	long
stigma	large papillae	small papillae
*pollen form**	smaller grains	larger grains
*pollen growth**	better on thrum stigma	better on pin stigma

* The pollen character is imposed by the genotype of the diploid plant.

Thus several kinds of difference between male and female organs have to be co-ordinated in the alternative types so as to allow of cross-pollination and also so as to ensure a successful result from it.[8]

[7] Sears, 1937.   [8] Darwin, 1877; Mather, 1950.

That heterostyly does in fact give a successful result is testified by its systematic extent. It occurs in large groups and it occurs in many groups; indeed in about thirty non-tropical families of flowering plants. All sections of the genus *Primula* have heterostyle species, altogether 354 species out of 419.[9] The property is continually being lost in small wild populations and in cultivated varieties and is often permanently lost in polyploid species. Yet it remains characteristic of nearly all diploid races or species. This gene difference is therefore at least as old as the genus *Primula*.

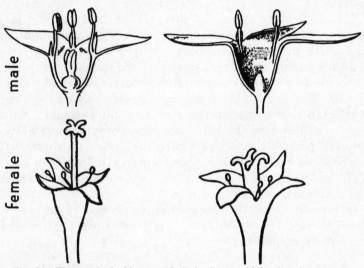

Fig. 24. The survival of heterostyly in both sexes of the dioecious species *Rhamnus catharticus* revealed by the flowers of the four types of plants. Left, long-styled; right, short-styled.   (After Darwin, 1877.)

Other evidence of the great age of heterostyly is provided by *Rhamnus catharticus* where, as described by Darwin, both the male and the female plants are of two kinds, those with long and those with short styles (Fig. 24). Dioecy seems to have been superimposed on heterostyly without having succeeded in erasing its expression. A wonderful field of enquiry is waiting for us when we care to study the genetic basis of such successions of breeding systems.

The co-ordination of the parts of the heterostyle gene we

⁹ Bruun, 1938.

should expect to have been built up by a long process of evolution beginning with the placing of the right genes next to one another. It can however be broken down in one step when 'homostyle' plants arise from heterostyle. The evidence from *Primula obconica* suggests that the step consists in a crossing-over between the parts of the *S* and *s* gene complexes in the *Ss* thrum plants.[10]

Dioecy, which we shall consider later, is certainly less frequent in the flowering plants and probably less durable than their incompatibility systems. But there is another system resembling dioecy superficially which is even less durable. It owes its interest to the fact that it needs no elaboration and probably comes and goes with great ease. This is the system of floating male-sterility—known to botanists under the unhelpful name of gyno-dioecy. It occurs in as many as a third of the species of the whole family of *Labiatae*. Certain plants in each population have the genetic property of developing no anthers. The normal hermaphrodite plants may self-fertilise or they may cross. But the exclusively female plants have to be pollinated by hermaphrodites; that is they have to cross. Since they can propagate only as female parents they must leave fewer progeny than the hermaphrodites. In these circumstances, if they maintain their type in the population, it must be because their progeny have an immediate and decisive advantage through hybridity over the progeny of hermaphrodites.

This is a somewhat surprising conclusion. Is it indeed correct? The mode of inheritance of male-sterility in these natural populations, as Lewis has shown,[11] reveals the need of a correction in the argument. The male-sterility is never determined by a single gene difference. As a rule it is inherited solely in the female line. Progeny of female plants are female; progeny of hermaphrodite plants, even crossed with the female, are hermaphrodite. Evidently the variation is not due to genes in the nucleus but to something carried not by the pollen but only by the egg; that is to something in the cytoplasm. This kind of property we shall return to consider later. For the moment let us notice that those kinds of pollen-sterility which appear in inbred maize all appeared to be due to the mendelian segregation of nuclear genes. Why then has a cytoplas-

[10] V. P. J. Dowrick, 1956.   [11] D. Lewis, 1941; Lewis and Crowe, 1955.

mic difference been picked up in natural populations as a means of encouraging crossing? Simply because in this way the crossing habit can be most easily established in the genetic system of a flowering plant. It is only in respect of the cytoplasm, that is of purely maternal inheritance, that female and hermaphrodite plants leave the same numbers of progeny.

iii. *The Second Adaptive Compromise*

The combination of change, crossing and selective elimination in any stable breeding group will work together to produce a certain *hybridity equilibrium*. Through their effect on this equilibrium they will react on the rest of the genetic system of the species. There must usually be, as Mather has put it,[12] a compromise between fitness and flexibility. But it is a compromise which, as we shall see, breaks down on certain occasions. The hybridity equilibrium may be measured in breeding experiments by the vigour and variety of the progeny from self-fertilisation or inbreeding. At meiosis, on the other hand, it may be measured by the frequency of bridges produced by inversion crossing-over.[13]

All sexual reproduction entails inbreeding simply because all breeding groups are limited by genetic isolation. But we can conveniently contrast the two extremes of self-fertilisation and of the widest crossing permitted by this limitation.

The effects of self-fertilisation or close inbreeding and cross-fertilisation with remote relatives are markedly different in a diploid species which is normally cross-fertilised. The one reduces the hybridity below the usual level, the other raises it. The one produces offspring of reduced vigour, the other of increased vigour. This property of increased vigour in crosses is known as *heterosis*. According to the one model it may be represented as due to the recessiveness of deleterious mutations in respect of some of which each of the parents is pure. Such crosses may be represented as $AAbb \times aaBB$ where both a and b are deleterious. The fact that such deleterious genes are present is due to their general protection from elimination by constant cross-fertilisation. The fact that a wide cross will suppress some that have been showing with the ordinary system of cross-fertilisation shows that elimination of poorer growing

[12] Mather, 1943.   [13] Darlington, 1937*b*.

individuals has not been rigorous enough for the previous size of the breeding group. In a word the genetic properties of a group are conditioned by its breeding system. Self-fertilisation is not deleterious in a group which has been selected under constant self-fertilisation in the past.

Such principles as these govern the evolution of the breeding system so long as the other side of the genetic system, namely the chromosomes, maintains a stable character. There are however several ways by which the relations of the two can be upset. One is by polyploidy.

A regularly cross-fertilised group is likely to be upset by allopolyploidy in three ways. First, the allopolyploid is a permanent hybrid whose recessive gene mutations cannot segregate when it is self-fertilised. If its diploid parents have a self-sterility system this system will not necessarily work in the new polyploid. Diploid hyacinths are self-sterile, triploids are not. Secondly, the new polyploid is in any case a breeding group by itself—the only member of a new species genetically isolated from its parents and with enforced inbreeding. And finally, as we saw, its method of variation is enlarged by a secondary segregation of ancestral differences. All these conditions are likely to change the character of the genetic system when a new polyploid species is formed. Later when such a polyploid by gradual differentiation of its sets becomes a functional diploid (if it was not so at first), in its general heredity, it will no doubt also recover some of the characters of its diploid ancestors, such as dioecy, in its breeding system. Others such as heterostyly may prove to be irrecoverable.

With polyploidy, or change in chromosome number, the genetic system suffers a sudden revolution in all its parts. With change in chromosome structure however the effect is graduated and its several and highly diverse steps can be studied in their effects on the system in a much more exact way. Moreover since these steps generate hybridity and restrict recombination they have a crucial position in the evolution of genetic systems. This position we must now study.

17

PERMANENT HYBRIDS

i. *Modes of Discontinuity*

An inversion, or at least a small inversion, can exist in a species in two common conditions. The first is that in which it is most likely to begin, the condition of free combination between the original and the changed structural types; here pure original, pure changed and hybrid individuals will exist side by side in equilibrium and freely intercross. Such a condition of inversions is found in *Campanula persicifolia*, but equilibrium has not been reached throughout the population of this widely distributed species. Crosses between plants from different regions are in general more hybrid than the wild plants drawn from any one region. Evidently new inversions are continually spreading in the species. This stage of development may be described as the stage of the *floating* inversion.[1]

The second stage in the history of an inversion is that where it becomes fixed in a given part of the species, a geographical or an ecological race. This stage is reached in *Drosophila pseudo-obscura*.[2] Chromosome differences between different species of *Drosophila* or *Lilium* are found to consist largely of inversions such as those which are here found developing and becoming fixed within species. Evidently they have arisen in the same way.

The question now arises as to why an inversion should become characteristic of a particular race having particular genetic properties which are not implied by the inversion itself. We find the answer in the discovery that the characteristic groups of differences between species or races are often found to be closely linked or even inherited as a single unit. In *Secale* several interchanges seem to hold together a group of differences between species. In *Rubus* the distinction between the raspberry and blackberry sections of the genus can segregate as a

[1] Darlington and Gairdner, 1937.
[2] Dobzhansky and Sturtevant, 1938.

single unit.[3] In the case of the speltoid and fatuoid complexes
which distinguish important ancestral groups in wheat and oats
it seems that inversions are what maintain this unity. They do
so by suppressing crossing-over between the group of gene
differences which are associated in the complexes. Inversions
isolate segments of chromosomes just as seas and deserts isolate
segments of a species. We can have an endogamy of chromosomes as much as an endogamy of populations. We can have
a genetic isolation of segments as much as a genetic isolation
of individuals.

Inversions may promote discontinuity within a species in two
ways, gradually and suddenly. Small inversions will largely
inhibit crossing-over and, floating in the species, will survive if
they happen to pick out a useful combination of genes. They
will act as a brake on recombination amongst these genes.

Such inversions have been found floating—as well as fixed—
in all species of *Drosophila* that have been studied. The effects
of these inversions, which are detected in the polytene chromosomes, may not be visible to the experimenter although they are
obviously important to the fly. Such a situation has been
described as a chromosome polymorphism. How is it related
to the visible polymorphism which has been shown to be
characteristic of visibly variable species in plants and animals
generally? Visible polymorphism is due to floating genetic
differences whose chromosome basis is not as a rule directly
observable.[4] They have been most extensively surveyed in
regard to the blood group antigens of man. Such differences
have become increasingly recognised to be compound differences owing both to their complexity and to their occasional
breakdown by crossing-over. As a rule their chromosome basis
has not been directly observable. They could be due to the
placing of compatible groups of gene-differences either in short
inversions or in other regions of low crossing-over. Later we
shall see evidence of both kinds of situation.

Large inversions, like translocations of any size, will establish
discontinuity by making the hybrid infertile through too much
crossing-over taking place within them. They will isolate, not
the chromosomes, but the organisms, and in consequence are

[3] Riley, 1955*d*; Darlington, 1949*a*.
[4] Ford, 1945; Huxley, 1955; Mather, 1955.

less likely to occur except in a largely self-fertilised species. They seem accordingly to be of little importance in nature. If inversions have acted as crossing-over suppressors and not as sterilisers we should find that short inversions are most frequent and that inversions including the centromere are absent. We should also find that inversions are disproportionately frequent in the longer chromosomes which have a wide enough margin of chiasma frequency to ensure regular pairing in the inversion hybrid. This seems to be true of races of *D. pseudo-obscura*.[5]

Interchanges demand other special properties if they are to float in a heterozygous state. Thus the distribution of inter-changes depends not only on whether the species is normally self- or cross-fertilised, and on the size of the interchange, but also on the properties of chiasma movement of the species. If chiasmata remain interstitial as in *Zea* and *Pisum* the associa-tions of four produced in the hybrid are, half of them, parallel in co-orientation and give inviable gametes. If the interchange hybrid is sterile then interchange, like a large inversion, will cause immediate fission in the species. This has probably happened in *Pisum*.

If chiasmata are terminalised, a higher proportion of regular gametes are produced and interchanges large enough to form chiasmata can float in a cross-fertilised species as they probably do in *Campanula persicifolia*. The opposite result is found in *Datura Stramonium*, where interchanges have been fixed in local races which are pure for particular types of interchange.

ii. *The Interchange Hybrid*

Interchange has however given results of yet a third character in certain species of flowering plants. In these species inter-change hybrids breed true. In fact the whole species consists of one type, hybrid for a particular interchange or com-bination of interchanges. How did such a species arise? An interchange floating in a species widely cross-fertilised like *Campanula persicifolia* will always be hybrid at first and will have crossing-over reduced in its proximal segments, as we saw earlier. After a certain period of sheltering in this way it will be impossible for it to exist in the pure condition. If however the hybrid is favoured by heterosis the interchange will spread

[5] *cf.* Carson, 1955.

in the species and interchange hybrids will increase in gene hybridity as time goes on.

In a word, the course of evolution from the floating to the fixed stage can be diverted if the selection pressure in favour of hybridity is strong enough. This selection pressure can be increased, strangely enough, by a change, especially perhaps a sudden change, in the breeding system, a change from outbreeding to inbreeding. So long as plants with rings of four are outcrossed in *Campanula* they give the mendelian ratio of 1 : 2 : 1 modified by the elimination of the third class, the interchange homozygotes, which seem to be lethal. But if these plants are selfed the first class, the basic homozygotes, are also eliminated. This means that the ring of four breeds true. It is not that the selection in favour of gene heterozygotes is increased. It is merely that the interchange heterozygote is a more rigorous marker of the gene-heterozygote in the selfed than in the crossed progeny.[6]

Interchanges float in a large proportion of diploid plants and are known in several animal groups such as scorpions and cockroaches. They can be stabilised in the hybrid state by a change in the breeding system such as is bound to occur whenever a small population is cut off from the main body of a species.[7] As a rule the adaptation of the two parts of the genetic system, the chromosome and the reproductive mechanisms, must be slow. When, as in the *Campanula* experiment, there is an immediate and as it were automatic adjustment (carried out, to be sure, at the expense of fertility) the result may well be an explosive expansion of the new system. In the course of this explosion a whole series of consequences, some obvious, others not at all obvious, ensue.

The first obvious consequence is that inbreeding instead of decreasing hybridity will begin to act in the reverse way. It will gradually increase it. The structural hybridity will shelter an accumulating gene hybridity: it will react on the conditions which produced it by exaggerating them. The second obvious consequence is that two chromosomes are thrown together in one linkage group. What appeared impossible at a first consideration of the recombination index can thus be achieved.

[6] Darlington, 1956*b*.
[7] K. Lewis and B. John, 1957.

iii. *The Oenothera System*

The less obvious consequences were revealed only by a long series of experiments. These began with de Vries' discovery of mutation in the species of *Oenothera* which had come to Europe from the eastern United States. They continued with Renner's demonstration of the hybrid character of these species. And they culminated in an analysis of chromosome behaviour and the discovery of similar conditions in other genera in some of which the historical and geographical circumstances could be defined.[8]

In *Oenothera* hybridity for one interchange has favoured hybridity for a second and a third. The ring of four has thus in rapid succession increased to include six, eight, ten and finally all fourteen chromosomes. The steps in the growth of a hybrid ring can be specified with euclidean rigour. In no other system, let us note, can a sequence of evolutionary events be specified so exactly. For this reason the hypothesis that a ring of fourteen had arisen by six successive interchanges constituted a challenge, the most serious challenge, for the theory of natural selection as applied to genetic systems.[9] The advantage of the hybridity conferred by a ring of four will of course be increased by each increase in size.

It might be thought that irregularities in the distribution of the ring at meiosis would upset the system by increasing sterility, and this shortcoming undoubtedly restricts the occurrence of ring-forming hybrids to certain groups of organisms. Owing however to a happy adjustment of the sizes of the chromosomes and spindle, co-orientation is usually convergent and a majority of the gametes formed even by the largest ring in *Oenothera* are usually regular and viable. And this happy adjustment is to be taken quite strictly for it has been shown to be genotypically controlled and therefore subject to selective improvement.[10]

In the ring of fourteen there will be, not only two pairs of interstitial segments in which crossing-over is reduced, but five pairs of *differential segments* in which it is suppressed (x in Fig. 10). And not only crossing-over but all recombination. All the differential segments on each side are bound together in one

[8] Renner, 1925; Darlington, 1931; Cleland, 1949.
[9] Darlington, 1929.   [10] Thompson and Rees, 1956.

segregating unit. Being cut off from genetic recombination with homologous segments they are genetically isolated. And like two species that are genetically isolated they are free to change independently and to diverge in evolution.

The evolving interchange hybrid will thus become more and more of a gene hybrid and the two types of gamete which it produces will come to differ as much as those of two distinct species. Each chromosome will have a terminal pairing segment which will exactly correspond to a pairing segment in a chromosome of the other gametic type, or *complex* as it is called. And proximally each chromosome will have a differential segment which does not normally pair at pachytene or cross over with any homologous segment in the chromosomes of the opposite complex. It is within these differential segments that the genetic differences between the complexes will persist and accumulate.

These hypotheses, these explanations and expectations, have been confirmed or fulfilled by the breeding behaviour of the complex hybrids or hybrid species of *Oenothera*.

In the simplest case each hybrid species produces two kinds of pollen grains and two kinds of egg cells. Hence when two species are crossed four different kinds of hybrid can be produced (as *Oe. Lamarckiana* × *Oe. strigosa*), and each of these has its own particular properties of ring-formation as well as its own recognisable morphological type. Usually one or two of these fail to live. Similarly when a hybrid species is crossed with a non-hybrid species (such as occupy the western part of the United States) two types of crossed offspring appear. Thus the homozygous species *Oe. Hookeri* with 7 (2), from California, crossed with the European *Oe. Lamarckiana* (12) + (2), gives two hybrids. We may represent the cross in regard to its complexes in this way:—

Oe. Lamarckiana (12) + (2) *gaudens. velans*
Oe. Hookeri 7 (2)   *^{h}Hookeri. ^{h}Hookeri*

hybrids $\}$ *gaudens. ^{h}Hookeri* (10) + 2(2)
         velans. ^{h}Hookeri   2(4) + 3(2)

A special situation which we may regard as the most highly developed is found in *Oe. muricata* (14). This species produces pollen grains and potential embryo-sacs with its two complexes *curvans* and *rigens*. But only the *curvans* pollen grains and only the *rigens* embryo-sacs function. Why? The *rigens* pollen grains die; but on the female side a less direct mode of elimination has been discovered by Renner, one to which we have already had to refer in considering the reactions of the nucleus and the cytoplasm. The embryo-sac mother cell, as is usual, forms a row of four cells; but when the end cell of the four, which should from its position grow and divide to give the embryo-sac, happens to have the *curvans* complex it hardly ever grows. It is pushed out of its place by the growth of the cell at the other end, which of course is *rigens* (Fig. 25).

This appears to be merely a straightforward example of the cell-struggle and of the natural selection which results from it. In fact, as we have already seen, it also demonstrates principles of a different kind. There is evidently a gradient in the cytoplasm of the four spores. This gradient in itself favours the development of the top cell. But when the bottom nucleus is of a type much more favourable for embryo-sac growth it is able to overcome the disadvantage of the cytoplasm and supplant its rival. And this embryo-sac-favoured nuclear type is the very one which is killed by the pollen grain cytoplasm. Thus we see evidence of the interactions of varying nuclei and varying cytoplasms. And of how they are used for the differentiation of tissues in the plant. And finally of how they are used for the evolution of the genetic system in the species.

Such are the means by which the complex hybrid species yields pollen grains entirely of one type, and egg cells almost entirely of the other. The loss due to the formation of pure zygotes which would die is eliminated.

This difference between the male and female sides shows itself in many hybrid species of *Oenothera*: their reciprocal crosses with other species are different. When *Oe. muricata* is the egg parent the crosses are nearly all *rigens* hybrids; when it is the pollen parent the crosses are all *curvans* hybrids. These two kinds of hybrid can always be distinguished, both by their external forms and by their associations of chromosomes at meiosis. Such a complementary gametic adaptation clearly makes for economy in reproduction and is due to genetic change during or since the development of the complexes. The genetic action of each complex, it will be noticed, has been selected to make itself felt as soon as the genetic character of the cells is established by segregation at meiosis.

As we saw earlier, crossing-over can take place between the differential segments of chromosomes whose pairing ends are

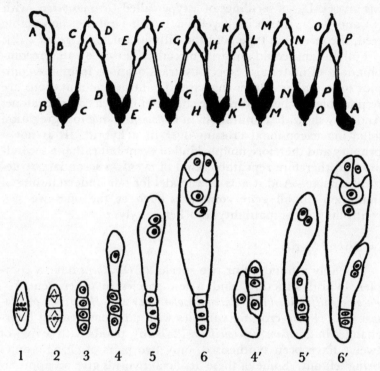

Fig. 25. Above, the regularly convergent arrangement of a chain at first metaphase in a species of *Oenothera* which is hybrid for six interchanges. Note that a complete set of the labelled pairing segments passes to each pole. *Cf.* Fig. 10. (After Darlington, 1932 *b*.) Below, the two possible series of events following meiosis in the embryo-sac mother cell of a hybrid species of *Oenothera* according to which cell receives the female-competent complex at the first division. (After Renner, 1921.)

not homologous. But it is exceptional. When it happens, there is a reverse interchange and the two whole complexes in effect cross over.[11] Gametes are produced, half of one complex and half of the other. Combining with normal gametes, wholly of one complex or the other, a new type of zygote is produced

[11] Sweet, 1937.

K

which is hybrid for half of its chromosomes, pure for the other half. Such plants are known as *half-mutants* and can themselves yield entirely pure offspring, half pure for one complex, half for the other. These are known as full mutants. Thus *Oe. Lamarckiana* gives 0·1% of seedlings of a type called *Oe. rubrinervis*, with (6) and 4 (2), which itself yelds a 1 : 2 : 1 ratio of non-viable seed, the *rubrinervis* type, and the full mutant, *Oe. deserens* 7 (2).

Full mutants could not arise directly. They show that recombinations of materials, especially translocations from one complex to the other, rather than specific intragenic mutations are responsible for the unworkable character of each complex alone. And they show that 'mutation' in *Oenothera* is due to segregation following exceptional crossing-over in a hybrid. It is not a primary and therefore unique kind of event but rather a secondary and therefore repeatable kind of event: a secondary structural change. And it acts as a model for our understanding of 'mutation' in all gene complexes such as the ones we saw controlling incompatibility and heterostyly.

iv. *Hybrid Species*

Probably a hundred or two species of *Oenothera* have a complex hybrid structure, and a few species in other genera— *Paeonia californica* (10), *Rhoeo discolor* (12) and *Hypericum punctatum* (16). From crossing varieties with different floating interchanges in *Campanula persicifolia* ($2n = 16$), plants with a ring of twelve have been synthesised, only two pairs of chromosomes being left out. Some of these artificial hybrids give an approximately Mendelian segregation in their progeny while others breed true with occasional mutation like the natural species of *Oenothera*.[12]

It is not however accident but a special circumstance that drives the genetic system of a species into complex hybridity. The experiments with *Campanula* show us that this special circumstance is the compulsion of an outbreeding species to inbreed. The situation of *Oenothera*, and probably *Paeonia*, in nature, corresponds with that of *Campanula* in experiment: the edge of the expanding species migrating on to new territory has been forced to abandon its outbreeding habit. Self-fertile

12 Darlington and La Cour, 1950.

plants alone have set seed and their progeny have of course been self-fertilising.

The same principle applies to the cockroach in a coalmine. Any species forced to inbreed at the edge of its range, and having the right type of chromosomes and of meiosis, will make use of interchange hybridity and fix it to preserve general hybridity and to make itself into a permanent hybrid.[13]

Complex hybrid species have gained by their special mechanism a high degree of hybridity balanced by a low degree of crossing-over. They have sacrificed flexibility to fitness, future variability to present variation; for as the system becomes more highly specialised, gametically and zygotically, crossing-over and mutation are more severely restricted and the species finds itself in an evolutionary blind alley. The changes that it has undergone with advantage in the first stage prove irreversible and presumably fatal in the last. This is the position of *Rhoeo discolor* with a ring of twelve chromosomes. The single surviving representative of its genus, it is restricted in distribution and almost invariable in form.

The device of complex hybridity is no doubt self-destroying for the species that indulges in it. But we shall find it instructive in considering many evolutionary problems. The foremost of these is the problem of genetic sex differentiation. By means of this sex differentiation hermaphrodite species of plants and animals have been enabled to become dioecious. Thus its function is not to permit inbreeding but to maintain crossbreeding. For this reason, as we shall discover, it is self-renewing as well as self-destroying.

[13] Darlington, 1956*b*.

18

EVOLUTION OF SEX

i. *Genetic Basis*

SEXUAL differentiation between gametes, distinguishes large stationary eggs from small motile sperm cells. Its origins can be seen in the Protozoa and Algae where all degrees of differentiation, all stages in its evolution, occur. In its simplest and probably original form this differentiation was a differentiation within the individual which therefore bore cells of both kinds. Most of the higher plants are still hermaphrodite, bearing both pollen and eggs. They have, as we saw, various special devices which assure cross-fertilisation. This end is achieved in most of the higher animals by having the sexes separated in different individuals. Here and there in a number of different families of plants we can see the same mechanism of sex differentiation coming into existence. In animals it is long established and indispensable. In plants it is a sporadic and short-lived alternative to other systems.

An experiment with *Zea Mays* provides the clearest evidence of how the mechanism can develop. One recessive mutation (*ff*) in the pure state causes sterility of the female flowers, which are on separate inflorescences from the male. Another mutation in the pure state (*mm*) converts the male flowers into female and the fertility of these is unaffected by the action of the *ff* gene. Plants of the constitution *ffmm* are entirely ovule bearers. Plants of the constitution *ffMm* are entirely male. A stock therefore which contains these two types in equal numbers will produce offspring with them likewise in equal numbers. The male is the hybrid sex.[1]

Provided such a new stock is isolated, genetically or geographically, from the original stock its system will be stable and self-perpetuating. An inversion including *f* and *m*, if they are near together in the same chromosome will give the necessary isolation. It remains to be said that it has proved equally easy,

---

[1] D. F. Jones, 1932, *cf.* D. Lewis, 1942.

using different mutations, to produce a stock in which the female instead of the male is the hybrid sex.

There is no doubt that in many plant species sexual differentiation is little more advanced than in this experiment. Nevertheless such a system is not likely to persist unchanged. So soon as the two types, male and female, are permanently segregated in the species, each will have special needs calling for special genetic adaptations. This can take place in one way alone, by the occurrence of mutations absolutely linked with the segregating *M–m* genes. Mutants linked with *m* will be selected if they are recessive and favour the female. Mutants linked with *M* will be selected if they are dominant and favour the male.

We usually call the *m* chromosome *X* and the *M* chromosome *Y*. Between them there is this essential distinction: the *X* chromosome occurs in both sexes, the *Y* is restricted to one sex and never meets an identical partner.

The *XY* sex is usually male, the *XX* female. The opposite holds good in birds and Lepidoptera. In dioecious mosses and liverworts the diploid generation is always *XY* and plants of the haploid generation either *X* or *Y*. There is no homozygous diploid *XX*: neither *X* nor *Y* ever meets an identical partner so that it is only by a secondary convention that we describe the sex chromosome of the female plant as *X*, of the male plant as *Y*.

Here we can see directly and with the utmost simplicity how other genes get attached to an original sex difference. In many liverworts, as in the genus *Sphaerocarpus*, the female is larger than the male plant, an obvious adaptive distinction. We then find that the *X* chromosome is much larger than the *Y*. In one genus, *Riccia*, the plants of the two sexes are equal and their corresponding sex chromosomes are also equal in one species (*R. curtisii*), while in another species (*R. bischoffii*) they are both correspondingly unequal. It is not often, of course, that sex differences can be even partly expressed in such crude terms.

Between the *X* and *Y* chromosomes and between the sexes which they determine, an important discontinuity arises. It can arise only if there is some restriction on recombination, some limitation on crossing-over. What methods the genetic system has at its disposal for limiting crossing-over we have already seen. Genotypically a localisation of chiasmata or structurally an inversion of the segment of chromosome containing either M or m genes will suppress crossing-over near these genes and make a system of sexual specialisation possible.

The available evidence suggests that genotypic control is primarily responsible, structural change secondarily. Thus the XY sex always has lower crossing-over than the XX sex, in the other chromosomes as well as in the sex chromosomes. The extreme example of genotypic control is found in *Drosophila*, where as we saw crossing-over is abolished in the XY sex, that is in the male. Such a general reduction can only be genotypic. Structural changes are likely to follow this genotypic suppression and are responsible, as we shall see, for great variation in the Y chromosome. The consequences of this suppression are seen when we compare the differences between X and Y chromosomes. In the *Bryophyta*[2] with haploid sex differentiation their divergencies are, as we saw, abrupt and startling. In plants and animals with diploid sex differentiation the different degrees of divergence between them fall into an evolutionary series.

ii. *Beginnings of Sex Chromosomes*

The earliest stage of differentiation has been found in flies from studies of the polytene chromosomes and in fishes by breeding experiments. In *Anopheles* two pairing chromosomes are distinguished by a complex of inversions in the polytene nuclei. One of the partners is found only in males where it is always in the heterozygous state. It thus has the character of a Y chromosome and its partner the character of an X chromosome. The same is true of *Chironomus tentans*.[3] But here there are different systems in different populations: sometimes one autosome may acquire the character of a Y chromosome with inversions to protect its differential genes from crossing-over; and sometimes another autosome may take over this function. Thus the whole system is evidently incipient and easily replaceable.

Closely parallel are the breeding experiments of Winge with the fish *Lebistes reticulatus*. In this species the males are usually XY. Free crossing-over of many genes is possible between X

[2] Lorbeer, 1934.   [3] Beermann, 1955a, b.

and Y. Only one, apart from the sex differential itself, is completely restricted to the Y chromosome; possibly the two genes lie in a small inverted segment together. Now certain stocks have a gene in one of the autosomes, i.e. in one of the chromosomes other than X or Y, which when pure turns the XX fish

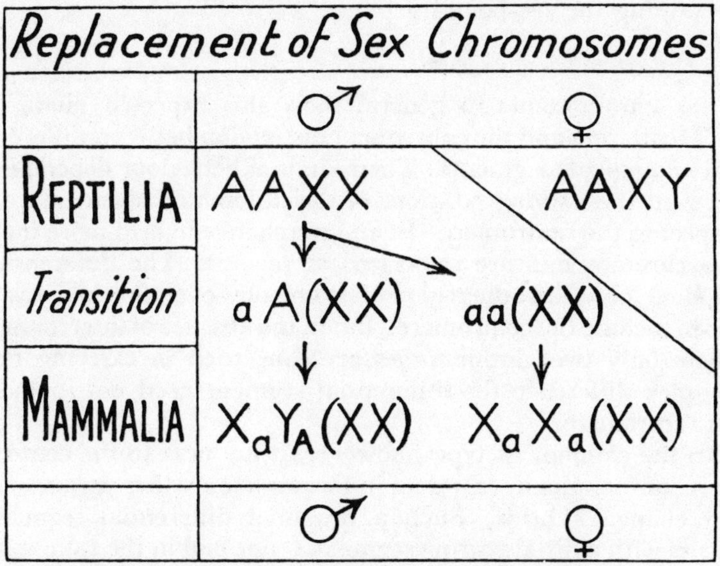

Replacement of Sex Chromosomes		
	♂	♀
REPTILIA	AAXX	AAXY
Transition	a A(XX)	aa(XX)
MAMMALIA	$X_a Y_A$(XX)	$X_a X_a$(XX)
	♂	♀

Fig. 26. The evolutionary stages by which a pair of autosomes (AA) can become the sex differentials in the XX sex, thus making it possible for the old XX sex to become the XY sex. The Y chromosome can also be displaced by direct loss as in Fig. 27, giving an XO system which itself can also be replaced as above by a new XY.

into a male; in the hybrid state for this gene the fish is a female.[4] Thus we have the beginnings of a system in which the old male type with its Y chromosome is eliminated and the female becomes the hybrid or XY sex, while the new male becomes the pure or XX sex. The related genus *Aplocheilus* has such a system. In the course of the evolution of the mammals some such change as this must have occurred once, if not several times, because the female is the hybrid sex in reptiles as well as birds, and the male in mammals (Fig. 26).

Now, so far as the Y chromosome is concerned, the species bearing it is a permanent hybrid. In the part carrying the sex differentials, crossing-over is suppressed. So long as X and Y

[4] Winge, 1932; Winge and Ditlevsen, 1947.

continue to pair and their segregation to be controlled by chiasmata their position must always be that of chromosomes in a permanent hybrid species of *Oenothera*. They must be made up of two segments, a *pairing segment* in which a chiasma is formed, and crossing-over occurs, and a *differential segment* containing the sex-bound genes.

iii. *Differentiation of Segments*

Sex chromosomes in general show this expected mode of differentiation and the consequent distinction between differential and pairing segments. Their kinds of behaviour depend indeed on the varying positions of the differential segment with respect to the centromere. In an interchange hybrid more than two chromosomes are associated at meiosis. The differential segment, or at least the region of no crossing-over, for this reason has to include the centromere. But in the absence of interchange where only two chromosomes are concerned in carrying the complex difference the differential segment need not include the centromere.

In the commonest types, however, it lies next to the centromere, or includes it, as it does in *Oenothera* and other permanent interchange hybrids. Such a proximal differential segment occurs with a distal pairing segment at one end in the campions of the genus *Melandrium*.[5] It occurs with pairing segments at both ends in the plants *Humulus* and *Rumex*, in both of which genera species occur with the Y fragmented in its differential region. The two ends of the X then each pair with a small Y; the female is XX, the male XY_1Y_2.

In the mammals the pairing segment is proximal, usually on both sides of the centromere, and the differential segment distal. This has interesting results which differ according to the part of the pairing segment in which the chiasma is formed. In most mammals, in man, the rat and the hamster,[6] there is a single long differential segment in one arm of the X and little or none in the Y (Fig. 27). The pairing segment is on both sides of the centromere. A chiasma may be formed in the short arm of the pairing segment on the opposite side of the centromere to the differential segment. This chiasma moves to the end and the two chromosomes separate reductionally, as is said, at

[5] Westergaard, 1940, 1946, 1948.   [6] Koller, 1946.

the first division. When however a chiasma is formed in the longer arm between the centromere and the differential segment, the two chromatids of this segment become attached to two different centromeres and the bivalent divides equationally at the first division, reductionally at the second (Fig. 6).

Owing to these chiasmata being formed at various points in the pairing segment we should expect that particular gene

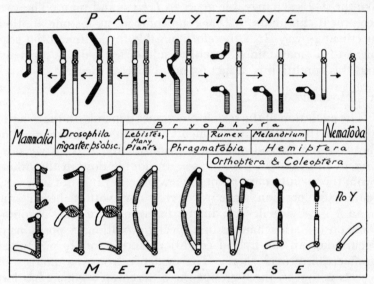

Fig. 27. The evolutionary divergence of *X* and *Y* chromosomes, shown by the pachytene pairing and by the metaphase association, following two series according to the relative positions of centromeres and differential segments (white in *X*, black in *Y*). Pairing segments hatched. The mammalian type corresponds to the unequal chromosomes illustrated in Fig. 5.

differences would cross over from the *X* to the *Y* chromosome and vice versa. Such gene differences would be more or less closely linked with the differentiation of sex instead of being absolutely linked, or rather bound, to *X* or *Y* like those in the differential segment. Without careful tests they would not be distinguishable from autosome differences. A number have now been recognised in man.[7]

Species of *Drosophila*, which also have proximal pairing segments, are distinguished from the mammals by two remarkable

[7] Haldane, 1936; *cf.* Darlington and Mather, 1949, Fig. 13.

properties of these segments. They always unite in the male by two reciprocal chiasmata between X and Y. Lying as they do very close to the centromere, they are inert except where they abut on the differential segment, where a single gene difference is known, affecting the length of the thoracic bristles. This gene, 'bobbed', sometimes lies between the two reciprocal chiasmata and so crosses over from the X to the Y chromosome like the X-Y exchangeable genes in *Lebistes* and man. The two reciprocal chiasmata in *Drosophila* compensate for one another in crossing-over. It is therefore possible for a differential segment to be maintained on either side of the pairing segment, and this condition is in fact found in several species.[8]

iv. *The Erosion of Y*

The evolution of the sex chromosomes depends on the genetic history of the differential segments. The differential segment of the X is in a special position physiologically: it is, as we saw, present in single dose in one sex, in double dose in the other. From the evolutionary point of view however it is not in a very remarkable position, since it can cross over with its homologue in an XX individual. The differential segment of the Y chromosome on the other hand is in a special evolutionary position; it occurs only in the hybrid condition, and is totally precluded from crossing over there. The evidence from mammals and insects is that in these groups the differential segment has lost most of its specific activity retaining only some polygenic effects. While the X chromosome of man reveals many major gene mutations in its differential segment, the Y chromosome reveals few or none. In *Drosophila melanogaster* the same is true, but in spite of this lack of mutations the genes are not entirely inert. A male with an X and no Y chromosome (XO) entirely resembles a normal male in form but it is sterile. Meiosis is abnormal and the sperm degenerate.

The capacity for free combination within the autosomes evidently gives them such an advantage in adaptive efficiency over the Y chromosome that they come to take over its work. The decisive difference between the sexes comes to be the difference in proportion of the X and the autosomes.[9] Two sets of autosomes and two X's give a female; two sets of autosomes and

[8] Darlington, 1934.   [9] Bridges, 1922.

one *X* give a male, irrespective of the number of *Y*'s which may be added to each. Further, three sets of autosomes and two *X*'s give an intersex. What we have seen earlier shows us that this change of balance has the same kind of effect that can be achieved also by gene mutation. The effect of the change is however more crudely obvious because it is on a larger scale.

The consequences of the *Y*'s inertness or lack of specificity are felt in two ways. First, the *Y* begins to vary very freely in size, not only as between related species of mosses or insects but also within the same species, e.g. in the neuropteran *Chrysopa vulgaris* and in *Drosophila pseudo-obscura*, as well as in species of *Humulus* and *Rumex*. Secondly, in certain large groups of insects (as we saw) and nematodes the *Y* chromosome has entirely disappeared. In any organism any chromosome is liable to be lost, particularly through failure of pairing at meiosis. If it is lost and the loss makes no difference the species will continue without it.

In the Coleoptera and Hemiptera we can see all the stages in diminution of the *Y* chromosome, ending in many species in its total loss. In the last stages the pairing segment is so reduced that pachytene pairing of *X* and *Y* no longer takes place. Or if it does, as in the crane-fly *Tipula*,[10] crossing-over is completely suppressed and the chromosomes segregate following a touch-and-go pairing, a momentary contact of their terminal pairing segments at the first or even at the second metaphase. When supernumeraries arise from fragmentation of the *Y* they can mount up to the number of six without effect. They are evidently lacking in specific activity. In the Orthoptera this process has gone even further. In the whole order, apart from some Mantidae, the *Y* has disappeared.

The differential segment of the *X* must always include the effective sex difference. But in a part of it there may also be a loss of specific activity. In *Drosophila melanogaster* the proximal third of the differential segment has been labelled genetically inert.[11] It is heterochromatic and in polytene nuclei it appears, not in the usual bands, but as small dispersed chromomeres. And in one species of the bed-bug *Cimex* supernumerary fragmented *X*'s vary in number from none to twelve. They have the physiological character of *B* chromosomes but the touch-

[10] B. John, 1957.   [11] Muller and Painter, 1932.

and-go metaphase pairing with Υ shows that their authentic sister is X.[12]

When the Υ is lost the males have a single unpaired X chromosome at meiosis (Figs. 3, 4 and 27). This univalent is somewhat more regular than other univalents and in most species divides either always at the first or always at the second division. Occasionally however, as in the bug, *Vanduzea*, it is less settled in its behaviour and divides at either division, just as a univalent will do in many plant hybrids. Like other univalents it lags behind the bivalents if it divides at the first division. Sperm are produced in equal numbers with and without X.

Loss of the Υ chromosome might seem to be the last stage in the evolutionary breakdown of the $X\Upsilon$ system. Yet the evidence shows that it is not. In the Coleoptera and Orthoptera as well as in the mammals the X chromosome, having lost its partner, often fuses with an autosome.[13] Thus X-O and A-A becomes XA-A. A, which becomes the new Υ, is distinguishable from an old Υ by the fact that it is not heterochromatic, and the gametic chromosome number has been reduced by one. In this way greater regularity of segregation is no doubt obtained. It seems possible that repeated fusions of this kind are responsible for reducing the chromosome numbers of marsupials below those of other mammals.[14] The same may be true in *Rumex* where the number of autosomes has been reduced to three in one species.[15] Such extremes of reduction no doubt facilitate or encourage polyploidy in animals as well as in plants and are therefore likely to be concealed by it.[16]

Another evolutionary aspect of the fusion of chromosomes is also probably its effect in fixing combinations by reducing recombinations. The suppression of crossing-over in the heterozygous sex of *Drosophila* achieves this result in another way. And a third way is in the generation of structural hybridity of the *Oenothera* type by interchange. This is found in an incipient stage in *Humulus*. And in the centipede *Otocryptops*[17] it has led to the formation of a chain of nine chromosomes which we may call, if we wish, five X's and four Υ's.

[12] Darlington, 1939*b*.
[13] S. G. Smith, 1953.
[14] Sharman and Barber, 1952.
[15] B. W. Smith, 1955.
[16] Sachs, 1952.
[17] Ogawa, 1954.

v. *Haplo-Diploid Systems*

A genetic method of sex differentiation occurs in many animal groups which in its origin seems to be unrelated to the alternative $X-Y$ system. The females are diploid; the males are haploid, arising from unfertilised eggs. This system is found in Rotifera, Acarina and four orders of insects. Thysanoptera, Hymenoptera, two families of Hemiptera and one of Coleoptera, represented by a single species *Micromalthus debilis*.[18]

Breeding and. chromosome studies of the parasitic wasp *Habrobracon* have revealed the kind of genetic situation which usually underlies the haplo-diploid system. With a change from outbreeding to inbreeding, as we have noticed elsewhere, the genetic system partly breaks down. Fertilised eggs on inbreeding occasionally give males which prove to be diploid. The explanation is that the females are heterozygous in respect of a kind of sex chromosome. In the haploid—and in occasional homozygous diploids—there is only one kind of sex chromosome. Of whatever kind this sex chromosome may be, the result is male. Now this sex chromosome does not exist simply in two alternative forms. Like the S gene in a self-incompatible plant, it exists in several forms. And like the S gene the difference has become by long evolution a complex gene. It reveals its complexity by a variety of kinds of mutations. We therefore have something between a complex gene and the differential segment of a sex chromosome, something with a natural history and evolution of its own in each of the haplo-diploid animal groups.[19]

How varied this natural history may be is indicated by study of the social bee *Melipona*. Here there are several chromosomes which have to be heterozygous if the progeny is to be a functional and fertile queen bee. When fewer chromosomes are heterozygous the diploid progeny are workers. Thus a genotypic switch for determining caste has replaced the nutritional switch that we know in the honey bee. And *Melipona* has made use of the genetic mechanism that has already been developed for sex determination.[20]

---

[18] Scott, 1936. *cf.* Darlington, 1937*a*.
[19] Whiting, 1945; Schmieder and Whiting, 1947.
[20] W. E. Kerr, 1950.

vi. *Sex Ratios*

In the Hymenoptera where the proportion of males and females depends on whether the queen has been fertilised the sex ratio becomes part of the social system. In animals and plants with segregating sex chromosomes however the sex-ratio is controlled more directly by the properties of these chromosomes. The means of control however are diverse. Especially they diverge in plants and animals as two examples will show.

In *Melandrium* the male plant produces two kinds of pollen grains, female-determining with an *X* and male-determining with a *Y* chromosome; these are formed in equal numbers. Correns found that putting too much pollen on the stigma gave more female progeny, too little pollen gave equality of the sexes. Why? Evidently the *X* pollen grains grow faster than the *Y*. Evidently also too many males would be a waste of reproductive effort but the system will correct in one generation any error of proportion it may have made in the preceding generation. Different males moreover differed in the sex ratios they gave so that natural selection could correct errors in the long-range character of the system as well as in its year to year operation.[21]

In *Drosophila* an entirely different mode of control has come into play. In a whole group of species there occur males which beget preponderantly female offspring. This 'sex-ratio' property is determined in these species by genes sheltered from recombination in a triple inversion which lies in the longer arm of the *X* chromosome. Evidently, like heterostyly, the genes of sex-ratio are in fact a complex of ancient origin. It operates by a remarkable example of the genotypic control of chromosome behaviour. It prevents the pairing of *X* and *Y* at meiosis; the *X* divides twice and the *Y* is lost; nearly all the sperm therefore contain one *X* and no *Y*. The proportion of female progeny in one strain which was 94 per cent at 25°C rose to 99 per cent when the temperature was reduced to 16·5°C. No doubt the frequency of this gene complex in each population is regulated by the modification of the normal or primitive sex-ratio which gives the thriftiest results for the population.[22]

A great number of different mechanisms may be used to

---

[21] Correns, 1927; 1928.   [22] Darlington and Dobzhansky, 1942.

separate the sexes on different individuals and to modify their proportions in the population. In the types we have taken, segregation of dissimilar chromosomes at meiosis or differential fertilisation is the basis. In certain species, both of plants and animals, the external conditions of development may determine the future sex. In the sea worm *Bonellia* and elsewhere eggs falling free develop into females, eggs falling on to females develop into males. The genotype of the species is such that it makes this differential response which is adapted to its reproductive requirements. The end result is the same whether it has been achieved by the action of external or internal differences. It may equally remain the same above all the increasing elaboration that we see in the internal mechanism of segregation. Beyond a very early stage we need not suppose that any necessary increase in elaboration takes place in the physiological differentiation of sex.

vii. *The Grounds of Instability*

How are we to understand the instability and indeed the cyclical evolution of the chromosome mechanism which underlies the differentiation of the sexes?

Evidently the mechanism has to change merely to keep pace with the mutations and structural changes which are constantly disintegrating it. But its instability does not touch the external differentiation it determines. The mechanism of segregation, however elaborate, merely releases a trigger which directs the processes of development along one of the two alternative paths of sex.[23] There is some evidence that even in the most advanced stages of developing this trigger, in *Drosophila*, it may be suddenly replaced by an entirely new device, much as in *Lebistes*. And the new system will work as well as the old.

The evolution of sex chromosomes shows a property in common with that of permanent hybrids. The suppression of crossing-over between two homologous parts of chromosomes separates them in evolution as effectively as if they belonged to different species. The discontinuities that arise as a result of the different kinds of genetic isolation are of the same order of magnitude and they have a similar adaptive significance. The principle is the same whether they arise from interchange

[23] Muller, 1932*a*.

hybridity in a complex hybrid species, or between the differential segments of two pairing chromosomes concerned with sexual differentiation, or in connection with an inversion which distinguishes corresponding chromosomes of two species. In this sense we may look upon paired complexes and also paired sexes as comparable with pairs of species, with this difference that they are mutually adapted for reproductive processes.

The instability of the sex chromosomes derives from this situation which may be expressed in very general terms. Two chromosomes are taken out of the set and subjected to different conditions of recombination and therefore selection from the rest. But their properties of genic and structural change are necessarily the same as the rest. An evolutionary disharmony is thus set up. We may say that the directive agent of change in the autosomes is selection, in the sex chromosomes mutation. The result is that no permanent balance can be set up between them. The sex chromosomes pass through a perpetual cycle of disintegration and replacement, no stage in which is physiologically preferable to any other.

19

STERILITY: THE CONTRADICTION

i. *Sterility of Crossing*

ZYGOTES which reach maturity must inherently have arisen from the fusion of viable gametes which have given viable products. The problem of sterility is how such a zygote can itself produce gametes, or its gametes produce zygotes, that are not viable; in other words how it can form gametes unlike those from which it is derived. It may do so under three kinds of conditions. First, an unfavourable environment may prevent development taking the same course as it has taken in the past. Secondly, differentiation may fail to provide uniform conditions of reproduction. A production of an excessive number of egg cells, or of unfavourably placed egg cells, where the young offspring are nursed by the female parent, may result in the destruction of some. All other instances of failure of development of gametes and zygotes fall into the third class. They are due to genetic variation.

Genetic sterility is in the simplest case *relational*. It arises from crossing dissimilar forms. The parents may fail to copulate in species crosses of animals. The pollen may fail to germinate on the style or grow down it in cross-fertilisation between races or species. The same is true *mutatis mutandis* in animals. These obstacles to fertilisation are physiologically similar to those producing self-sterility in hermaphrodite plants and animals, where as we saw they are due to lack of genetic differences. A specific gene mutation is known in *Zea mays* to cause cross-sterility.[1] Or again the new zygote produced may fail to develop beyond an early stage, either in the simplest case owing to its new and untried genetic constitution being unsatisfactory or, in the mammals, owing to the relationship of embryo to mother being unsatisfactory. In the higher plants the endosperm also plays a part. This can be most simply shown in the occurrence of differences between reciprocal crosses of diploid and polyploid plants.

[1] Demerec, 1929.

For example in crosses between diploid and tetraploid forms the normal products of reduction and fertilisation are evidently at a disadvantage in many species for a majority of the progeny are the results of aberrant processes of which we should not have evidence in normal breeding. Equally in *Primula sinensis* and *Campanula persicifolia* we find a discrimination against triploid progeny as follows:

	Primula		*Campanula*	
	fertility :	progeny	fertility :	progeny
$2x \times 4x$	nil	—	0·1 %	4x and 3x
$4x \times 2x$	0·1 %	3x and 4x	0·3 %	3x, 4x and 2x

The non-triploid progeny are of two kinds. They are either diploids arising from a lack of fertilisation of the eggs of the tetraploid parent. Or they are tetraploids arising from a lack of reduction of the pollen or eggs of the diploid parent.

These abnormalities are uncommon; hence the relative sterility of the crosses. The same principles hold for crosses between diploid and polyploid species.[2]

Each of these types of sterility involves physiological problems peculiar to the particular case. The effect of all of them is to restrict the size of the breeding group by genetic isolation, and they act as a direct limitation, as we shall see, on all the other types of sterility.

ii. *Sterility of the Individual*

Two other kinds of genetic sterility may be described in more general terms. They are properties of the individual irrespective of cross- or self-fertilisation. One is *genotypic sterility* and is due to the organism being different from its parent or parents in having some abnormality of its reproductive processes determined by its individual genotype. Such sterility may take effect (equally in maize or *Drosophila*) at any stage of development. It arises earliest by the abortion of the sexual organs, later by the suppression of chromosome pairing at meiosis through lack of precocity and last of all by a failure in the development of the germ cells which have been satisfactorily formed.

These genotypic properties may appear as a result of inbreeding or of crossing between two races or species. Usually in

[2] Darlington, 1937*a*.

either case they affect one sex alone. And usually in plants the anthers are more susceptible to abortion than the ovules, but in *Zea mays* and *Rubus idaeus* mutations are known affecting each separately. Such mutations may be used as we saw in establishing sexual differentiation. In animal crosses where the sexes are separated on different individuals it is usually the hybrid sex which is sterilised in this way.[3] The reason for this is fairly clear. The XX sex has one X and one set of autosomes from each parent, the XY or XO has no X from one parent and the Y being largely inert does not take its place. The hybrid sex is as we may say unbalanced. The result is that in crosses between species in *Drosophila* the pairing of the chromosomes is suppressed at meiosis in the male and the testes are under-developed. In the female however the chromosomes pair and the eggs are fertile if back-crossed to one of the parents. Some of the males in this back-crossed generation are fertile. They no longer have the wrong combination of X and autosome genes.[4]

The other kind of individual sterility, and the one which we are in a position to analyse most exhaustively, is due to a lack of uniformity in the products of segregation. This lack of uniformity we may describe as due to the formation by a zygote of gametes genetically different from those which gave rise to it. But what is more to the point is that it depends on the zygote having arisen from the fusion of genetically differing gametes; that is to its being a hybrid, and a hybrid which undergoes crossing-over and segregation at meiosis so as to produce new combinations of genes in a gametic set of chromosomes.

The failure of fertility that we get from these recombinations expected at meiosis in hybrids we may describe as *segregational sterility*. We may consider it in relation to the three kinds of hybrids in which it occurs, gene hybrids, structural hybrids and numerical hybrids, using at the same time the special behaviour of tetraploids of hybrid and non-hybrid origin as a test of our conclusions.

iii. *Sterility and Balance*

We may see the effect of segregation on sterility most simply in a triploid plant. Spores are formed with all numbers of

---

[3] Haldane, 1931.   [4] Dobzhansky, 1937.

chromosomes between the haploid and the diploid. Those with intermediate numbers are unbalanced. They develop on the female side to produce egg cells. On the male side however, on account of the longer life of the spore, a proportion usually die before the pollen grain germinates. When they survive the balanced and unbalanced grains have to compete in growing down the style; only a small proportion succeed in fertilising the egg cells, and these are likely to be the balanced ones. When a triploid is crossed as a female with a diploid as a male the result is therefore a higher proportion of unbalanced progeny than in the reciprocal cross. This is notwithstanding a certain differential mortality among the young embryos which also reduces the proportion of unbalanced ones. When the triploid is the male parent very few progeny except diploids and simple trisomics are usually produced.

Sterility of a triploid is thus due to unbalance in the progeny. Now there are occasional plant species which do not show any serious effect of unbalance. This is sometimes due to the basic set being itself polyploid in origin, and sometimes to there being so much translocation and duplication of segments of chromosomes that a mechanical diploid is physiologically a polyploid. This is evidently true of *Hyacinthus orientalis*, $n = 8$, for in this species different plants with all chromosome numbers from 16 to 32 are equally vigorous. In keeping with this lack of depression from unbalance, they are also almost equally fertile: how fertile exactly we still need to know. It is also in keeping with this situation that vigorous diploid plants deficient of chromosome segments have been found both in cultivation and in wild populations.

How are we to describe the *Hyacinthus* situation? There are various ways of representing it. But for the present the easiest is no doubt to say that each chromosome is nearly self sufficient. Each chromosome has its own balance. Differentiation there must be; but it is as much within as between chromosomes.[5]

Absolute deficiency is, in the normal situation, an even more serious cause of sterility than unbalance. *Rhoeo discolor* having a ring of twelve chromosomes can produce, through errors in the orientation of the ring, pollen grains with five and seven chromosomes instead of six. Those with five never reach the

[5] Darlington and Mather, 1944; Darlington, Hair and Hurcombe, 1951.

first mitosis. Those with seven may germinate and they may perhaps grow down the style. They never give rise to offspring. Or so it seems for the seedlings all have the same uniform number and appearance as the parent.

These examples show us why a hybrid like *Raphanus-Brassica* is sterile. Owing to lack of pairing, pollen grains and embryo-sacs are produced with all numbers and combinations of chromosomes; none of the parental types are reproduced except by a rare chance, and a balanced combination will arise only by complete non-reduction; that is by omission of one of the two sexual processes.

In an entirely opposite way, as we saw, following complete pairing and crossing-over in every chromosome of the diploid *Primula kewensis* the original parental combinations are even less likely to be produced. In consequence likewise the hybrid is absolutely sterile. In the tetraploid through pairing and segregation of similar chromosomes, uniform and balanced gametes are produced and the plant is fertile.

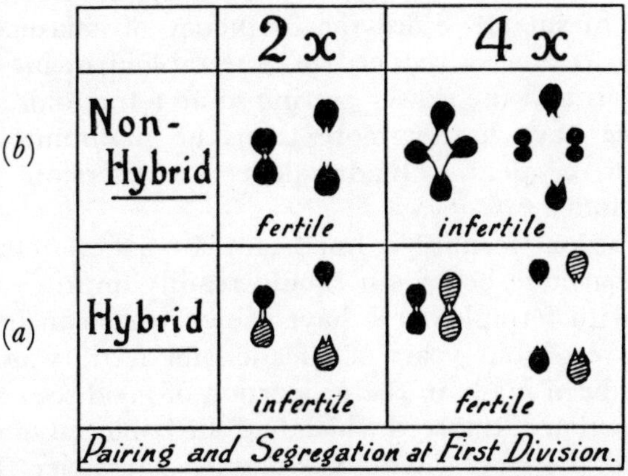

Fig. 28. Diagram showing the alternative conditions of segregational sterility (*a*) in a hybrid diploid, (*b*) in a non-hybrid tetraploid. (After Darlington, 1932*a*.)

The position of an autotetraploid is significantly different. Its chromosomes, as a rule, change partners at pachytene and, forming chiasmata in these different associations, they remain quadrivalents at metaphase. These quadrivalents are, except perhaps under very special conditions, incapable of regular orientation and segregation in every cell. With linear orientation three-and-one segregation often results. In this way a tetraploid cherry with eight potential quadrivalents has given a segregation of 19 : 13 instead of 16 : 16. With indifferent diamond-shaped co-orientation of the four chromosomes two may be left on the plate at anaphase to divide as univalents. Moreover, trivalents and true univalents often occur (Fig. 28). Thus there is irregularity of segregation in the autotetraploid and infertility is the result.

iv. *Selection for Fertility*

There are two kinds of exceptional circumstance under which these rules do not hold. The first is that of the undifferentiated chromosome complement, as in *Hyacinthus*, where tetraploidy and even triploidy fail to destroy fertility. The second is that revealed by comparison of a number of species of *Tulipa* which are evidently autotetraploids. These vary in the number of quadrivalents they form at meiosis subject to two conditions: the numbers of changes of partner at pachytene and the frequency of chiasmata. Since the frequency of chiasmata per chromosome is always reduced in a tetraploid owing to the larger nucleus and the slower pairing some tetraploids such as *T. chrysantha* have hardly more than the minimum of one chiasma per bivalent. Quadrivalents are therefore almost entirely excluded.[6]

Thus, if sexual fertility is important for a new tetraploid, selection in meiotic behaviour should readily improve it. Experiments with tetraploid rye have shown what can be done. In the course of four years of selection for fertility improvements have been made in the proportion of good seed set and in the proportion of this seed which had the balanced tetraploid number and therefore gave good plants. Moreover this improvement was correlated with a reduction of laggards and of unequal segregation at meiosis in the pollen mother cells.[7]

Rye is an outbreeding plant. In rice, an inbreeder, parallel results have been obtained but only where the diploids have been produced by crossing varieties. Inbred diploids give tetraploids in which selection has no effect: there is no variation in the genotypic control of meiosis from which the breeder can select.[8]

⁶ Upcott, 1939a.   ⁷ Bremer *et al.*, 1954.   ⁸ Mashima *et al.*, 1955.

By such processes of selection we may suppose that *Dahlia variabilis* which seems to have arisen as an autotetraploid garden plant in pre-Columbian Mexico has come to combine regular quadrivalent formation and seed-fertility with free tetraploid segregation.[9]

The new unselected autotetraploid however always forms univalents. It thus yields unbalanced gametes, and its fertility is reduced. Now here is the contrast and, if you like, the paradox. The fertile diploid gives an infertile autotetraploid. The sterile diploid gives a fertile allotetraploid. There is a negative correlation between the fertility of diploids and that of the tetraploids they give rise to. Hence autotetraploids in nature do not usually establish themselves as new species unless sexual fertility can be to some extent dispensed with.

If we enquire into their occurrence among plants we are at once led to discover how this happens. We find that the autotetraploid forms nearly always arise in individuals or varieties which differ from the average character of the species in having a greater propensity for vegetative reproduction. They are, we may say, pre-adapted to polyploidy. Or, better still perhaps, we may say that polyploidy and vegetative propagation mutually select one another.[10]

v. *The Splitting of Groups*

Let us return with the knowledge which these principles give us to consider sterility within a natural diploid breeding group of common size and stability. Within such a group cross-fertilisation takes place between pairs of gametes which differ in respect of a varying number of changes in genes and in their arrangement. We find that a proportion of the zygotes produced fail to develop and we can trace this failure to the recombinations that occur at meiosis. Sometimes it is due to crossing-over within inversions giving deficient gametes and zygotes. Sometimes it is due to irregularity in segregation following failure of pairing at meiosis. Sometimes it is due to two chromosomes which are necessary to one another failing to pass to the same gamete. They may be complementary to one another either through one containing a segment of chromosome actually removed from the other (as we see was the case

[9] Lawrence, 1931.   [10] Darlington, 1956*a*.

in *Oenothera*) or they may contain independent mutations which cannot work separately.

What happens to a breeding group in which variation increases and fertility consequently decreases? Clearly any change which will reduce the amount of variation in the group will enjoy an increasing advantage. How can this be done? By any means which will split the group into parts; that is by any kind of genetic isolation. Any self-fertilising individual, any new polyploid, any asexually propagating type, at once breaks itself off from the main group and escapes from the disadvantages. Any divergence from the normal breeding system will separate the divergent race and split the group. Any structural change which binds together genes in the hybrid will achieve a similar result. For it will limit recombination. It will mitigate segregational sterility. Its effect will also depend on a genetic isolation, but an isolation of chromosome segments, from which an isolation of individuals, a splitting of the group or the species, will only later be derived.

The group breaks into two. Sterility brings its remedy. The new smaller groups have less variation within their limits and are more fertile than the old. But if cross-sterility does not readily develop, if genetic isolation does not crop up, or if sexual reproduction can be to a great extent dispensed with, as in some sections of *Rosa* and *Rubus*, a population will arise which will vary between moderate fertility and absolute sterility. In such a population the discontinuity of species may cease to be recognisable.

Sterility is therefore the contradiction inherent in variation and recombination. A stock that is invariable will become pure breeding and completely fertile. Even if it varies, and yet suppresses the recombination of variants that would occur by the crossing of individuals or by the crossing-over and segregation of chromosomes, it will still remain pure-breeding and completely fertile. Sterility is the price the species pays in the death of a part of its immediate progeny for the advantages of recombination and adaptation in its more remote posterity. It may be said that this price is inevitable. That is not true for every group of plants and animals; there are some species which avoid paying it, or postpone paying it, or pay it in a different currency. We will now see how they are able to succeed.

20

APOMIXIS: THE ESCAPE

i. *Asexual Cycles*

UNTIL the sperm nucleus or the generative nucleus of the pollen fuses with the egg nucleus the egg does not develop. That is the rule in most organisms reproducing sexually. Without a sequence of this kind sexual reproduction could not have been established. But the sequence is not, for all organisms and under all conditions, so obligatory as might be expected. With eggs of frogs, sea urchins and seaweeds it may be replaced by artificial devices such as shaking or pricking, or by alteration of the surface conditions with specific reagents. In plants, pollination often suffices, and if the pollen is of a different species in *Datura* or in *Rubus* it may fail to enter the egg, which then develops without fertilisation. The stimulus of development has then become indirect, like that of a conditioned reflex. In cotton (*Gossypium*) and in the threadworm *Rhabditis* special stocks regularly allow the development of their unfertilised eggs.

Where this parthenogenesis is occasional and accidental, it is due to the coming of the sperm too late; or the coming of too few of them. Very often supernumerary egg cells in a plant will be stimulated to develop in this way merely by the fertilisation of their sisters. The development of a haploid egg cell to maturity depends however on its genetic constitution. In a group with a high hybridity equilibrium many recessive mutations such as would have a depressive effect in the pure condition are floating in the population protected by a hybrid condition. A haploid being pure and unprotected must always reveal these recessives. Haploid parthenogenesis giving mature haploid progeny is nevertheless known in fifty or more genera of flowering plants. But it is commonest in the relatively inbred stocks found in some cultivated plants and in polyploid species where the 'haploid' is itself physiologically diploid or polyploid. Non-reduction is therefore needed together with non-fertilisation to maintain the two together as a permanent system. But it is also needed to permit the survival of the egg which goes unfertilised. And the casual occurrence of parthenogenesis combined with non-reduction will generally pass unnoticed. It seems therefore that the observations of haploid parthenogenesis, abundant though they are, must give an inadequate notion of the widespread occurrence of this capacity of egg cells to develop without fertilisation.

The various combinations of non-reduction and non-fertilisation under cover of the external forms of sexual reproduction are known in plants under the collective name of *apomixis*. In animals where the reproductive processes are simpler and more uniform the abnormality can be given the specific name of *parthenogenesis*. How do these aberrant modes of reproduction arise in nature? It is possible that apomixis is sometimes thrust upon a sexually fertile stock by mutation or exceptional conditions causing both the compensating aberrations to occur at once. This has happened in the nematode *Rhabditis* in experiment.[1] A strain arose by mutation in which reduction was suppressed by the failure of one of the meiotic divisions and the egg developed without fertilisation. Such a strain would have a longer or shorter lease of life in nature according to the merits of the sexual type from which it came.

Obligatory parthenogenesis can also get into a fertile species indirectly. In aphids summer broods are parthenogenetic. The egg suppresses its first meiotic division and only one polar body is expelled. The egg with its diploid nucleus can then develop without fertilisation. This property in the genetic system of the aphid economises its reproductive processes by dispensing with the males. At the same time it lengthens the sexual cycle, the intervals between recombination, to a reasonable period, much as paedogenesis, the reproduction of immature animals, may be said to broaden it. Now parthenogenesis in summer aphids is a genetic reaction with summer conditions. When winter returns the XX parthenogenetic females begin to produce offspring capable of sexual reproduction: there are XX sexual females and also XO offspring, lacking one sex chromosome, which are males: thus a sexual generation arises; the XX female gives an XO male by loss of one X chromo-

[1] P. Hertwig, 1920.

some at the single non-reductional division which replaces meiosis. When such a species spreads to a warmer climate the sexual generation is omitted. Obligatory parthenogenesis has got in by the back door.[2]

Thus mutation or migration, if favoured in their effects by natural selection, may lead to the replacement of sexual by asexual reproduction. Apomixis has been found however in all groups of plants and animals where it has been thoroughly sought. It has been found, not merely by observation of breeding, but even more by the comparative study of chromosome complements. And although our knowledge in animals is still no more than fragmentary it allows us to conclude that in animals as well as in plants the mutation that is most usually effective in establishing apomixis is one that concerns the whole chromosome complement. How does this happen?

ii. *The Evidence of Polyploidy*

A new tetraploid animal of a sexually differentiated species will reproduce with difficulty as a male since it must usually cross with diploid females to beget sterile triploid progeny. That is why polyploid species are so rare amongst sexually differentiated animals.[3] A new tetraploid female however can perpetuate herself as a tetraploid if the pairing of chromosomes, and indeed the first meiotic division as a whole, is suppressed. Such is the condition in the shrimp *Artemia salina*: diploid races are sexual: tetraploid races, which have spread to new habitats, are parthenogenetic.[4]

How, it may be asked, can both meiosis and fertilisation be conveniently stopped at the same time when neither is any longer needed? There are two answers to this question. In the first place the normal sequence of meiosis and fertilisation is only 99 per cent effective in most organisms. A new tetraploid individual will often exist by virtue of its female parent being able to forgo meiosis as well as fertilisation. If there is a selective advantage in forgoing both processes no species producing polyploids will have to wait long to produce one with the right gene combination for undergoing regular parthenogenesis. In the second place the new parthenogenetic tetraploid nearly always repeats its mistake. In many species of animals with

[2] Vandel, 1927.   [3] Darlington, 1953a.   [4] Barigozzi, 1946.

parthenogenesis, including *Artemia*, there are octoploid as well as tetraploid races.

The position of the triploids is even simpler. Their inherent segregational sterility cuts them off from sexual reproduction at once. Triploid species can survive only by apomixis or by vegetative propagation. Moreover owing to the awkward segregation of trivalents and univalents they are particularly likely to have an abortive first division in meiosis and thus to produce two triploid products of meiosis instead of four irregularly reduced ones. At one stroke triploidy can remove the possibility of reduction and the need for fertilisation. If in a triploid the egg cell can develop without the stimulus of fertilisation, apomixis is thus automatically established. Such is its origin both in the isopod *Trichoniscus elizabethae* and in many species of flowering plants, for example in *Hieracium*, *Taraxacum* and *Artemisia*.

These principles are illustrated by the parthenogenesis found in species of earthworms which, like the flowering plants, are hermaphrodite.[5] Among 29 species 13 polyploid races have been found; ten of these are obligatorily parthenogenetic. In one species *Eisenia rosea*, $4x$ and $10x$ races are sexual, $3x$ and $6x$ are parthenogenetic. The parthenogenetic forms undergo a regular doubling of chromosomes in a pre-meiotic nucleus of the egg. Owing to the property by which the earthworm chromosomes form only one chiasma in each bivalent at meiosis, no multivalents are formed: meiosis is normal and the result is fertile. Provided however that fertilisation is omitted. Clearly it has not always been successfully omitted and the property of pre-meiotic doubling has not always been regular. Hence the mixture of types and behaviours found in one species.

In the weevils (Curculionidae) parthenogenesis has been studied in many parts of Europe. It is characteristic of the polyploid races which can be recognised by having a body size in proportion to their polyploidy. Among 30 parthenogenetic races studied the following types were found:

$2x$	$3x$	$4x$	$5x$
1	21	6	2

Two of the triploid races had diploid sexual races of the same

[5] Omodeo, 1952; Muldal, 1952.

species. Triploidy was thus demonstrably the immediate condition of their origin.[6]

iii. *Genetic Conditions*

These examples make it clearer what is the origin of apomixis
in diploids. In the triploid we see that hybrid sterility must be
the immediate cause since an act of hybridisation in the genetic
sense, the fusion of diploid and haploid gametes, was the last
sexual act in its history. In the diploid any condition that would
cause sexual sterility and permit a failure of reduction would
have the same result. And that is indeed what happened in
Rhabditis.

Many kinds of genotypic conditions such as appear in inbred
rye and maize lead to a suppression of pairing or a suppression of
chiasma formation or a suppression of the spindle at the first
or second meiotic division. Hence there can be a fairly regular
replacement of the two meiotic divisions by one mitosis. There
is thus a failure of reduction.

The autotriploid and the inbred asynaptic diploid both have
the properties necessary for instituting apomixis. These properties of irregular meiosis are of a kind which has usually in
the past been held to be characteristic of 'hybrids' in the sense
in which the systematist uses the term. That is in the sense of
a cross between members of different species. There is indeed
no reason why apomixis should not arise from crossing species.
But there is at present no evidence that it has ever done so.
Enforced inbreeding rather than enforced outbreeding is more
likely to be the immediately determining condition.

Since we see the conditions of non-reduction arising both
with polyploidy and with special genotypic combinations in all
groups of plants and animals, while apomixis is specially frequent in certain groups, the limiting condition must be the
capacity of the egg to develop without fertilisation. This
capacity gives the sterile polyploid or the sterile mutant a
means of escape from its sterility.

The stimulus of the male gamete is not however so readily
dispensed with. In most apomictic races or species both of
plants and animals the capacity to develop without pollination
or insemination is not in fact perfectly developed. The new

[6] Suomalainen, 1954.

strain can do without fertilisation. But it cannot always do without its antecedents. That is why we find that the egg in asexual races still needs the action of the sperm (in *Rhabditis*) or the pollen (in *Rubus*) in starting its development. They are said to be *pseudogamous*. In plants there are many kinds of pseudogamy owing to the fact that the alternative sexual process of endosperm formation still continues with marvellous variations.[7]

iv. *Versatility and Competition*

The new apomictic form has to compete, from the start, with its sexual parental type. This competition at the very beginning is seen in the apomictic embryos produced by plants which are facultatively apomictic, plants whose mode of reproduction we may describe as genetically *versatile*. Some such species, like

	FERTILISATION	NON-FERTILISATION
REDUCTION	*Sexual Reproduction*	*Haploid Parthenogenesis*
NON-REDUCTION	*Polyploidy*	*Diploid Parthenogenesis Vegetative Embryony*
REPRODUCTIVE METHODS OF VERSATILE SPECIES		

Fig. 29. The combinations of reproductive methods found in versatile species, sometimes all in the same plant competing with one another.

the diploid *Allium odorum*, resemble the aphids. The normal egg is capable of development only after fertilisation. Sometimes however a bud in adjoining tissue grows into an embryosac with an egg nucleus and its seven customary attendant

[7] Rutishauser, 1954*a*, *b*.

nuclei. But this embryo-sac is purely vegetative; its nuclei are diploid and its egg cell develops without fertilisation.

Why should the vegetative embryo sometimes replace the normal embryo and sometimes not? The answer is provided by experiments with similar species of *Rubus* and *Poa*. When fertilisation is attempted with pollen of a closely related plant it is successful; with that of a different species it is usually unsuccessful. The union is a false one for, although seeds are obtained, they are apomictic. Evidently the vegetative embryo develops when the sexual one fails. Neither develops without pollination for the plant is pseudogamous.[8]

The evidence of competition between sexual and vegetative embryos reminds us of the competition between potential embryo sacs of different genetic constitution in *Oenothera*. This competition amongst embryo-sacs is probably very common in hybrids generally although only in *Oenothera* has it been studied in genetically controlled material. It shows a struggle for existence between cells and between individual embryos within the ovule analogous to that between free growing plants. Its effect is like facultative parthenogenesis in the aphides, an economy in the reproductive resources of the species.

Genetic versatility probably reaches its extreme in certain polyploid species. In *Poa pratensis*, for example, we may have every conceivable combination of reduction and non-reduction on one or both sides with fertilisation and non-fertilisation. Thus a $12x$ plant when crossed with an $8x$ plant may yield $6x$, $10x$, $12x$, $14x$ or $16x$ progeny. The particular types of progeny will depend again on their success in competition as well as on the sexual propensities of the parent. For example since the numbers actually found in the species do not generally range beyond the extremes of $6x$ and $18x$ it is clear that non-reduction must be more successful with $6x$ plants and non-fertilisation with $18x$. The non-reduction is occasioned apparently by high autopolyploidy, which at the same time makes it possible for the progeny to forgo fertilisation without exposing too many undesirable recessive combinations and also makes it possible for plants with unbalanced chromosome numbers to show very little effect of unbalance[9] (Fig. 29).

[8] Crane and Thomas, 1940.

[9] Åkerberg, 1939.

v. Subsexual Reproduction

The obligatorily apomictic plant or parthenogenetic animal shows a regularity in its behaviour comparable with that in a sexual species; or indeed exceeding it, for where sexual reproduction is entirely lost we find uniformity of individuals in reproduction as well as in all other respects. As we have seen, this condition can, in some circumstances, be reached at one stroke.

There is one form of obligatory apomixis where further enquiry is needed before we can discuss its mode of origin. This is the type best known in the earth-worms but recently found also in tetraploid species of *Allium*.[10] Here meiosis on the male side is normal for an autotetraploid with many quadrivalents. But on the female side it is preceded by an endomitosis. Each chromosome therefore finds itself next to an identical sister which enjoys a complete spatial advantage in pairing. Hence $4x$ bivalents are regularly formed and reduction restores the tetraploid number with invariable regularity and, of course, with no recombination. We cannot yet say whether such a system has arisen at one step or by several.

In many plants however the steps are now visible.

Comparative study of related groups reveals the sort of evolutionary succession of stages that we might expect from a gradual selective improvement. It also shows how, at each of these stages, there arises the variation on which selective processes could work.

The grass *Agropyron scabrum*[11] which is basically hexaploid exists in a series of populations in New Zealand which pass from inbreeding sexual types of uniform appearance in the north, through facultatively apomictic types of variable appearance, to an obligatorily apomictic type, which is again of uniform appearance, in the south.

In the extreme and obligatorily apomictic type meiosis is completely suppressed on the female although not on the male side. In the embryo-sac mother cell there is no pairing or crossing over of chromosomes and there is often only a single mitotic division instead of meiosis. The chromosome evidence agrees with the study of the population of plants in nature: all

[10] Håkansson and Levan, 1957.   [11] Hair, 1956.

recombination has ceased and reproduction we may say is purely asexual.

Again in the facultatively apomictic populations meiosis is more often suppressed on the female side than on the male side. Let us note that this difference in suppression cannot be due to hybridity. It must have arisen by the selection of genotypes

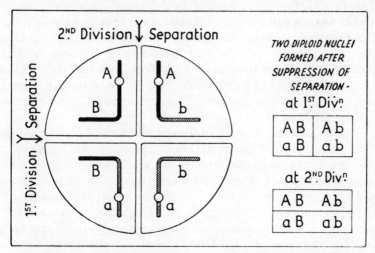

Fig. 30. The results of segregation at meiosis in a hybrid diploid *ABab*. *A-a* (and likewise *B-b*) may be taken to represent a pair of alternatives, either genes or segments, in one pair of chromosomes.

Normal reduction and segregation following crossing over at one chiasma gives 4 haploid nuclei. Reduction can be avoided by suppressing either the first or the second division of meiosis. But in either case segregation is only partly suppressed: homozygous types segregate and subsexual recombination occurs.

Note: (i) The centromeres are represented by circles and the homozygous genes or segments are distal to the chiasma with suppression of the first division, proximal to it with suppression of the second division. (ii) On the same principle, in tetraploids members of quadrivalents which form chiasmata may go to the same pole; an *AAAa* zygote can thus yield *aa* gametes where *Aa* is distal to a chiasma. (After Darlington 1932, fig. 109.)

favourable to the success of the genetic system. That is by the selection of genotypes tending to suppress meiosis in the mother cells on which the plant relies for its reproduction. And when the facultatively apomictic hexaploid yields a triploid or a nonaploid seedling it is giving us evidence of the occasional failure of these selective adjustments.

Now what happens at meiosis in the embryo-sac mother cells

of these populations? The first meiotic division is usually sup-pressed and a single unreduced nucleus is re-formed. But usually there has been pairing; there has indeed often been multiple pairing. The suppression is due to the lagging of un-paired chromosomes at anaphase. The paired chromosomes have crossed over with one another to give new chromatids. The two chromatids attached to the same centromere are no longer always sister chromatids but come in part from different chromosomes. These chromatids will pass to the same pole as their true sisters in half the unreduced second divisions in which they occur. Where there is crossing-over there will therefore be a limited amount of segregation (Fig. 30) even though there is non-reduction. The amount of segregation and recombination will be *subsexual*.[12]

The evidences of subsexual reproduction are clear in the facultative stage of the evolution of apomixis. In *Agropyron* at the facultative stage they appear as variations both of chromo-some number and of external form. But traces of meiosis are still expressed in what we may call subsexual reproduction in the obligatory stage of apomixis. In *Taraxacum*, which triploidy proves to be obligatorily apomictic, there are parallel processes. In *Taraxacum*, as in *Agropyron*, meiosis in the embryo-sac is replaced by a single division and reproduction gives a nearly uniform product. But occasionally a single bivalent is formed. And from this simple cause two quite different results ensue. On the one hand crossing-over has taken place and leads to recombination. On the other hand the suppression of meiosis is impeded and embryos are formed with one chromosome too many or too few. Or both divisions are suppressed and, as in so many parthenogenetic animals, hexaploid progeny are the result[13] (Fig. 31).

Subsexual variation probably arises with most kinds of par-thenogenesis. Wherever it arises it is a symptom that the asexual mechanism is still imperfectly adapted to the needs of reproduction. And it is using the relics of the sexual system as a means of making good this defect. The numerous names given by the systematist to what prove to be chromosome variants in *Taraxacum* bear witness to the effectiveness of sub-sexual variation in contributing to the adaptive development

[12] Darlington, 1937*a*.   [13] Sørensen and Gudjonsson, 1946; Hair, 1956.

of each apomictic strain. Such development will be as important in adapting the character of the genetic system as it is in adapting the character of the vegetative individual.

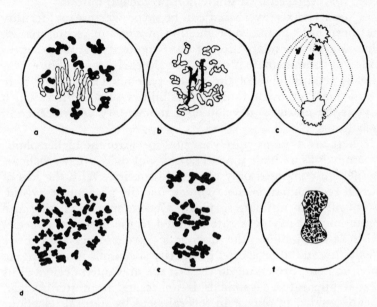

Fig. 31. Partly suppressed meiosis in pollen mother-cells of obligatory apomicts in the grass *Agropyron scabrum* ($6x=42$). *a* and *b*, first metaphases with 8 and with 2 bivalents. *b*, a univalent has developed centric activity at the ends. *c*, three lagging univalents at anaphase. *d* and *e*, abortive anaphases with scattered and grouped univalents after complete failure of pairing. *f*, restitution nucleus arising from *b*, *d* or *e*.
× 1000   (from Hair, 1956.)

vi. *The Blind Alley*

In this way the new and still evolving apomictic species will have a limited scope of recombination and variation so long as pairing and crossing-over can take place between its chromosomes. The result is shown to the plant or animal breeder by the appearance of mutant types in his progenies. Or, if he makes accurate measurements, by the appearance of quantitative variation.[14] It is shown to the systematist by the appearance of innumerable trivial species in nature, in such genera as *Hieracium* and *Taraxacum*. It is also shown by the development

[14] Haskell, 1953.

in its last stages of a more precise and fertile system of apomixis. The abandonment of sexual reproduction is progressive and irrevocable. Meiosis is completely suppressed on the female side; it is replaced by a single non-precocious mitosis.

Thus apomixis saves what can be saved when sexual fertility has been lost. Sexual reproduction provides in recombination the basis for the adaptation of all its posterity. Apomixis provides for its immediate progeny. In the early stages of its evolution it retains relics of the sexual system. These allow it to enjoy new although limited possibilities of variation which give it the means of developing a momentary efflorescence of new forms.

There are as many purely asexual species of the higher plants or animals as we have time to name. But there are, we believe, no genera composed only of asexual species. With the loss of sexual recombination the apomict, like the permanent hybrid, is cut off from ultimate survival. Recombination ceasing and mutation still having a rate adapted to the needs of a species with recombination, the apomictic species loses its genetic flexibility and after a brief prosperity succumbs to a changing environment, preserving to the last the unwanted devices of its sexual apparatus. Apomixis is an escape from sterility; an escape guided in one or in several steps by natural selection; but it is an escape which leads only to extinction.

21

THE INTEGRATION OF THE CELL

i. *Interactions*

THE first problem of heredity is that of the parts played in it by the nucleus and the cytoplasm. It is also the last, for we can deal definitely with the less definable cytoplasm only when the nucleus has been accurately defined. The nucleus showed us that there were two methods of investigating long-range processes in life namely microscopy and experimental breeding. For treating the cytoplasm the two methods reappear in parallel but their relative values have proved to be different. When we consider the cytoplasm we have to leave behind for the most part the visible determinants which are so useful in dealing with the nucleus and rely more on inferences from heredity and development. These inferences are less obvious but they need not be less rigorous.

Another parallel between the study of nucleus and cytoplasm is in the cardinal need for separating the effects of heredity and environment. But again the cytoplasmic problem has proved to be somewhat different from the nuclear one because development comes into the picture in a different way. Indeed our next task must be to separate heredity from development, and in order to do this we must know something about how genes act during development. We have already considered much of the evidence in special connections. Let us now bring it together.

Cells can exist without nuclei. Special cells like red blood corpuscles are even adapted to do their specialised work for a limited period without nuclei. But they do not grow or multiply. Successful regeneration of parts of unicellular organisms depends on the presence of the nucleus. In short the nucleus is constantly acting on the cytoplasm whenever anything new is being done.

Now we know that the action of the nucleus is balanced. Its different parts produce a co-ordinated effect. Where does this co-ordination take place? The answer is that mechanically most of the co-ordination takes place within the nucleus. Each chromosome is synchronised in spiralisation throughout its length. This synchronisation is probably controlled by the centromere. The different centromeres are also synchronised. They are able to communicate with one another or with the cytoplasm. This mechanical co-ordination however has no peculiar physiological character. It is merely adaptively necessary. And it means that the nucleus has its internal system of communications which it can use when it needs must.[1]

Another kind of evidence of internal co-ordination is derived from the position effect. The position effect of genes which we saw earlier shows that exceptionally two genes have a different effect if they are close together in the chromosome from what they have if they are far apart. Here then their products must interact inside the nucleus. As a rule however they do not. They interact in the cytoplasm and through it.

The intermediacy of the cytoplasm is perhaps most obvious in the genotypic control of chromosome behaviour, since the uniformity of the action of the nucleus always arises in a reaction with its substrate. Hence the old fallacy that it was indeed the cytoplasm which ultimately controlled nuclear behaviour and not the nucleus itself.

The next question is how quickly the nucleus can act on the cytoplasm. Instantaneous action can be recognised in many ways. We saw one example in the pollen of *Allium cernuum*. In the diploidisation of fungi the guest nucleus divides in every cell it enters, the host nucleus does not. In this instance a single gene difference may be all that distinguishes the two nuclei. More important differences distinguish pollen grains and potential embryo-sacs which live or die according to whether they have the right or the wrong numbers of chromosomes or genetic complexes. And here we may note that precisely the same difference of viability that marks certain genetic complexes in *Oenothera* may be determined, and usually is determined elsewhere, by relative position of the nuclei in the organism. We shall return to this reaction later.

Some genes therefore act as quickly as diffusion in a liquid substrate can allow them to act. And multiple differences are

[1] Darlington, 1957.

therefore likely to act rapidly. But individual genes differ in
their time of action.[2] They are set going at a specific time in
development. Thus the detailed properties of pollen grains—
shape, colour and kind of starch—are usually determined by
the genetic action of the mother plant, although if this plant is
hybrid for genes affecting these properties the pollen grains
will differ in these genes. Exceptionally however in *Zea*, *Oryza*,
Sorghum, *Pisum* and *Oenothera* the pollen grains show their own
individual properties. In a word the nucleus reacts with the
cytoplasm and the cytoplasm changes its properties throughout
development. These properties at any one stage are the
resultant of the reactions of the genes at all previous stages.

In unicellular organisms these previous stages include many
mitotic generations. And in the higher organisms they include
the preceding generation. Of course it is the maternal side that
matters. The maternal character invariably determines the
direction of coiling of a snail's shell. And in some animals like
the dung fly *Sciara* it invariably determines the sex of the offspring: the eggs of each mother are all male or all female. Thus
the cytoplasm may determine or carry determinants of properties of importance for many future cell generations: indeed
it seems to do so whenever it has proved useful to the organism
that it should do so.

By these carrying properties the cytoplasm maintains and
propagates through many cell generations something that has
been put into it by the nucleus; or at least has been modified
by the nucleus. These properties are most developed and best
known in animals. They are related to a differentiation or
mosaic character, or in its simplest form a polarity or asym-
metry, in the animal egg. They persist throughout development
and not merely in space but also in time. The different parts
of the animal at one time are as different from one another as
are the same parts at different times. Their relations in time
and space are established by the formation and diffusion of
chemically recognisable organisers.[3] And they are expressed
by the changes we have noted in the integration and dispersion
of genes in the polytene chromosomes at different stages of
development and in different tissues. Thus we have evidence
that the integration of gene action is due to the reactions

[2] Haldane, 1932.   [3] Waddington, 1939.

between genes and cytoplasm being chemically and spatially determined in specific successions and arrangements.

The delayed effect of the cytoplasm is shown by the preponderant influence of the egg on early development where its recent genetic history has been different from that of the sperm nucleus. This is shown most crudely by the breakdown of development in most distant hybrids in animals, whether in sea-urchins, fishes or amphibia. This breakdown is always associated with gross malformations. The same breakdown follows in animal eggs where the egg nucleus is removed and a sperm nucleus from another species allowed to develop in the maternal cytoplasm. Here it can sometimes be shown that the early development is maternal and the breakdown occurs when the nucleus tries to assert itself. Or rather when the nucleus should be reacting with the chemical stimuli of a compatible cytoplasm which then prove to be lacking.[4]

Less violent conflicts between nucleus and cytoplasm arise through the treatment of *Paramecium* or *Drosophila* with heat or various poisons. Abnormalities are produced which are inherited only through the egg (in *Drosophila*) and persist for a limited number of generations.[5] Specific differences showing the same maternal influence are found in several crosses between animal species and races and indicate a prolonged failure of the cytoplasm to adjust itself to the nucleus. Whether any such cases imply the permanence of the cytoplasmic elements concerned was long considered doubtful. It was not until the discovery that susceptibility to CO_2 in *Drosophila* was inherited only in the female line that such a determinant could be assumed in animals.[6]

So much is true of animals. In the past the same rules have often been thought to apply to animals and plants in regard to cytoplasmic effects, because the same rules apply in regard to nuclear effects. This is certainly not true. Not only are the processes of development less highly organised in plants and regeneration, especially in the lower plants, vastly easier, but the genetic results tell a different story.

'Hybrids', containing the nucleus of one species and the cytoplasm of another, live and flourish in plants: not only when the

---

[4] Hadorn, 1937.   [5] 'Dauermodifikation.' Jollos, 1934.
                    [6] L'Héritier, 1955.

difference is between species, as in *Fragaria* and *Nicotiana*, but also when it is between genera. Under natural conditions the sperm nucleus of *Vicia sativa* may expel the egg nucleus of *Lens esculentum* and proceed by doubling of its chromosome number to develop a normal plant, with the alien cytoplasm of the maternal parent. Furthermore distant hybridisation which is so disastrous in animals is remarkably successful in plants. Crosses between genera are frequent. Crosses between subfamilies in mosses, grasses and crucifers give vigorous progeny. Hybrids between *Saccharum* and *Bambusa* are fertile. Only that between *Saccharum* and *Zea* shows vegetative abnormality.[7]

There is however an important similarity in the part played by the cytoplasm in plants and animals. In both it is the agent of nuclear activity and of differentiation. In both it consequently passes through a cycle of adjusted changes. In animals this adjustment seems more complex, more rigid and more persistent. But we must remember that in ferns and mosses parthenogenesis can give a haploid sporophyte and non-reduction can give a diploid gametophyte. It is not therefore the difference in chromosome number which decides that a spore shall develop into a gametophyte while a fertilised egg shall develop into a sporophyte. It is the character of the cytoplasm at different points in the life cycle which is decisive. The differences arising in the cytoplasm of the plant as of the animal are immediately responsible for switching the processes of differentiation.

ii. *Organellae*

What can we see in the cytoplasm to explain its properties?

In the cytoplasm there are various structures large enough for us to study their reproduction and behaviour. These structures vary in the course of development and differentiation. Their variations appear to be not controlling differentiation so much as being controlled by it. But they are self-propagating. That is to say they always seem to arise, like the nucleus or the chromosomes, by reproduction of a previous body of a similar kind. They have a genetic continuity and we must speak of them as *genetic particles*. There are two generally important types of genetic particles having visible effects in the cytoplasm,

[7] Janaki Ammal, 1938.

those which produce fibres and those which produce pigments.

Fibre-producing bodies include the centrosomes responsible for organising the mitotic spindle in animals and in the lower plants. These bodies are no doubt similar to the centromeres of chromosomes but they live and work outside the nucleus. As we have seen, they react with the centromeres and like them are activated cyclically by the cytoplasm. Like them also they can be activated in other ways, for example in producing the motile fibres of sexual cells at the gametic stage.

The largest development of fibre-producing bodies is in the protozoa where they give rise to an elaborate differentiation not between cells but within the single cell (Fig. 32). Within the ciliates, for example, there is a body studied in detail by Lwoff and known as the kinetosome.[8] This body is related to the centrosome but it has more varied properties in organising cilia and other fibrous structures on which the life of the organism depends. Again, the type of activity of the kinetosome depends on the part or layer of the cytoplasm in which it lies. Just as the differentiation of the cytoplasm within the cell can be demonstrated by the reactions of the nuclei in a pollen grain, so also can it be demonstrated by the reactions of the kinetosomes. Every active body in the cell is reacting with its substrate and its reactions change with the changes of the substrate which may equally be changes in space or in time.

If these fibre-producing bodies are genetic particles we might expect them to change, to mutate. Differences between races and species are of course evidence of such mutation but we need experimental evidence to show us how the difference may have arisen, its causes and its consequences.

Two kinds of experiment have been used. In most ciliates the organellae are not genetically differentiated. Small fragments containing nuclei will reconstitute the whole. But in *Paramecium* differentiation is sharper. Fragments without a gullet cannot regenerate one and therefore die.[9] Genetic particles in the ciliates are thus evolving and changing their status.

Again, in animals the centrosome is believed to be carried by the spermatozoa. It should prove to be a patrilinear cytoplasmic particle. In race crosses of *Culex* there is sterility which

[8] Lwoff, 1950.   [9] Tartar, 1954.

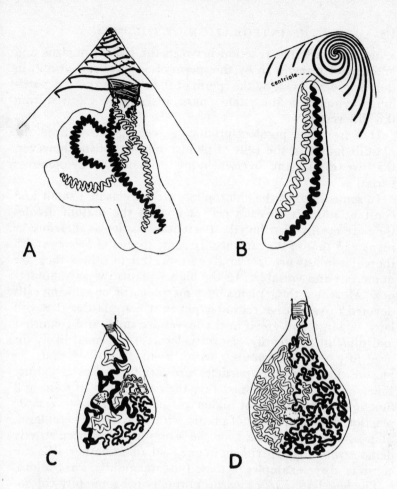

Fig. 32. Organellar plasmagenes in the mitotic cycle of the organism with the largest known chromosomes, the parasitic flagellate *Holomastigotoides tusitala* ($x=2$). The four stages shown cannot without reservation be given the names used for mitosis in the higher organisms because the nuclear membrane remains permanently intact and the chromosomes remain permanently differentiated and attached to the fibre-producing plasmagenes (centrioles and flagellar bands) without an ordinary resting stage.

A. *Prophase:* sister chromatids separated: centromeres attached to divided centrioles which are attached to sister flagellar bands and are being pushed apart by the developing spindle fibres.

B. *Telophase:* centromeres lying on nuclear membrane; full spiralisation retained.

C. *Late Telophase:* nucleolus developed; relic coils growing; new spindle fibres formed by divided centriole.

D. *Resting Stage:* full uncoiling but no split visible in the chromosomes. Chromosomes 35μ long at full contraction: × 1500 (from Cleveland, 1949).

arises from a lethal reaction between the hybrid nucleus and an element brought in by the sperm of one parent but not, in the reciprocal cross, by the sperm of the other parent. A patri-linear cytoplasmic inheritance must, it seems, be inferred from this difference.[10]

It is from the pigment-producing bodies, that is from the plastids found in the cells of plants and of protista, however, that we derive the overwhelming evidence of cytoplasmic variation.

In some diatoms the chloroplasts are present in a small and constant number in each cell and when the diatom divides they are evenly distributed. Their transmission is therefore as regular as that of the nucleus. In some species of *Spirogyra* also the chloroplasts are few and constant, but in others they are numerous and variable. In the higher plants they are numer-ous. Moreover these plants have meristematic or growing cells devoted to vegetative reproduction in which plastids·that will later be large and green in the leaves are small and colourless and difficult to identify. Nevertheless it has seemed likely for over fifty years (beginning with Erwin Baur)[11, 12] that the plastids like the fibre-particles are strictly self-propagating. Likewise it has also seemed that their variations in form and function in the tissues of higher plants are due to a versatile reaction of a single type of plastid with a changing cytoplasm. Step by step during this time the assumption has been strictly demonstrated by experiment in one field after another. We can consider three examples of these fundamental demonstrations.

The flagellate *Euglena gracilis* normally has some fifty chloro-plasts. Kept in the dark on peptone broth it multiplies faster than its plastids which consequently decrease in number. In the end a mitosis produces organisms without plastids. And they are never formed again. We have a new race of colourless *Euglenae*, such as is also found in nature.

This change has an evolutionary interest to which we shall return later. It is of genetic interest to us at once as demon-strating the basis of genetic continuity. And finally it is of physiological interest as showing one of the principles of inte-gration in the cell. The different genetic organs or organellae of the cell have their own individual rates of multiplication

[10] Laven, 1953.   [11] Baur, 1909.   [12] Chittenden, 1927.

which are affected differently by changes of conditions. It is not surprising therefore that the character of the cell can be altered (as in the evolution of meiosis) by changing these conditions and thus putting them out of step with one another and with the nucleus.

The same result can be achieved with *Euglena* in quite a different way. High temperatures and also treatment with streptomycin will produce colourless races by killing the plastids.[13] Parallel with this experiment is the discovery that in *Trypanosoma* a nucleo-protein body of unknown function, known as a kinetoplast, can be prevented from reproducing by treatment with an acridine dye. Trypanosome races have thus been produced destitute of this easily recognised body. They have bred true for twenty years.[14]

Again we have evidence of genetic continuity. But we also have evidence of a specificity of chemical interference with a genetic particle. The reaction is comparable with that of maleic hydrazide (an isomer of the uracil in a nucleotide of RNA) which specifically interferes with the reproduction of heterochromatic parts of chromosomes and causes their breakage.

The third type of experiment is concerned with the genetic and physiological properties of the plastids of higher plants.

In hundreds of plant species genes are known which control the colour of the plastids. The albino type appears as a Mendelian recessive which usually dies. In a number of species, however, the cross white-by-green is entirely white and the cross green-by-white entirely green. The colour of the plastids is maternally inherited. Actually a purely white parent cannot be used, but it so happens that white tissue arises by mutation in very many plants and owing to the regular separation of layers in the development of the plant an arrangement comes about by which a glove of white tissue is growing over a hand of green tissue. The subepidermal layer of white tissue produces the germ cells, the green layers do the work. Such chimaeras of *Pelargonium zonale* can be bred as though they were white, and from this breeding Baur was able to conclude that the plastids were self-maintaining organs of inheritance.

Plastid mutations from green to yellow or white occur in all

[13] E. and O. Pringsheim, 1951. [14] Hoare, 1954.

species of green plants in nature. They occur once in 2000 *Oenothera* plants, wild species or crosses. They appear as pale flecks or if they come early enough they develop into layers of pale tissue. The cells in which these mutations have occurred are at first mixed cells: they are seen to contain large plastids with numerous chlorophyll grana and small defective plastids with few grana.[15] Evidently the plastids maintain themselves, but also, unlike the genes, they are capable of sorting themselves out at a mitotic cell division. Thus purely white and purely green cells arise from mixed cells. This sorting out takes place slowly in *Antirrhinum* and *Mirabilis*, more quickly in *Pelargonium* and *Oenothera*, where egg cells for example are never mixed.[16]

Another property in which species differ is in regard to the plastids being carried over by the pollen tube. In *Antirrhinum* and *Zea* they are inherited exclusively through the egg. In *Oenothera* a few usually enter from the pollen. A flaked plant is then produced from the cross green-by-white. The reciprocal cross dies too young for us to see the flakes.

These situations are instructive but not unexpected. In *Pelargonium* however the results are unexpected, so much so that their implications were overlooked by those who discovered them. The reciprocal crosses between green and white gave the following percentages of green, variegated and white seedlings[17]:

♀ × ♂	G	V	W	Total
G × W	77	13	10	*280*
W × G	72	28	—	*93*

Here it seems that the green plastids in some way come to predominate over the white. This is not surprising. What is surprising is that their predominance is greater when they come in with the male germ cell.

Thus the male germ cell makes a greater contribution of these cytoplasmic particles. And the female cell sometimes fails to contribute anything at all. The rule that we might expect to hold for an evenly dispersed particle, that the larger cell carries most, holds for most plant plastids. But it breaks down

[15] Maly and Wild, 1956.   [16] Renner, 1934, 1937.   [17] *cf.* Darlington, 1949*b*.

in *Pelargonium*. It breaks down no doubt because the particles are localised or aggregated in special ways according to the kind of cell and according to the species of plant.

What then is the relationship of nucleus and plastid? It seems in some cases that the nucleus controls the colour of the plastid. Yet in other cases it seems that the plastid is as autonomous and permanent as any gene. This apparent conflict is resolved by certain critical experiments with *Oenothera*.[18]

As we saw earlier, the hybrid species *Oenothera muricata* produces two types of gametes, *curvans* and *rigens*. The homozygous species *Oe. Hookeri* on the other hand produces only one kind of gamete whose haploid nuclear complex is known as *hHookeri*. These two species can be crossed reciprocally to give two kinds of progeny in respect of the nucleus: and there are two kinds of each of these in respect of the cytoplasm. If we take only the *curvans* progeny we find that the progeny of the reciprocal crosses is different:

Hookeri ♀ × *muricata* ♂ —*hHookeri . curvans*: yellow
muricata ♀ × *Hookeri* ♂ —*hHookeri . curvans*: green.

This means that *Hookeri* plastids are yellow with the $H . c$ nucleus. Yet they are green with a pure *Hookeri* nucleus, and *muricata* plastids are green with the $H . c$ nucleus.

The table shows us what is happening:

NUCLEI	PLASTIDS	
	Hookeri	*muricata*
Hookeri	green	green
hH. curvans	yellow	green

Now the yellow seedlings die, but a few *Hookeri* plastids have been brought into the green seedlings with the pollen where *Hookeri* was the male parent. Some of these develop yellow flakes and yellow layers by sorting out during development. Yellow-over-green shoots should then breed from their yellow subepidermal layers as though they had pure *Hookeri* plastids. When selfed these shoots gave the two kinds of progeny that we should expect on this view (*curvans . curvans* being, as we know, lethal):

    (i) *hHookeri . curvans*: all yellow.
    (ii) *hHookeri . hHookeri*: all green.

[18] Renner, 1936

As we should expect also, when these shoots are back-crossed with *muricata* pollen all the progeny is of the first type; with *Hookeri* pollen, of the second type.

Thus *Hookeri* plastids which become yellow with the *H . c* nucleus become green again with the pure *Hookeri* nucleus, and indeed with certain other nuclei in other crosses.

Tests of this kind show that the behaviour of the plastids depends on their reaction with the nucleus and that both partners to this reaction are permanent and autonomous. Hence although most plastid mutations to white or yellow are incompetent in any nucleus with which they can be combined by crossing, we are bound to suppose that the plastids and the nuclei of each *Oenothera* species have become mutually adapted for chlorophyll production by mutation and selection on *both* sides.

Microscopic studies show the physiological and structural bases of these differences in plastid behaviour. In cells of *Oenothera* hybrids with mixed plastids each type has its own rate of propagation under a particular nucleus and therefore its own competitive position.[19] With the electron microscope the degrees of efficiency of different genetic types of plastid and the stages of breakdown of those which are not efficient can be determined.[20] The scope of variation of plastids is indeed comparable with that of nuclear genes with this limitation that the plastogene must always be selected for a somewhat specialised physiological function.

iii. *Invisible Particles*

Knowing the special properties of extra-nuclear inheritance shown by the visible plastids, we are in a better position to test the evidence for invisible determinants outside the nucleus. We must not expect absolute constancy; we must allow for sorting out. We must allow for differential rates of propagation subject to changing external conditions. We must allow for varying aggregations and localisations. We must not therefore expect absolute matrilinear descent in plants; indeed we may expect a reversal of it; and accordingly we must be prepared for the predominance of either one side or the other in reciprocal crosses.

[19] Schötz, 1954, 1955.   [20] Maly, 1951; Wettstein, 1957.

Reciprocal crosses between many pairs of species in plants differ, for example in *Epilobium*, *Streptocarpus*[21] and *Geranium*. They differ, not in resembling the mother plant more closely, but in new and precise modifications. Reciprocal crosses between *Funaria mediterranea* and *F. hygrometrica*, for example, differ in sporocarp shape. By regeneration meiosis can be avoided and diploid gametophytes produced vegetatively. These again differ in leaf shape. They still differ if maintained vegetatively for 13 years. And further, if haploid gametophytes are back-crossed to the male parent eight times, so that the product has the nucleus of the male parent and the cytoplasm of its matrilinear ancestor, it still does not agree in form with its male parent.[22]

Such tests show the action of a permanent cytoplasmic determinant. Or, should we say, system of determinants? The answer depends on the nature of the crosses. In a particular difference between reciprocal crosses of individuals with a single gene difference, a specific cytoplasmic determinant may be assumed. In *Linum* a special gene from the tall flax aborts the anthers in a quarter of the F_2 progeny of its cross with a procumbent species when this species is used as the female parent. A gene mutation has been accompanied by a corresponding cytoplasmic change.[23] In these circumstances it is not surprising that plant populations have been able, in the ways we have seen, to seize on cytoplasm-controlled male-sterility as an instrument in correcting their breeding systems.

Where generalised or multiple effects are concerned a number of different determinants must be supposed to take part. Thus in *Vicia Faba* a number of plasmatic differences are to be inferred from reciprocal crosses between the subspecies *major* and *minor*. Amongst other effects the *minor* cytoplasm seems to eliminate the F_2 segregates which are pure for certain genes from the stock. There are six genes concerned and they are linked in one complex.[24] When we recall the importance of such complexes in developing the discontinuity between species it begins to appear that this action on linked genes is not a coincidence but a consequence of special adaptation of the cytoplasm to the nucleus during the differentiation of the two

[21] Oehlkers, 1938.
[23] Gajewski, 1937.
[22] Wettstein, 1937.
[24] Sirks, 1931.

N

races. It implies the existence of a number of different and specific determinants in the cytoplasm.

The variety of changes in plasma types similarly argues a specificity in these changes. In *Epilobium hirsutum* half a dozen stocks from different localities differ in their plasmatic properties, as shown in reciprocal crosses with one another and with *E. luteum*. They differ not only quantitatively but qualitatively and give in the extreme cases a variety of probably unrelated effects.[25]

The cross *luteum-hirsutum* has been back-crossed to the male parent thirteen times so as to give a *hirsutum* nucleus in an approximately *luteum* cytoplasm. This product may be represented as Lh^n. We then find that $Lh^{14} \times luteum$ resembles *luteum* $\times$ *hirsutum* and not the reciprocal cross. For example, it is male sterile. The cytoplasm of Lh^{14} remains after fourteen generations essentially *luteum*.

This is not the whole story. When a white-over-green *hirsutum* is used as the male parent of Lh^{14} one in 400 plants shows white flecks. Evidently this is due to the sorting out of pollen plastids from egg plastids. Examination of this generation shows that about one in 400 also has shoots with fertile anthers. Further, the male-fertile flowers selfed give fewer sterile progeny than the male-sterile flowers of the same plant (using presumably the pollen of the fertile flowers). The plasmatic determinants therefore just as much as the plastids are sorted out in development. In fact plasmatic inheritance of all kinds, like Mendelian inheritance, is particulate.

Particulate inheritance of the plasma does not mean that a single type of particle distinguishes *luteum* from *hirsutum*. As we saw, the several effects in *Vicia* and the several races in *Epilobium* indicate several kinds of particle. This is brought home to us in a special way by the same mutating plants of Lh^{14}. When the fertile flowers of Lh^{14} are crossed with *luteum* pollen they give less fertile progeny than do the sterile flowers in the same cross. The sorting out of a determinant affecting the fertility of pure *hirsutum* nuclear type does not mean the sorting out of a determinant affecting the fertility of a *hirsutum-luteum* hybrid. Different and independently assorting determinants are at work.[26]

[25] Michaelis, 1935.   [26] Michaelis, 1937.

Taking these experiments together we see that genotype must be supposed to embrace three elements, the nucleus, the determinants of plastids and organellae, the pigment and fibre producers, and the submicroscopic particles which we cannot yet identify because they have no products attached to them.

All of them depend on self-propagating or genetic particles. The nucleus, to be sure, consists of particles of different sizes and is subject to variation of different kinds: for the other genetic particles we are still in the dark about these things. Yet if we give the name of genes to the particles in the nucleus, we have to use the same kind of name for the free particles in the cytoplasm. Those in the plastids and the cytoplasm may be treated more rigorously if we also think of them also as genes— *plastogenes* and *plasmagenes*. To be understood, and even sometimes to be discovered, we need to know them in relation to specific differences in nuclear genes. But this in no way robs the free genes of their specificity or integrity. It merely shows that we cannot so exactly control them.

In order that we should find out something more about these free genes we must try to form a more precise picture of how they live, move and multiply. It seems likely that they are nucleo-protein molecules or aggregates. Evidently they are such that, like true genes, they can rise only from nucleo-proteins of the same kind—apart from mutation. Unlike true genes however their reproduction is not controlled by a *mechanical* equilibrium but will be subject rather to conditions of equilibrium genotypically controlled but specific for each type of gene. Where the particles are as large and complex as plastid determinants we may describe their equilibrium as *physiological* and we have seen how this equilibrium may be physiologically upset by light and nutrition. Where the particles are smaller as they doubtless are for most plasmagenes we may imagine that their equilibrium approaches nearer to a condition of *chemical* equilibrium. The conditions of cytoplasmic heredity are therefore likely to show a wide variation according to the type of equilibrium to which the plasmagenes concerned are subject. Probably also the varying kinds of differentiation found in animals, plants and micro-organisms will favour the development of varying types of plasmagenes.

The possible nature of the plasmagene is indicated by what

we know of virus diseases. The virus is a protein molecule which, introduced into one organism, disappears; into another, multiplies to give a neutral equilibrium; into yet another multiplies without limit and has deleterious or fatal results. If we look upon the virus as a protein taken out of one organism (usually by a parasite) and injected into another to which it is not properly adapted, we see that it has the properties often shown by a plasmagene in crosses between species. This is to suppose that a virus is not a primitive enemy of nature but just a protein out of place. Such is the position of the cytoplasm of one species which harbours the nucleus of another, and the varying behaviour of the one indicates the varying possibilities of the other.

22

TYPES OF PLASMAGENE

i. *Male Breakdown*

So far we have considered evidence of genetic particles that was mostly available twenty years ago and the conclusions that could be derived from this evidence.[1] We may now consider the new enquiries and new interpretations which have sprung from the notion of the plasmagene: a genetic particle which is versatile in its behaviour like the larger organellar genes, but with even more remarkable consequences of this versatility owing to its free situation.

These enquiries and interpretations have confirmed the expectation that there are physiologically and genetically many kinds of ultra-microscopic plasmagenes. Four of them may be usefully described.

The first class of plasmagene includes those responsible for male-sterility in plants. It is stable and purely maternal and for this reason it was the first kind to be identified. Also, of course, the anther is the first organ the plant produces which can be upset without upsetting the general vegetative life. This action in upsetting the development of the anthers always depends on the failure of the cytoplasm to react with a particular nucleus. Each species or race therefore has a nucleus and a cytoplasm each capable of varying in its effect on the development of the anther and with the two therefore nearly always adjusted in nature.

The co-adaptation, as we may call it, of nucleus and cytoplasm is best shown in *Zea mays*. Here numerous local and varietal differences in nucleus and cytoplasm are found to go together. Crossing therefore readily produces male-sterile forms. Just as cytoplasmically male-sterile forms are of value in the breeding systems of species in nature, so these are of value in the raising of hybrid seed in cultivation.

How do these cytoplasmic differences arise? They arise

---

[1] that is, in the first edition of this book.

from mutation which can be induced, or rather vastly increased, by the choice of special nuclear genotypes. In many species of plants particular gene-differences render the plastids unstable. They thus cause irregular variegation. And, since the plastids are maternally inherited, the progeny include white seedlings. In maize a recessive gene, *iojap*, has this effect. It also causes patches of male-sterility in plants where it is homozygous. This male-sterility is also maternally inherited. The patches of aborted anthers do not however correspond with the stripes of white leaf. Thus it seems that the *iojap* gene has the effect of rendering unstable some cytoplasmic element or process which reacts independently with the two kinds of genetic particle.

This evidence of a genotypic control, or more strictly a nuclear control, of the stability or mutability of plasmagenes is worth connecting with the corresponding evidence for the control of nuclear genes. For this kind of control is a key property in the evolution of genetic systems. It was in maize also that a particular gene Dt had the property of causing another gene a_1 to mutate to A_1 and so give a purple flaking on green leaves. Or we may say the allele of Dt has the property keeping a_1 stable. This gene difference has no other known effect. Evidently this is the same relation as that found between nuclear genes and plasmagenes. For the stability or instability of each element in the cell-system all the elements are bound up together; they are mutually adjusted, or selectively balanced.[2]

Male sterility plasmagenes are now known in many plants to be strictly matrilinear and stable in inheritance. Only those which happen to have these qualities have any possibility of being discovered and identified. Many more that are less predictable may therefore also exist.

Floating in several populations of *Drosophila bifasciata* is a plasmagene of a similar kind. It kills nearly all the *XY* embryos, that is the males, in the progeny, before hatching.[3] This reaction of nucleus and cytoplasm thus produces much the same effect on the population and on its breeding system as the sex-ratio gene complex in other *Drosophila* species: it raises the proportion of females in the whole population. In its effect on the individual, that is physiologically, the reaction is much the same as those producing male-sterility in plants.

[2] Rhoades, 1938, 1950.   [3] Magni, 1953.

ii. *Age Breakdowns*

A second class of plasmagene is that which arises frequently as a mutation during development and seems indeed to be a symptom of development. It suggests a quantitative rather than a qualitative change in the effective particles. The classical example is Bateson's rogue pea.

Rogues in peas arise in certain varieties (that is in certain nuclear and cytoplasmic genotypes). They have narrower leaves and fewer flowers than the normal type. The rogue pea passes on its character to all its progeny. Selfed it always breeds true. When crossed with the type either as male or female it yields progeny which become rogue gradually or suddenly during development. On these changing plants the selfed progeny of successive flowers also show a changing proportion of rogues. The heredity goes with the development.

Here we have cytoplasmic inheritance since there is no segregation. But it is biparental. Indeed the crosses become rogue more quickly if the rogue parent is the male than if it is the female. Thus once again the plasmagene contradicts what was formerly the critical test of cytoplasmic inheritance, the predominance of the maternal influence. But from the genetic point of view influences are of no more use than essences. We have to think in terms of the propagation of particles. We must then say that, like the plastid-determinants in *Pelargonium*, but not of other plants, this type of plasmagene seems to multiply or to be localised in one tissue more than in another, in the pollen rather than in the embryo-sac.[4]

Similar to the rogue in peas is the breakdown in strawberries which seems to make their plastids unstable in the strongest light and is known as June Yellows. Like the rogue, this breakdown is an irreversible and hereditary change which has been attributed to plasmagene mutation.[5] It takes place in clones after a certain number of years of vegetative propagation. All the plants in different places behave in a roughly similar and therefore predictable way. And like the rogue in peas, the yellows in strawberries is transmitted more strongly and at an earlier stage of life through the pollen than through the embryo-sac.[6]

A third type of plasmagene is that responsible for several

[4] Darlington, 1949c.   [5] Darlington and Mather, 1949.
[6] H. Williams, 1955.

other kinds of mutations in plants. The most notable is the rogue tomato with poorer fruiting than the otherwise pure-breeding varieties in which it occurs. Among tomatoes grown in glasshouses in England the seed is germinated at a higher temperature than when the crop is grown in the open in warmer climates. Also seed is used from fruits of the later, the higher, inflorescences. These two circumstances to which the species is not adapted combine to induce a proportion of seedlings, up to one half, of the abnormal type or rogue.

How do these rogue tomato seedlings breed? Unlike the rogue peas they have no more rogues in their progeny than their normal sisters. Hence we might argue that this is not a genetic or hereditary problem in the ordinary sense at all but a developmental one. A high temperature merely shifts the mode of development of the young seed from normal to rogue without having any effect on the next generation. But this is not the whole story. Seed from the top inflorescence of any plant gives a higher proportion of rogues than seed from the bottom inflorescence; the two lots are grown of course at the same temperature. Thus seedlings of the variety Ailsa Craig grown at 14°C give 5 per cent of rogues from the two bottom, 10 per cent from the two top inflorescences. At 30° they give 15 per cent of rogues from the two bottom, 22 per cent from the two top inflorescences.

How are we to describe this? The seeds in different parts of the tomato plant differ in their inherent inborn capacity. And we cannot fail to ascribe this difference to variation in a genetic particle. The plant changes in its genetic capacity during development in the same way as the normal-rogue crosses do in peas. But the genetic difference which in peas can be a difference between whole rogue plants and whole normal plants is never more than a difference between the parts of a rogue plant or the parts of a normal plant in tomatoes.[7]

The importance of this genetic aberration is twofold. On one hand it shows a relation with development like that of the rogue pea combined with a kind of physiological response like that of the *Euglena* plastids. In these respects it has the character of a genetic particle. On the other hand it shows where one of the fundamental antitheses of genetics seems to break down, that

[7] D. Lewis, 1953.

between genotype and phenotype. Lewis overcomes this diffi-culty by saying that 'the difference between rogue and normal is phenotypic and not genetic'. To this however we must add four peculiar circumstances:

(i) Its determination arises or begins in the preceding generation. (ii) It varies in development. (iii) It is in part a maternal effect carried over to the progeny. (iv) The maternal effect does not vary in relation to the phenotype of the mother.

In these circumstances we find the distinction between heredity and development breaking down. The breakdown is genuine in the sense that a particle whose variations are evi-dently playing a part in development can have these variations transmitted through germ cells, that is in heredity. The same kind of genetic particle, which we may call a plasmagene, can be effective both in heredity and development. We may also notice that organisms benefit from separating the two modes of change; and they are usually successful in their natural environments in so organising their genetic materials that the separation is effective. Here the cultivated tomato fails.

iii. *Heredity and Development*

The genetic properties of rogues in peas, tomatoes, potatoes and many other cultivated plants compel us to admit that genetic particles which vary in heredity may also vary in de-velopment. The distinction between heredity and develop-ment, which is so general and so useful under natural conditions, breaks down here and there with artificial plants and artificial treatments. We must then refer to variations occurring within vegetative individuals, variations which for different reasons can be transmitted by sexual reproduction, as genetic and due to the action of genetic particles. In the higher animals the im-portant group of such variations concerns cancer. In micro-organisms the important group concerns the antigens whose transmission has been studied in *Paramecium*.[8] In plants the important group concern the transformations of development in long-lived trees and shrubs.

Trees, in the course of their development, undergo certain irreversible changes of character. These prevent the propagator

[8] Beale, 1954.

using their shoots as cuttings for they deform the tree that is produced. The most striking of such changes are known in *Cedrus*. In the Cedar of Lebanon side branches may be propagated and they produce a tree bearing no resemblance in habit to the ordinary cedar or indeed to any other conifer. This situation is in marked contrast to that in the small ornamental and fruit trees which are regularly propagated by grafting. It indicates an irreversible change in the normal vegetative life of the cells which stands half-way between the differentiation of the higher animals and the abnormal development of rogue plants.

Three other types of vegetative change are well known in plants under cultivation. One is the witches' broom an irreversible dwarfing mutation spontaneous in hundreds of tree species which is responsible for many of the dwarf trees of miniature gardens.[9] A second is fasciation, the potentially permanent flattening of growing points so common in herbaceous garden plants which gives, for example, the ornamental varieties of many succulent plants known as *monstrosa* or *cristata*. A third is the climbing sport which has arisen in some hundred varieties of modern garden roses and which is sometimes reversible by bud-propagation. All of these might be attributed to an upset in a cell system responsible for the orientation of mitoses. They might be referred to changes in a constellation of particles from one steady state to another. But there is yet a fourth type of change, that from a juvenile to a mature habit, in which the results of experiment seems to require single and specific genetic particles.

The flowering shoots of ivy have regularly lost the capacity which the juvenile shoots had of creeping and rooting. They may be propagated from cuttings and remain stable indefinitely in their arboreal habit. Indeed nurserymen offer them under the learned name of *Hedera helix* var. *arborescens* Loudon. The flowering shoots have thus the character of having undergone an irreversible change in regard to a cytoplasmic particle. Irreversible except in the normal course of seed formation. The flowering shoots may however be changed back to the juvenile state by two kinds of experimental treatment. The first consists in treating them with a low temperature shock or with an

[9] Hornibrook, 1923.

X-ray dose.[10] The second consists in grafting, or growing together in the same solution, juvenile and flowering shoots. The first of these effects may be due to direct actions on the relevant particles. The second seems to be indirect: a water-soluble substance in minute concentrations is altering the conditions of propagation of the particle so as to shift the genetic character of the flowering shoots back to that of juvenile shoots.

The overlap between the work of genetic particles or plasmagenes in heredity and in development is manifested only under exceptional conditions in the flowering plants. And in animals its existence is still a matter of conjecture. In the fungi however this overlap is not exceptional. It is widespread. There are in the fungi examples of strictly matrilinear inheritance. These are attributed to plasmagenes and the plasmagenes may undergo, like those of protista, mutation by the action of specific reagents like acridine.[11] But on the other hand there is also evidence of cytoplasmic variation during development which is transmitted to offspring arising from spores. It seems to be more effectively transmitted from asexual than from sexual spores. And it is most effectively transmitted by the fungal mode of vegetative propagation.[12] Evidently in the fungi as in the flowering plants sexual cells are adapted to restrict or regulate or exclude cytoplasmic variation.

In this range of possibilities we see an analogy with the range of behaviour in rogues, whether peas or tomatoes. Later it will no doubt be possible to amplify the analogy and use the studies in one group of organisms to guide the exploration of another group. For the present however it is enough to say that in general the processes of sexual reproduction are adapted to distinguish sharply between two kinds of genetic particles in the cytoplasm. There are those whose variation in quality or quantity, in character or concentration, is sufficiently independent of the nucleus to be used in sexual reproduction. And there are those whose variation is sufficiently dependent on the nucleus to be used in development and differentiation. But there is no intrinsic difference, no difference in chemistry and physiology, which distinguishes between plasmagenes of heredity, the field in which they were first postulated, and plas-

[10] Frank and Renner, 1955; cf. Darlington, 1949b.
[11] Ephrussi, 1953.   [12] Jinks, 1956, 1957.

magenes of development, the field to which they later had to be applied.[13]

We now have to carry the same enquiry into a third field, that of infection.

[13] Darlington, 1944; Sewall Wright, 1945.

23

HEREDITY AND INFECTION

i. *Higher Organisms*

IN all species of plants and animals that have been closely studied special particles of nucleoprotein are known which propagate themselves out of proportion with the other proteins of the cell. These particles are usually composed of RNA combined with protein. Usually also they are filterable and ultra-microscopic and they have the capacity of diffusing from cell to cell. They often come to produce the symptoms of disease. And when in addition they are habitually passed from one individual to another by infection in nature they are known as viruses.

Viruses are recognised in an enormous number of stable and distinct types. They are genetic particles. How are we to distinguish them from plasmagenes? In regard to structure, since protein production is found to be correlated with the presence of RNA in cells generally, we must suppose that plasmagenes are RNA-proteins. In regard to effect, we find among both viruses and plasmagenes a wide range of relationship between the host (or mother) and the particle. Some viruses kill quickly; in plants they turn as much as four-fifths of their host's cell proteins into their own substance. Others, like the one responsible for breaking the colour in tulips, can reach equilibrium with their host which they will maintain for centuries. A smaller but similar range of types occurs, as we have seen, among plasmagenes.

The best distinction we can make, the nearest to a distinction that we can reach, is to say that plasmagenes are transmitted, while viruses are not transmitted, through the germ cells in sexual reproduction.[1] Turnip Yellows is carried by grafting and not by the seed: it is due to a virus. Strawberry Yellows is carried by seed and not by grafting: it is due to a plasmagene.

This distinction is a basis of discussion. It is of great practical

[1] Darlington, 1944.

193

value for reasons which we shall consider later. But it is not ultimately valid. It breaks down in the same way as the distinction between the plasmagenes which are carried through germ cells and those which are not. And its breakdown naturally concerns the evolution of genetic systems. Let us take certain examples of this breakdown.

Cell contents of the King Edward potato injected into other potato varieties generate a virus which produces symptoms in the other varieties although not in King Edward. Similarly, cell contents of *Beta maritima* seedlings (at a certain stage of development) injected into plants of *Vigna sinensis* generate an infectious agent which multiplies in the new host: they generate a virus.[2] Again susceptibility to nodule bacteria is cytoplasmically inherited in clover and characteristic for each species.[3] But seedlings of *Phaseolus vulgaris* are susceptible to *P. lunatus* bacteria if their parent has been grafted on roots of *P. lunatus*. Thus in all these instances a plasmagene is graft-transmissible or infectious.[4]

Much more striking is the change when a plasmagene spontaneously or through treatment breaks through its reproductive equilibrium in its own mother organism and, having multiplied without limit, becomes infectious. This crisis is known to happen in a number of species of moths where polyhedral viruses arise without infection inside the caterpillar. In the silkworm they arise after feeding with specific chemical agents.[5] In the tiger moth they arise after inbreeding, that is after changing the nuclear genotype.

The spontaneous virus in the moth *Abraxas grossulariata* takes the argument a step further for it arises only under specific genetic conditions. The origin of the virus is confined to a particular recessive nuclear genotype, that of the mendelian segregate known as the variety *lacticolor*.[2] Having arisen in *lacticolor* the virus can infect moths which are not of this genotype. The simplest assumption to make is that particles which exist as part of the normal cytoplasmic systems of the moths can become dangerous and infectious viruses. And this change can be induced by conditions which are either nuclear or nutritional: either internal or external to the organism.

[2] K. M. Smith, 1952.   [3] Nutman, 1949.
[4] Darlington and Mather, 1949.   [5] Yamafuji *et al.*, 1954.

It has been frequently suggested that potatoes or moths which generate viruses spontaneously must have always carried such viruses in a 'latent' state. But there seems to be no more reason for ascribing the harmless condition to a latency of a virus than the dangerous condition to the virulence of a plasmagene. Indeed there is less reason. We do not know the past history of such a particle. We can assume that it has a history of self-propagation. Since the virus is fatal no ancestor of *A. g. lacticolor* could have developed it. We therefore have to suppose that the effective particle was not carried through the egg but was generated during development by the action of the newly-constituted *lacticolor* nucleus. In the same way we have to assume that a virus comes into being by the action of a *Vigna* nucleus on a *Beta* plasmagene.

There are thus genetic particles which play a normal part in the organism in nature but which develop the capacity of multiplication and diffusion necessary for infection under conditions which do not occur or have not previously occurred in nature. Such particles are conveniently described as *proviruses*.[6]

ii. *Proviruses*

Complete ambivalence, the existence of a particle which is both plasmagene and virus, is never attained. But it is often approached on the plasmagene side. Thus a form of mottling appeared twice in field crops of *Capsicum annum* in Japan. It was transmitted to all progeny through pollen or eggs. It was also transmitted from one plant to another by bottle-grafting.[7]

How are we to classify the particle responsible? Clearly it had arisen in the cytoplasm. It was a plasmagene. It had two abnormal properties, one of them unfavourable to the race that bore it. It interfered with the synthesis or maintenance of chlorophyll; and it multiplied itself so fast as to allow of diffusion through grafting. It had evidently not acquired the properties of a true virus, however, since it was not spread naturally by infection, and would quickly have died out in nature. It was a potential virus, a provirus. And how has the difference from a normal plasmagene which made it into a provirus been acquired? Either through innoculation from another species by an insect, as in the virus experiments. Or

[6] Darlington, 1949*b*.   [7] Ikeno, 1930.

through mutation in *Capsicum* itself, a mutation in the cytoplasm no doubt conditioned by an abnormal nucleus.

Why do we say that the distinction between virus and plasmagene by their mode of transmission, infection or heredity, is a practical one? Because any new self-propagating particle in the organism will depend for its survival either on the success of its host, the organism in which it multiplies, or on its own success. If it depends on the success of its host the closer its combination, or we may say identification, with its host the better for it: and the closest combination, the only identification is by heredity, by egg-transmission. If, on the other hand, it depends on its own success the greater its freedom from its host the better for it. No freedom is possible in plant or animal heredity. But in the cytoplasm freedom is possible by changing heredity to infection. Thus, where the particle is balanced in its propagation and benefits its host an adaptation towards heredity must be favoured. Where the particle is unbalanced in its propagation and injures its host an adaptation towards infection must be favoured. The nucleus, as we have learnt from plastids and from rogue plasmagenes, is continually reacting with all cytoplasmic particles in regard to their propagation and mutation, indeed in regard to the integration of the cell. The materials for selection are therefore always available. In these circumstances an intermediate or ambiguous position cannot long be maintained in the evolution of a particle.

The instability of intermediate positions is quite unconnected with another kind of instability which is to be inferred from the developmental evidence. In rogue peas and rogue tomatoes the process of development shifts the character or concentration of a plasmagene. In *Drosophila* we find the same.[8] The plasmagene responsible for sensitivity to CO_2 is not naturally infectious but it can be inoculated into a non-sensitive female. She then produces some sensitive and some non-sensitive progeny. Only in some of the sensitive progeny does the condition become stabilised and true-breeding like the rogue character in peas. But the change L'Héritier is able to prove is a change, not in the sensitivity plasmagene itself, but in other cytoplasmic constituents; it is a change induced by the introduction of a new plasmagene into the system. He has demonstrated inter-

[8] L'Héritier, 1955.

action and integration in the plasmagenes of the cell as a whole.

iii. *Microbes*

The next connection in which we have to study the relations of heredity and infection and the integration of the cell is that of micro-organisms.

The discovery of the means of sexual breeding in yeast by Winge and in *Paramecium* by Sonneborn, both in 1936, opened the field of microbial genetics. Now in most unicellular organisms only the one cell fusion of fertilisation and the two cell divisions of meiosis separate mature representatives of successive generations. Inevitably therefore the contrast between heredity and development partly breaks down. For the same reason the distinction between body cells and germ cells also disappears. Genetic particles which have gained admission to a cell by infection cannot be excluded from heredity save by a differentiated life cycle. As yet we have no evidence of such an exclusion. It is not surprising therefore that the contrast between heredity and infection also partly breaks down in unicellular organisms.

Certain individuals of the infusorian *Paramecium aurelia* carry in their cytoplasm some hundreds of self-propagating particles. These are known as kappa particles. They consist of DNA-protein and are about 2 microns in diameter. Their existence and their properties Sonneborn discovered first from breeding experiments and later from direct observation.

The kappa particles, like the plastids, demand a suitable constitution in the nucleus to provide for their propagation and, like the plastids also, they exist in various genetic forms with their own sizes, activities and rates of propagation.[9] Unlike plastids however they produce a substance which kills individuals not carrying kappa. The population is therefore divided into Killer and Sensitive individuals. The particle, at a cost of a trifling tax on its host, removes competitors,[10] and the species enjoys what for nuclear variants is described by Ford as a balanced polymorphism.

When, by special arrangement, Killers are brought to mate with Sensitives the kappa particles do not usually pass over during the exchange of nuclei. They are thus always cyto-

---

[9] Dippell, 1950.   [10] Beale, 1954.

o

plasmically inherited and usually maternally inherited. And they are not in any sense infectious either in nature or in experiment: they kill at a distance if they kill at all.

The kappa particle may have arrived in *Paramecium* by infection. But it may equally have evolved through many ages like the plastids of plants which chemically, physiologically, and genetically, it so closely resembles. And today it certainly exists in *Paramecium* by virtue of the good it does to its host and not the harm. It has followed the selective line of a plasmagene and in no respect that of a virus.

Perhaps the greatest interest of kappa to us is in bridging the gap between genetic particles in the higher organisms and in bacteria. For in bacteria, where also the whole body is a germ, the evolutionary distinction between heredity and infection becomes crucial for the understanding of heredity itself.

iv. *Bacteriophages*

An infection of bacteria was discovered by d'Hérelle in 1915. He gave the name of *bacteriophages* to the infective particles. Today we know that most species of bacteria found in nature are subject to infection by bacteriophages which arise usually from individuals of their own species. And no other form of infection of bacteria is known.

Phages consist of particles of nucleoprotein. They are from 200 Å to 1000 Å in diameter. Like nuclear genes they contain DNA; but their DNA has an inert coat of protein. When a single bacterium breaks down its explosion releases a hundred or more of these filterable particles each of which can infect another bacterium. The new host, if it happens to be susceptible, in turn breaks down twenty minutes later. Its metabolism has been shifted from producing its own DNA and protein to that of the phage. It is therefore able to release a hundred phage particles instead of itself reproducing.

If this were the whole story a species of phage would work its way through the whole susceptible population of a species of bacterium and that would be the end of it. It would then disappear. The evolution of this particular system would be as explosive as the susceptible individuals. It would have no future and its past would be beyond enquiry. Another part of the story however was exposed when it was found (as is found in all infections) that in each species of bacterium there were resistant genotypes.[11]

Phage-resistant bacteria are now believed to be of two kinds. There are some that are able to absorb the particular phage without breaking up; and there are some that reject it because they have already absorbed it. The resistant bacteria which contain the phage have it propagating itself in equilibrium within them, like kappa particles in *Paramecium* or the plastids in *Euglena*. Indeed the host cell may under special conditions multiply too quickly for its guests. Thus, as happens with *Paramecium* or *Euglena*, its progeny may become guest-free. Then they are again susceptible to invasion by a new phage particle.

How does the phage exist in its permanent bacterial host? The first steps in solving this problem have been the remarkable experiments of Lwoff.[12] Phage cannot be extracted artificially by rough handling. Anaerobic conditions or chemical lysis do not release it. Only certain treatments have this effect. And then only after a delay during which DNA production is shifted back from the bacterium-making state to the phage-making state. These special treatments are of the kinds which cause gene mutation and chromosome breakage in the higher organisms. That is X-rays, reducing agents, and the wavelength of maximum absorption by the pyrimidine bases of DNA (about 2600 Å). The treatment must be accompanied by a complete nutrition. And even so the reaction of the bacterium is genotypically variable.

The evolutionary relations of bacterium and phage are thus partly intelligible. The invading particle exists in alternating states, as Lwoff suitably describes them, of phage and prophage. These states correspond in a general way with the virus and provirus of cytoplasmic particles in higher organisms.

Which is the original state? It is part of the problem as to whether heredity or infection came first. Here the answer does not seem to be disputed. The prophage, the hereditary phase, is the original state. It constitutes a gene of the bacterial species. By mutation, both in itself and in the rest of the bacterium, it has come to react in special circumstances to cause a lysis of the bacterium and an infection of many new

[11] Burnet and McKie, 1929.   [12] Lwoff, 1952.

bacteria. It becomes embodied in their heredity by returning to the prophage state or—to use the expression of L'Héritier—the integrated state.[13]

v. *The Bacterial Chromosome*

What is this integrated state? The great initial difficulties of the breeding-infecting type of experiment with bacteria have now been overcome. Temperate strains of phage which combine more and kill less have been brought into use. The results in three or four groups which bear the names of different genera reveal certain of the relations of the bacterial genetic system with that of higher organisms.[14]

In the first place, in *Salmonella* and *Escherichia*, phages produced by lysis in one strain can, through a filtrate, infect another strain. In certain respects in which the two differ they then permanently change the character of the infected bacteria. This process is known as *transduction*. The changed individuals may be only one per million of those exposed to the filtrate, but the change is significant. For sometimes two differences may be concerned in the change. And transfer is even possible between different genera.[15]

In the second place, in *Pneumococcus*, normal cultures of one strain may be broken up with bile salts and the filtered product may be applied to another strain. It then similarly changes the character to that of the first strain. This process is known as *transformation*. Again several kinds of difference can be carried over and recombination can even take place between them. The filtered product remains an effective agent of transformation when it has been purified. It then appears from all test to be free from protein and to consist only of partly polymerised DNA.[16]

In the third place, in *Escherichia*, individuals of two types, motile with flagella and non-motile without flagella, have been seen to mate. They conjugate and then separate and later individuals appear which show the recombined characters of the parent strains, characters concerning not only motility but also sexual incompatibility and flagellar antigens.[17]

---

[13] L'Héritier, 1955.
[14] Lederberg. 1948; *cf*. Hartmann, 1957; Jacob and Wollmann, 1957.
[15] *cf*. Stocker *et al*., 1953.   [16] Ephrussi-Taylor, 1951.   [17] Lederberg, 1955.

Finally, in *Escherichia*, marker differences which show linkage in conjugation experiments are carried over together in transduction experiments.[18] The recombinations arising in these three ways, two of them natural ways, rest it seems on the same basis of structure. And from them we can conclude something with regard to this structure. Bacteria must contain genetic materials with the linear permanence of chromosomes and like chromosomes depending for this permanence on a DNA fibre. Further processes analogous to nuclear fusion and meiosis, that is analogous to a sexual cycle, must also occur in bacteria. Direct observation of nuclear structures does not help in extending this conclusion. The mechanism of transduction may, on the other hand, provide the clue to the nature both of the gene string and of the sexual cycle in bacteria.

To find this clue we must pose the question: how is the free genic material, either with phage transduction or with chemical transformation, fixed in the gene-string of the recipient bacterium? The simplest assumption is that it takes the place of a small polymerised segment of DNA in the reproduction of the gene-string. The introduced polymerised particle slips into position in sequence with unpolymerised nucleotides and so produces a changeling copy.

This kind of supposition involving chemical competition was formerly used to account for crossing-over and chiasma formation at meiosis in higher organisms. But it failed to account for the frequencies and arrangements of chiasmata. Here however the frequencies of transduction depend on the opportunities of infection and not on the regulated mechanics of chromosome pairing. And they are of the order of one per million cells not ten or twenty per cell.

On the assumption of chemical competition certain consequences would follow from polynemy. If, as we suppose in higher organisms, the chromosome is based on 4, 8 or 16 DNA fibres then transduction should often be incomplete. The origin or segregation of the changed fibres should be delayed. Or, if the propagation of the multiple fibres were so arranged, a condition of continuing hybridity should follow. There are suggestions that both these kinds of irregularities sometimes occur.[19]

[18] Lennox, 1955.   [19] Lederberg, 1955.

vi. *The Gene-Virus Cycle*

How then are we to conceive of the genetic system of bacteria? They contain a nuclear element composed of gene-strings or chromosome-like fibres. This element controls the hereditary properties of the organism and the genetic character of the vegetatively propagating clone. The gene-strings in the course of their reproduction can incorporate small fractions, short pieces of polymerised DNA, which come to them by infection. If such fractions fail to be incorporated or integrated or intercalated in new gene-strings they may multiply on their own as prophages to be again propagated by explosive infection.

So much we know. But we do not yet know whether the process of sexual reproduction in bacteria depends on an exchange of phage-like particles as in transduction or whether it corresponds with the processes of higher organisms. Consequently, we cannot unreservedly speak of haploidy or diploidy or even of chromosomes at all. Nor can we certainly distinguish on the breeding evidence between genetic particles in the nucleus and in the cytoplasm. Or, if we distinguish between nucleus and cytoplasm, we must say that phage particles choose on each occasion whether they will propagate themselves in one or the other. On the evolutionary scale however they have no choice between heredity and infection: they are committed to both.

This is true of the temperate phages. On the other hand there seems to be a complete gradation among bacterial genes between violent phages strongly committed to infection and steady particles completely committed to heredity and the chromosome.

From what we now know, the phage-prophage cycle is a key process for the bacterial population as constituting a genetic system. By the alternation of lysis and infection the bacterium achieves the same general result as is achieved by sexual recombination. It accomplishes an exchange of the genetic material responsible for an adaptive and balanced polymorphism.

The exchange is superficially under deep disguise. The wastage of genetic material is even higher than that arising from the production of the germ cells of the higher organisms.

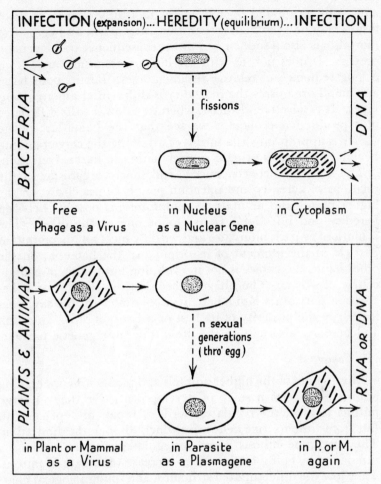

Fig. 33. Diagram to show how the same genetic particle may behave alternately as a virus and as a plasmagene, being transmitted at one stage by infection, at another by heredity.

Above: the Lwoff cycle in bacteria which depends on changing geno-typic-environmental reactions within one species. Below: the cycle in higher organisms which depends on a relation between two species of higher organism, host and parasite; either plant and insect (e.g. *Trifolium* and *Agalliopsis* for Clover Club Leaf) or mammal and tick (e.g. man and *Dermatocentor* for Rocky Mountain Spotted Fever).

Note: it is always in the parasite (to which the virus is innocuous) that it becomes inherited, and always cytoplasmically, i.e. in the female line. (*cf.* K. M. Smith 1957*a*.)

And with phage and bacterium the mortality of the results of fusion may be even higher than that with sperm and egg. The mortality is also a sudden and direct consequence of the genetic process. It does not, as with the higher organisms, arise from a long sequence of relative disadvantages. But in both large and small organisms the mortality is differential among genotypes. It is selective. Indeed, when we allow for the difference in reproductive economy, we see that the bacterium-phage device is appropriate as a means of attaining the corresponding benefit. It exposes genetic recombination to natural selection.

The contrast between micro- and macro-organisms in the relations of heredity and infection now becomes clear. In the higher plants and animals no compromise is possible between heredity and infection. It has to be one or the other. The evolutionary path bifurcates and we only meet an uncommitted particle at the moment of its origin. In the bacteria, on the other hand, the choice is not in evolution but in the immediate course of events. The phage either destroys its host or it becomes a part of its host's heredity: only later in this case does it destroy the posterity of its host or a fraction of it. Infection and heredity alternate in the life of the same genetic particle.

vii. *Cancer*

Most tissues of the higher animals and plants stop undergoing mitosis at a certain stage of development. Or they undergo mitosis to meet the regulated needs of repair or replacement. But from time to time cells arise which disobey this limitation. They continue mitosis in an unregulated way to produce a tumour. Or, going further, they increase their rate of mitosis. They lose the differentiated structural and immunological character of their cells. They return to an embryonic condition. Even, in animals, they may acquire motility and spread in the body fluids to other parts of the body setting up centres of malignant growth.

Such is the nature of cancer. Clearly its origin lies in a change occurring in a cell at a particular moment. It must be a genetic change for two reasons. First it may be induced by special treatment with so-called carcinogenic substances which are different for animals and for plants. And, secondly, it can continue for ever in the progeny of the changed cell. It can also be transplanted unchanged from one animal to another.

The evidence of a genetic change is shown conversely by special situations in which a pseudo-cancerous condition arises not by genetic change but as a regular event. In a certain species of *Sorghum*, as we noticed earlier, the pollen grains of plants having extra B chromosomes regularly undergo extra mitoses. DNA and protein are, as it were, pumped into the nucleus. The pollen grain by this polymitosis turns almost its whole substance into nucleus and becomes what in medical terms would be called an encapsulated tumour.[20] Now, here the fatal event is regular: it is fixed in time and place. It must therefore be directly determined by the character of the genotype with its observably odd chromosome complement. It cannot be the result of mutation either in the nucleus or in the cytoplasm.

The frequency with which the genetic change of carcinogenesis occurs is indeed characteristic of the type of cell in which it occurs. That is to say it can be specified for a particular strain, or particular genotype, of animals, such as rats and mice, and also for a particular tissue and particular stage of development. Such a degree of predictability is found in both gene and plasmagene mutations.

The question now arises—and it is the second fundamental question for cancer—where does the initial change or mutation occur? Is it in the nucleus or in the cytoplasm? It cannot be in both. We know that mitosis demands a doubling of nuclear contents, protein and DNA. We also know that the new materials must come from the cytoplasm. Either nucleus or cytoplasm, we likewise know, might be the site of the genetic change. There are however two means of discrimination at our disposal.[21]

In the first place, mitosis in tumours is often exceedingly rapid. In consequence the distribution of the chromosomes is irregular. Cells are formed with a great variety of chromosome numbers. One tumour may even give rise to diverse fixed strains with diverse fixed chromosome numbers. These maintain the cancerous property of morbid mitosis.[22] It is difficult to imagine a gene mutation which could regularly override in its

[20] Darlington and Thomas, 1941.   [21] Darlington, 1948, 1949*b* and *c*.
[22] Koller, 1957.

effects such gains and losses of whole chromosomes which follow from it.

In the second place, the primary cancer mutation is characteristically followed by secondary changes enhancing the exaggeration of the rate of mitosis. How such a sequence of changes could take place following gene mutation is likewise difficult to imagine. But any great change in the rate of mitosis affects differentially the genetic particles in the cytoplasm.

What is the alternative, the cytoplasmic, view of the origin of cancer? It is that at different stages of development different plasmagenes are balanced in their propagation in the cell. They are balanced in reaction with their nucleus to produce the amount of growth and the kind of growth characteristic of each tissue. A change in one of these plasmagenes, especially favouring its own propagation, will upset the balance. It may lead to a deficiency or an excess of mitosis. A deficiency will have no detectable effect. An excess, on the other hand, will further distort the balance since the mutant plasmagene will propagate out of proportion to the rest of the plasmagene system. Secondary and exaggerating effects will therefore be likely to occur such as are always the basis of malignancy.

There are, as we have seen, many other kinds of situation in which specific plasmagenes multiply out of proportion to the rest of the cell. It is true of plastids, of kappa and of rogue agents. It is also the effective change in the origin of plant viruses from plasmagenes. It is not surprising therefore to find that cancer-forming particles are often diffusible and infectious and sometimes in addition they are egg-transmissible or hereditary. This is true of leukaemia in mice.[23] The diffusible cancer particle is sometimes infectious in nature like the agent of myxomatosis in rabbits. And sometimes it is only infectious by human intervention like the agent of the Rous Sarcoma in fowls. In the first case we have a genuine virus which may very well have arisen recently by plasmagene mutation. In the second case we have a provirus which can certainly have arisen in no other way than by plasmagene mutation.

Our immense knowledge of cancer which we owe to the vast proliferation of cancer research in the present century is here

[23] L. Gross, 1956.

summarised in a short space. It is summarised in its purely genetic relations. These are clarified by our general knowledge of genetic systems which tells us what is possible in the reactions of nucleus and cytoplasm and what is impossible. They also justify to the more practical student the trouble we have taken in analysing such apparently inconsequent properties as CO_2-sensitivity in *Drosophila* and rogues in peas.

viii. *Particle Genetics*

When we look at the external properties of organisms, those properties with which a biologist begins his study, we notice various aspects of behaviour under which we are compelled to classify our observations. Heredity, development and infection seem to be the great headings of our subject. But when we get inside these problems microscopically, chemically and experimentally, the great headings are seen to be descriptively and superficially convenient but not ultimate. The ultimate agents are the particles of molecular size and organisation whose capacity for self-propagation must underlie all genetic processes. What are these genetic particles?

All genetic particles are, it seems, proteins combined with nucleic acids. Many, especially the larger and more elaborate particles, are combined with DNA. They are organised in the chromosomes of nuclei, in the larger viruses and in bacteriophages. The smaller particles are combined with RNA; they are the smaller viruses and the plasmagenes which in part seem to be interchangeable.

If we may judge from the crystallisation of viruses these particles have a variety of structures. But what interests us here is to classify them by their behaviour, or more particularly their movements. Particles in the cytoplasm fall into three groups in respect of their movements or mobility.

First, there are organellar genes or plastogenes which, like the nuclear centromere with its spindle fibre, are attached to their products. And also marked by their products. They are localised or specialised in different ways according to the organism or the tissue. Such are the plastids in plants and the kappa particles in *Paramecium*.

Secondly, there are those particles which although unattached and unmarked are nevertheless fixed in the cell where they began. They may then multiply evenly during development and in consequence pass predominantly through the egg in heredity. They may also multiply unevenly in development with the variety of consequences, such as passing predominantly through the male germ cell, seen in rogues and elsewhere. If these particles are long-lived they will appear to be independent of the nucleus and independent also of the cyclical changes of development: they are then described as plasmagenes of heredity. But if they are short-lived they must owe something to the initiation of the nucleus. They then appear as plasmagenes of development. And they are the basis of differentiation both normal and abnormal.

Thirdly, there are those particles which can diffuse from cell to cell. They are therefore transmissible by grafting. And they are useless in differentiation. But they sometimes have the capacity, if transplanted by experimenters or predators, of becoming viruses. They prosper differently in different tissues and are usually excluded from the germ cells altogether. These are the proviruses and the new viruses of the higher plants and animals.

For the ambiguous or uncertain particle we have to consider carefully its known or possible history. It is not enough to ask what it is. We have to ask also how it came there. Above all we have to distinguish experimental from natural conditions. Sometimes we have to suspend judgment on origins; often we do not even know whether a particle is of animal or plant origin.

In addition we have to keep in mind yet another class, another world, of near-genetic particles, which has been provisionally sketched by Burnet.[24] This world includes adaptive enzymes in microbes. It includes also the 'self-markers' or self-propagating antigens which constitute the genetic basis of individuality and specificity of reactions in the cells of higher animals. These seem to depend for their initiation on a modified reproduction of true genetic particles under the influence usually of exceptional substrates in microbes or alien proteins in animals. They also reflect, so far as self-markers are concerned, important processes by which tissues mature in the development and inhibition of immunological responses.[25]

[24] F. M. Burnet, 1956.　　　　　　　　[25] cf. Medawar et al., 1956.

These variations of reproduction are now widely attributed to a distortion of the copying process which underlies the reproduction of genetic particles; a distortion which can maintain itself for a short or long period in the absence of the original stimulus. Such subordinate kinds of genetic particle we shall return to consider later.

If we now compare the relations of our series of genetic particles we see them falling in to a hierarchy which begins at its most permanent and most elaborate and most independent with the organisation of the chromosomes and ends at its least permanent and least elaborate with particles which can actually react with things outside the organism, that is with the environment. A scheme of this hierarchy is represented in the diagram.

Stability of equilibrium in relation to the cell as a whole concerns us in all cytoplasmic particles. The nucleus and most organellar genes are fairly strictly co-ordinated and synchronised with the cell as a whole. Where the co-ordination fails, as we have seen, polyploidy and other kinds of mutations arise. But the free plasmagenes are not always so co-ordinated. Variations of development and of temperature upset the co-ordination and have been of crucial value in analysing the cytoplasmic system.

The effects of temperature on cytoplasmic particles are of two kinds. On the one hand, a continued high temperature may remove one kind of genetic particle by reducing its rate of propagation relative to that of the host cell. In this way *Paramecium* may be freed from kappa. And a low temperature, as we saw, will change the arboreal *Hedera* back to its juvenile form. On the other hand, the shock of a high temperature may inactivate or kill a plasmagene. During maturation and cleavage divisions 26°C will 'cure' a *Drosophila* of its sex-ratio plasmagene. Sometimes the cure is permanent: succeeding generations are free. Similarly a high temperature will kill the plastids of *Euglena*. It will also kill a number of plant viruses and thus rid the plants of their infection.[26]

The great source of variation in cytoplasmic particles however arises from their relations with the nucleus. Some nuclei, as in the tomato, may pass plasmagenes into the cytoplasm. Some

[26] A. D. Thomson, 1956.

nuclei, as in *Paramecium*, may maintain plasmagenes in the cytoplasm. And some nuclei, as in maize, may cause plasmagenes, either free or organellar, to mutate. Our experience being so fragmentary, it is no more than an experimental accident that one of these relations has been found in one

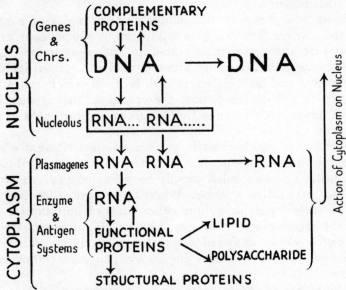

Fig. 34. Diagram of the Genetic and Synthetic Hierarchy in the cell
Downwards: sequence of developmental production with RNA columns of decreasing length.
Rightwards: sequence of hereditary propagation with DNA and RNA columns of fixed length.
(After Caspersson 1941, Darlington 1944, Sewall Wright 1945, Darlington and Mather 1949, and Burnet 1956).
Note: Just as the bacterial gene can be propagated by DNA alone, so the virus in the cytoplasm can be propagated by RNA alone (Fraenkel-Conrat *et al.*, 1957.)

organism and one in another. In general all the genetic components of the nucleus, the genes of the chromosomes, are accurately balanced by the selective processes of evolution. They have to be balanced because they are fixed and because they interact. We also see that all the elements of the cytoplasm, although they are not fixed, are similarly balanced at any one time because they similarly interact. The whole of the nucleus and the whole of the cytoplasm, all the genetic particles in the cell, are mutually selected and adjusted to make a successful cell. And the whole succession of processes is selected and adjusted to make a successful organism.

In one evolutionary respect we must note an important distinction between genetic particles in the cytoplasm and in the nucleus. In the cytoplasm they often respond directly to changes in the environment. Particles that are not needed in the dark are lost in the dark. An adaptive change occurs. The effect of disuse is inherited. When this happens in microbes where each cell division gives rise to a new organism we have the appearance of a Lamarckian principle in evolution. We may accept this description with the proviso that it is evolution backwards and it is evolution in a subordinate particle, a cytoplasmic particle. The exception helps us to understand the predominant role of the nucleus, the peculiar functions of the chromosomes and of DNA in evolution as a process of forward change.

The greatest, most elaborate and most enduring of these processes of forward change is in the evolution of heredity itself and this we must now consider.

24

EVOLUTION OF HEREDITY

i. *Steps in Evolution*

PROPERTIES of heredity and variation, methods of reproduction and the control of breeding, we now realise are in various ways bound up together in each group of organisms. They constitute a genetic system. The genetic systems of different groups of organisms differ widely. They make the complete revolution from asexuality to sexuality and back again. And they make many smaller revolutions. How do these changes come about? The genetic system has been shown at many points to be itself subject to heredity and variation. Is it then subject at all points? It is itself adaptable and it is certainly often adapted by natural selection. But does this alone enable us to explain the results? Or are there reservations that we must make, limits that we must define, laws that we must modify? These are the questions we must now ask ourselves.

A first stage in this enquiry is to find out how far the present variation in genetic systems can show us the steps in their past evolution. This method has proved of value in comparative morphology and biochemistry. In comparative genetics we have even more to expect from it because the steps are fewer and many of them are still susceptible of the combined tests of experiments with cells and with organisms. Let no one imagine that the definition of these steps is a work of supererogation, a mere catalogue of superfluous conjectures, for no one can undertake a serious study of genetics or evolution without being compelled to make one or other of the alternative series of assumptions that are implied by the evolution of genetic systems—whether he knows that he is making these assumptions or does not know.

In the first place, the properties of heredity and mutation are common to all organisms from the virus to the many-celled animal or plant. We know them to be characteristic of life, heredity by definition, mutation by experience. The chemical

212

basis of heredity is however twofold. The mainstream of evolution which takes us from a common origin to the nuclear
materials of all plants and animals and bacteria seems to be
based on DNA-protein. But a secondary parallel stream run-
ning through the cytoplasmic materials of all organisms is based
on RNA-protein.

Within each of these streams there is no decisive discontinuity
of materials. There is a chemical distinction between different
nuclear genes only in the proportions of the nucleotide units
which make them up. Between different plasmagenes and elementary viruses there are also physical distinctions of RNA-
protein types in regard to the pattern of crystallisation. But
between the two groups there is a decisive chemical discontinuity. No intermediate type of molecule is now known. It
may exist and may be discovered. Or it may have disappeared.
Within the nucleus no doubt DNA gives rise to RNA but this
is no evidence of a sequence in evolution. How one gave rise
to the other and which gave rise to the other, these remain open
questions, perhaps the great open questions in our consideration
of the origin of life. Within the main DNA series, on the other
hand, we can define the possible course of evolutionary change
with some confidence (Fig. 35).

The evidence of the first stage in the evolution of heredity
has come to us in two steps. First, the study of meiosis showed
that crossing-over occurred wherever there was sexual reproduction. Secondly, the occurrence of recombination within
bacteriophages has shown that even at this lowest level a linear
organisation of genes goes with something like crossing-over.
Thus it seems that DNA alone, without the co-operation of
protein in forming a chromosome, may provide the basis both
of a linear differentiation of genes and of the necessary recombination between them.

The second stage in the evolution of heredity arose from the
development of chromosomes and the organisation of mitosis.
It depended, as we now believe, on the exploitation of the
capacity of DNA nucleotides for unlimited polymerisation to
form fibres. The Protista provide us still with a large number
of experimental types of mitosis with a far wider range of
behaviour than is found in multicellular organisms. But many,
perhaps all of them, are compatible with the development of

P

the next stage of evolution, the discovery of sexual reproduction. This stage arose from the invention of meiosis.

The fusion of cells, and at mitosis the fusion of nuclei, are both such commonplace accidents that the introduction of fertilisation involves no novelty. It is however an abrupt change. Organisms, cells, and nuclei, either copulate or they

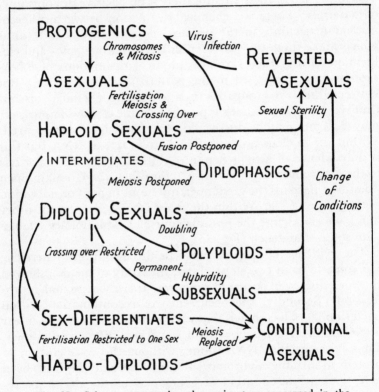

Fig. 35. Scheme representing the main steps concerned in the evolution of genetic systems.

do not. Meiosis likewise is an abrupt change which permits of no half-way house. The chromosomes must either reduce or fail to reduce if they are to keep their genetic character. Anything intermediate upsets the apple-cart. But meiosis is an elaborate process whose failure only too easily gives rise to just this result. And it must regularly alternate with fertilisation.

The origin of meiosis and sexual reproduction therefore must represent the most violent discontinuity in the whole of evolution. It demands not merely a sudden change but a revolution. It is impossible to imagine it as the result of a gradual accumulation of changes each one of which had a value as an adaptation. If the material processes underlying sexual reproduction had been understood at the time neither Lamarck nor Darwin could ever have thought of evolution as depending on the adaptive accumulation of entirely continuous variations.

In all sexually reproducing species of organisms from *Amoeba* or *Euglena* to maize or man, meiosis has a certain basic uniformity of character from which it departs only in detail. The basic uniformity and the detailed differences are both important. The uniformity consists in the occurrence of crossing-over between chromatids of pairing chromosomes. This crossing-over is responsible for the later segregation of old and new, parental and recombined, chromatids in the course of two nuclear divisions to four daughter nuclei with halved chromosome complements.

Crossing-over, in this basic and also universal type of meiosis, is thus the key to the recombination of genes as well as to the recombination and reduction of chromosomes. Two conclusions follow. In the first place this basic meiosis must represent the common origin of meiosis at the beginning of sexual reproduction. In the second place, although many substitutes for this process have been discovered, none can satisfactorily compete with the basic type of meiosis over a long period of time.

So much for the uniformity. The lack of uniformity, the differences of detail, reveal something almost as important. They show that restrictions of recombination and especially restrictions within chromosomes, that is in regard to crossing-over, are continually arising and surviving in small groups of organisms. They are therefore evidently being favoured for shorter periods of time. These restrictions are of two degrees. The extreme degree consists in the replacement of sexual by subsexual or asexual modes of reproduction. The mild degree consists in the widespread occurrence of a restriction or localisation of crossing-over. This restriction reaches its limit in the abolition of crossing-over in one sex in animals.

Restriction of crossing-over has two advantages. On the one hand it helps in the differentiation of sex chromosomes. Thus the secondary or derived types of meiosis with reduced crossing-over which are developed in many insects are always confined to the heterozygous sex. On the other hand, it reduces the total amount of crossing-over and what we have called the recombination index in the population. No reduction below one chiasma per bivalent is possible with standard meiosis. Now, as we have seen, recombination is the chief cause of sterility in hybrids. Any restriction of crossing-over is therefore not only a means of stabilising useful combinations of genes under ordinary conditions. It can also turn a dangerous genetic emergency into a fruitful evolutionary opportunity.

Could meiosis have accomplished reduction by any other course than the one it has taken?

There is one other course that meiosis could have followed and that is in fact a simpler one. If chromosomes entirely failed to divide in the first division they might pair and separate very much as they do in meiosis in the male *Drosophila*. There seems no mechanical difficulty about such a system and it may indeed be found to occur some time in one sex in an animal. The reason why it has not provided the basis of sexual reproduction is clear. It does not allow of crossing-over, which depends on the division of threads while they are paired and coiled. And without crossing-over recombination is limited to whole chromosomes. Without crossing-over indeed sexual reproduction is meaningless. And genes are also meaningless since each chromosome becomes a single gene.

In view of what we now know of genetic processes in bacteria this apparently theoretical statement has an immediate practical application. The causal sequence: crossing-over—chiasmata—pairing—segregation and reduction, once recognised made it necessary to suppose that recombination in the form of crossing-over was co-extensive with sexual reproduction. Now we know from the properties of phages that this is an under-assumption. Recombination extends beyond sexual reproduction. It goes back before meiosis. It goes back indeed precisely to the beginning of chromosomes. Recombination by a process which resembles crossing-over in its effects begins at the level of the bacteriophage. The fact that it also goes down to the DNA particles artificially separated from bacteria means even more than this. It means that recombination in one form or other is co-existent with the function of DNA in heredity and evolution. Or, to put this in another way: no self-propagating material, it seems, could undergo evolution without the physical aptitude for rearrangement which is possessed by the DNA-protein system.

ii. *Invention of Meiosis*

The original change to meiosis would be one affecting all nuclear divisions in the cycle. We have to remember that a special timing of the action of a gene is an adaptation which can hardly be there before the gene itself has arisen by mutation. The precocity mutation causing meiosis would therefore act as soon as a diploid nucleus had been formed. The haploid nucleus would have its precocious prophase which would not however upset mitosis since its chromosomes could not pair. The original sexual cycle would therefore be one without any phase of diploid mitosis. Comparative morphology reaches the same conclusion. The simplest sexual organisms are those with meiosis immediately determined by the fusion of nuclei.

Two ways are then open to make a diploid phase possible. The first is the postponement of fusion found in the Basidiomycetes.[1] Nuclei are exchanged between different individual mycelia so that cells in each have two different nuclei. These do not fuse. The invader divides and its daughter moves on to the adjoining cell until the whole mycelium has double-nuclear cells each of which can divide to form double-nuclear daughters. Fusion occurs only when meiosis and spore-formation is about to occur. This curious method of 'diploidisation', with its long engagement and its short marriage, has been retained because, as Buller first showed, it permits the fertilisation of one fully developed mycelium by another. Like so many other genetic devices it reduces the cost of reproduction.

The co-existence of unfused nuclei has given rise in the Ascomycete fungi to a variety of new genetic systems. In the products of crossing (which are known as heterokaryons to distinguish them from heterozygotes where diploid nuclei are formed) the nuclei may multiply beyond two per cell. The two dissimilar nuclei then vary in proportions. Thus the genetic character of the mycelium can adapt itself directly to changes

[1] *cf.* Darlington, 1937*a*.

in the environment. The adaptation of course is not permanent; it is not a long-range adaptation. It shares the remarkable
property with certain plasmagene variations of being a genetic
change that would be a Lamarckian change if it could establish
itself in evolution. But it cannot.

A second remarkable property has been discovered in *Aspergillus* and *Penicillium*.[2] Once perhaps in ten million cells the
two unlike nuclei may fuse. This is a rare event among cells;
but among populations it may be a significant event. For the
new diploid nucleus in an organism unaccustomed to diploidy
behaves as we might expect. Symptoms of spindle inadequacy
and abortive meiosis appear. Once perhaps in a hundred cells
a chiasma is formed which does not lead to co-orientation and
reduction but only to mitotic crossing-over. More frequently
haploid nuclei are reconstituted with mixed chromosomes.

Both these events are notable as showing the difficulty of
changing the life-cycle and establishing diploidy where it has
not existed before. But they are also notable as constituting
genetic recombination. They enable an asexual species to vary
like a sexual species. And, since a large part of the species of
Ascomycetes are believed to be asexual in the ordinary or
legitimate sense, this means that illegitimate recombination is
taking the place of legitimate sexual recombination in the
evolution of the group. For this reason Pontecorvo describes
such a genetic system as *parasexual*.

The parasexual system can replace the sexual system in
Aspergillus niger; it can supplement the sexual system in *A.
nidulans*. In either case we must note that it seems to be a permanent even though an irregular competitor of regular sexual
reproduction. The various forms of subsexual reproduction we
find with parthenogenesis in the higher organisms are steps in
breaking down the sexual cycle. This seems to be rather a step
in imitating it suited to the peculiar modes of life in fungi.

iii. *The Alternation of Generations*

The second method of making a diploid organism possible is
by doing precisely what most fungi seem to have failed to do.
It is to postpone meiosis by an efficient differentiation in development between mitotic and meiotic divisions of the cell.

[2] Pontecorvo, 1954.

This change prepared the way for the origin of all the higher plants and animals. In all of them it led to the evolutionary development of the diploid phase at the expense of the haploid one.

The question now arises: has this postponement of meiosis and establishment of a diploid phase happened only once? Or has it happened independently many times in the course of evolution. There are indications that it has happened many times,[3] as follows:

i. In the green algae, a group which is mostly haploid, we find the genus *Cladophora* in which a mixed haploid-diploid cycle suddenly appears and culminates in some species with a diploid cycle where only the germ cells are haploid.

ii. In other groups of algae an alternation of haploid and diploid generations seems to have arisen early, perhaps as early as their common ancestors.

iii. In the Sporozoa, as in the green algae, there are both extremes, purely haploid and purely diploid.

iv. Among the Phycomycetes, which are believed to be otherwise purely haploid, a purely diploid cycle has arisen in the water moulds of the *Allomyces* group.

v. In certain Ascomycetes we have parasexual diploidy.

vi. and vii. And finally, the higher plants and animals may well have developed their diploid phases independently of these changes in the still unstable groups of lower organisms.

This frequency of change from the obligatorily haploid to the facultatively diploid type of life cycle suggests that the change itself is not profoundly serious for the genetic system. But rather the contrary is true: it is the second most important change in evolution after the invention of meiosis itself. Its importance however only very slowly makes itself felt. It makes diploidy possible but only slowly does its effect appear in the immensely increased scope of expressing variation within the species or within the breeding group. Its immediate effect is the trivial one that it makes possible, or vastly facilitates, the various abnormalities and breakdowns of sexual reproduction which we have discussed. For example at once in the genus

[3] *cf.* Darlington, 1937*a*.

Allomyces we have polyploidy and parthenogenesis appearing.[4]

A survey of life cycles confirms us in respecting the importance of diploidy. It is rare to find any reduction of the diploid phase: that is any reversal of its evolutionary origin. There are two circumstances in which diploidy has been known to give ground. One is in *Pediculus* and other lice. Here meiosis in the male is followed by six mitoses which give 64 sperm and 64 abortive cells. Thus, the haploid phase, unlike that in higher plants, produces 64 gametes of each genotype.[5] Thus too the genetic system sacrifices a part of its potentialities for recombination. If the sacrifice were made with eggs we should have reason for surprise. But since the sacrifice is made with sperm, we need not take it seriously. For with the sperm of animals many serve for advertisement and only few for perpetuation.

The other kind of reversal to a haploid phase is the important instance of animals with haploid males; animals in which the male may be described as economically the less important sex. In one case he falls to the lowest level of animal individuality. In the bug, *Icerya*, meiosis is shifted back in development and thus gives a reversal to haploidy within the life cycle. The female produces a haploid structure within her. This structure is male. It constitutes a testis and on its account the female is usually described as a hermaphrodite; she is rather to be regarded as two individuals and two stages of a life cycle wrapped up within one integument.[6]

One evolutionary advantage of the haploid male is easily overlooked. He provides a means of abolishing crossing-over in one sex; and indeed of abolishing recombination altogether.

These rare or special exceptions emphasise a general rule. In the regulation of diploid and haploid phases the simplest organisms show some elasticity, the higher organisms on the other hand an extreme conservatism. In the higher plants it is therefore possible to trace the ancestry of groups on this basis. The end of the process is seen in the highest flowering plants. For them the haploid generation is reduced to four, three, or even two, mitoses in the embryo-sac, and always to two in the pollen grain. And in the higher animals the haploid phase has almost ceased to have any physiological existence of its own.

---

[4] C. M. Wilson, 1952.   [5] Hindle and Pontecorvo, 1942.
[6] Hughes-Schrader, 1948.

iv. *Integration and Mutual Selection*

Let us now consider the principles shown by some of these evolutionary changes. In the first place what is the reason for this evolutionary conservatism? The spores of a fern can be changed to spermatozoids by a single mutation.[7] But a co-ordination of male and female organ production is necessary. They can therefore be changed only by the association of mutations. Hence the profound changes that have taken place must have been by slight mutations each of which would make another more desirable. Each of which, we may recall, would require a recombination with the mutations of other genes.

The interlocking action of gene changes is well shown by the development of a differential sexual effect in the autosomes where sex chromosomes are differentiated from them. This as we saw is due to gradual atrophy of the Y chromosome. This atrophy in turn is due to the failure of natural selection to eliminate changes in the Y, involving loss of specific or integrated activity. This failure again is no doubt due to a lack of recombination of old and new genes following the suppression of crossing-over between the X and Y, the suppression on which their original differentiation depends. Such long chains of compensating or interlocked or mutually selective changes may be regarded as typical of all evolution at the highest level. They are always slow because they are integrated in their effects at every stage. For the same reason also, we may suppose, they are nearly always irreversible.

Such integrated effects arise, although to a less extent, in the course of genetic adaptations of form. Every new variation of importance throws the organism into a new environment. In fact we may say that it is not the environment which changes the genes but the very opposite: it is the genes which change the environment. In adaptation every gene change demands others to act in concert with it. The stabilisation of a new combination depends in turn on structural change in the chromosomes at the right time and place to act in suppressing crossing-over. Hence the part that structural hybridity plays in setting up the major discontinuities from which in turn genetic isolation so frequently arises.

[7] Andersson-Kottö and Gairdner, 1936.

A special chapter of these reactions concerns polyploidy. For the new polyploid is changed at once in its vegetative structure and in its genetic system. At one step it is adapted to a new environment. If it is not sexually sterilised it is certain to be genetically isolated. In these circumstances new polyploids in nature must always have survived by virtue of having had unusual and selected parents. There is a mutual selection between polyploidy and all the other elements of the genetic system.[8]

This is a first corollary of integration. A second is no less important. It is that the unit of variation is not the unit of selection. Changes in the chromosome are determined by conditions of molecular stability. They are biologically at random. Recombination of these changes shifts the object of selection from small numbers of gene differences to great numbers of gene-combination differences. The sorting out of these changes by mutual selection together with selection by environments: these are what take us from the chemical level of mutation to the biological level of adaptation. It is the business of the genetic system to accomplish this sorting out.

It is a third corollary of integration that genetic systems and vegetative systems are capable of evolving independently. This is shown by the evolution of sex chromosomes. In any one group of organisms such as flies, higher mammals, or flowering plants, the difference between the two sexes is remarkably stable. It is stable because the complementary functions of the two sexes remain similar and demand the same structural, physiological, and in animals emotional, basis. But the chromosome system determining this stable group of differences is, as we have seen, continually shifting. It is compelled to shift according to laws of its own.

The same principle can be shown in other ways. Chromosomes can determine evolutionary discontinuities which are not morphologically visible. Two geographically separated varieties of *Hordeum sativum* give a vast array of segregation in their progeny which is not seen when parents with similar differences of form come from the same region.[9] The same kinds of gene difference in two species of *Gossypium* have different properties of dominance.[10] Certain cryptic species of *Drosophila* although scarcely distinguishable in form have chromosomes differently

[8] Darlington, 1956a.   [9] Karpechenko, 1935.   [10] Harland, 1936.

arranged and are inter-sterile.[11] All these properties go to show that the genetic basis of form may change although the form itself does not. We need not suppose that the external stability of a *Lingula* depends on an unchanging complement of genes. The genes must change. Forms and their determinants are not necessarily related in the same way in different species at the same time, or in the same species at different times. And because the copulatory system of a particular kind of fly, or the root system of a particular kind of buttercup, happens to be simpler and is therefore deemed to be ancestral to that of its relative, its chromosome system is not also to be deemed ancestral or, as it is often said, primitive.

By chromosome system, small changes are to be understood, such as changes in chromosome number or gene arrangement. It is another matter with the grand evolutionary changes in the genetic system. The advanced type of sexual cycle is, as we saw, ultimately responsible for the advanced organisation in higher plants and animals.

A fourth corollary of integration in the genetic system is compromise. Integration means that all the components of the genetic system are related to more than one function, all the functions to more than one component. The requirements of the different functions of the same component always differ. They may even be opposed. Hence selection enforces a compromise.

The most fundamental compromise is that between high and low crossing-over. High crossing-over is demanded for the pairing of chromosomes, low crossing-over for the preservation of combinations. Another and related compromise is that between the requirements of hybridity, fertility and stability, a compromise which is resolved in entirely different ways in different species. A third compromise is that between true diploidy, which gives a sensitive balance, and polyploidy, which buffers the organism against unbalance and mutation. The vastly different ways in which these compromises are reached imply the imperfectibility of genetic systems.

v. *Modes of Selection and Compromise*

The genetic system works at different levels of integration—

[11] *cf.* Darlington, 1940*c*.

the gene, the chromosome, the nucleus, the cell, and so on—and its activities at these different levels are interlocked in development and reproduction, in heredity and variation. Knowing something of this we can now consider afresh how selection works in more general terms.

The limits we can set to natural selection must depend on the limits we can set to variation. For Darwin, as for his predecessors, variation, that is genetic variation, was undefined. It was a function of heredity; in his original theory it was no more than a principle of uncertainty inherent in heredity. The uncertainty might be negligible except in evolutionary time, as Johannsen's experiment showed, but it was universal.

For Darwin also the uniformity he assumed in variation naturally implied a uniformity in selection. He admitted only one special category—sexual selection. For us variation has to be split into its parts. It arises from two causes: the origin of new changes and the recombination of old changes, the old changes being of diverse kinds, the new changes still more diverse. And the effects of variation are more diverse than all their causes. Now these many types of variation mean many types of selection. They raise problems in regard to selection of kinds that can be realised only in the light of the evolution of genetic systems. Let us see what they are.

In the first place new changes cover in their effects the whole range from what is unobservably slight to what is gross and drastic. At the slight end of the spectrum are the minute polygenes which are believed to underlie most quantitative variation. We cannot speak of them as being individually beneficial since they are individually undiscernible. The preservation of a store of polygenic variation is necessary, not for the individual but for the population, and its origin by mutation will therefore benefit the population and the benefit will be extended indefinitely in time.[12] The widespread development of supernumerary chromosomes is, as we have seen, probably only a peculiar symptom of the storage of polygenic variability.

At the drastic end of the spectrum are those changes which quickly kill the cell that bears them. Losses of parts of chromosomes in nuclei of pollen grains or meristematic cells have had one effect far beyond the death of the deficient cells: they have

[12] Mather, 1954.

favoured the multicellular meristem of flowering plants at the expense of the unicellular meristem of ferns. Here the cell is the direct object of selection, its death is unconditional, and its direct effect is conservative. But it has an indirect effect at a higher level which is constructive.

In the middle part of the spectrum we find large causes with slight effects and slight causes with large effects. The large causes are the structural and numerical changes in chromosomes. These may have only the mildest immediate consequences indistinguishable from polygenic variation. But in their long range consequences, as we know, these are the indispensable materials of evolution. They achieve their results by recombining with the other kinds of stored variation.

The slight causes with large effects are the major gene mutations. As they arise these are usually deleterious or lethal in the homozygous or pure state. But in diploid outbreeding species they can be stored in the hybrid state. Continuing in this state for great periods of time they will stand the chance of combination with other genes, especially polygenes which will reorientate their activities, in beneficial ways. They will also stand the chance of reappearing in other and more favourable environments. It is in this sense that we can understand the inversions floating in species and preserving gene combinations where they are hybrid and releasing them where they are homozygous[13]; and likewise the development of the complex adaptive genes which control breeding systems.

It is thus not by acting directly on a single change in a gene or a chromosome or on a single cell or a single individual that selection is constructive. Nor is it by acting on a 'character', that is a difference in properties considered at one level of organisation. It is by acting indirectly on combinations of changes of many kinds through their effects which are of many kinds. None of these changes are inherently or unconditionally beneficial in whole populations over long periods, and some of them are operating merely mechanically to control combination or variation.

These kinds of selection have aspects in the cell which are bound to be concealed from the outside observer. What appears in breeding experiments as a competition between

[13] H. L. Carson, 1955.

mendelian alternatives, appears in the cell in its long-term results as the evolution of complex from simple genes; the evolution of euchromatin from heterochromatin; the evolution of chromosomes whose parts are organised in regard to the positions of their diverse components to suit their mechanical properties to their physiological needs.

This mutual adaptation of mechanical and physiological variables is something of which we are only beginning to learn.[14] Consider a simple example.

Crossing-over is probably less frequent immediately adjoining the centromere than in other parts of the chromosome. Genes in this region, like those in the differential region of the Y, are therefore not capable of being freely recombined. Nor can they be freely selected. If they are large, integrated or major genes their mutations will be largely disadvantageous. But if they are small non-specific polygenes, they can serve the modest but effective purpose of polygenic adaptation and the efficiency of the genetic system as a whole will be enhanced. Hence the differentiation we often find between parts of the chromosome in regard to activity and inertness, a differentiation which will itself necessarily stabilise the crossing-over system that gave rise to it. Thus gene mutability comes indirectly to promote stability at other levels of behaviour.

Again Darwin's theory of selection regarded the whole life cycle as a unit. Now we are able to realise the special implications of haploid selection. In plants the haploid generation is selected as such. The possibilities of adaption of the diploid generation are therefore limited by the difficulty of restricting the action of many genes with precision to one time in the life cycle. Or, we may say, they must act satisfactorily pure in the haploid as well as hybrid in the diploid stages.

The absence of elimination of gametes in the offspring of hybrid animals, where grossly deficient sperm and eggs are usually believed to be effective in fertilisation, means more elimination of zygotes. Sterility therefore, in this respect, establishes genetic isolation more readily. The size of the breeding group and hence its hybridity equilibrium are reduced. Mobility with the consequent ability of individuals to select favourable environments, and highly developed discrim-

[14] Darlington, 1957.

inative mating, both favour the same course. But regular differentiation of the sexes with the abolition of self-fertilisation counteracts all these effects. These are basic and partly correlated contrasts between the genetic systems of plants and animals whose evolutionary consequences are still unexplored.

The differentiation of selection in the life cycle has consequences which can be studied experimentally. There may be a conflict between the needs or capacities of haploid and diploid phases. Thus in populations of *Sorghum* extra B chromosomes which must be favoured in the vegetative plant are disastrous to some of the pollen. The opposite situation is shown by a particular group of recessive mutant genes widespread in populations of mice. In the pure state these are lethal to the diploid mouse; but they favour either the development or the competitive effectiveness of the sperm that carry them.[15] Such conflicts enforce compromise in the frequency of B chromosomes or of sperm-promoting genes in the population, compromise which will change as the genetic system adapts itself to the new element. Clearly in *Sorghum* we already have the kind of compromise existing in most populations of plants and animals with B chromosomes. But in the mouse we have the introductory phase in a process, so costly to the vegetative system, by which the efficiency of the sperm, so vital to the genetic system, is maintained or enhanced.

Selection therefore acts at every level, gene or chromosome, cell and individual, and in every stage and process, haploid and diploid, mitotic and meiotic, embryonic and adult. But as well as the parts it is also acting always on the genetic system as a whole, a system which resolves the conflicts of all these elements by means of diverse and unstable compromises.

vi. *Environment and Adaptation*

We may return now to the simple axiom with which we began, the axiom that the genotype reacts with the environment to give the phenotype. We see that it is indeed the indispensable means of discovering the causes of the differences between living things. Every difference has an internal and an external component. The object of observation and experiment must be to separate them. When we think, not of individuals in experi-

[15] Dunn, 1953; *cf.* Beatty, 1956.

ment, but of populations in nature, we still need to make the same separation. The reaction however is no longer so simple or direct. It is compounded of a series of reactions. Mature organisms in nature are the small fraction of survivors of those which began and were selected in different environments. With them the environment selects the organism. Organisms which are mobile as zygotes, animals which can move and choose, are better off. With them the organism selects the environment. This gives them an advantage over plants, which move only as male gametes and usually move without choosing. It spares them a vast loss due to elimination of the unfit and speeds the process of adaptation to a varying environment.

Nor can we leave the environment here. There are other relations where we need to consider how what is inside the cell or the organism reacts with what is outside. Thus for the cell in development, as we saw, the environment expresses itself through the intermediacy of the cytoplasm. Now the cytoplasm is an internal environment. It is also a changing environment and one which, like other environments, is changed by the genotype, the nuclear genotype.

Quite another situation arises with the genetic system itself. For the genetic system in its adaptation and evolution depends on the selection of individuals. But in this relationship the environment of the individual consists of the rest of the breeding group. All changes in the genetic system are, or can be, entirely neutral with regard to other parts of the external world. But any of them may enlarge or diminish the size of this group, the size of the world in which the genetic system works.

In all these relations—development, heredity and adaptation—we therefore see that the effective environment is itself dynamically subordinate to the genotype, to the internal component in variation. And there is no point in discussing the environment in any sense in which it is not effective.

vii. *Uncertainty in Heredity*

The founders of genetics were concerned with the importance, the overpowering importance, of the distinction between genotype and environment. In their view, and this was most true of Galton and Johannsen, it had to govern every discussion of the problem of heredity. In this they were right. But their very rightness distracted their attention from another distinction which, beginning with the classical mendelian experiment itself, is also universal in its application to heredity. For heredity, the principle of family resemblance, is not an elementary principle. It consists of two components.

The first component of heredity is the principle that the character of the fertilised egg determines the character of the individual that develops from it with almost complete certainty. Development is a process on which selection is continually operating to remove uncertainty under the conditions of living to which each species of organism is accustomed. Under unusual conditions, such as those leading to the origin of one-egg twins in man, uncertainty frequently arises. But under usual conditions the adaptation is so successful that a residual uncertainty is impossible to detect by the experimental resources available to us.[16]

The second component of heredity is the principle that in sexual reproduction differences are recombined with various degrees of uncertainty. This uncertainty rests on two factors: the segregations of the paired chromosomes which are random with respect to one another; and crossing-over with its own special system of linear relations and of genotypic control.

These two factors, segregation and crossing-over, let us note, were at first treated statistically by Mendel and later by Bateson, and above all by Morgan. Only later were they separated and ascribed to observed and single events in single cells. These events in turn (in our present discussion) have been related to supposed mechanical antecedents operating in a causally uniform or deterministic way.

This separation of the certain and the uncertain components of heredity enables us to put the evolution of genetic systems as a whole in a new light. In sexual reproduction a uniform distribution of recombination is probably the basic, the ideal, or more strictly, the continuous system in evolution. From it the various kinds of restriction are probably irreversible changes offering short-lived advantages. And the crowning restriction of all by which apomixis arises, either directly or through sub-sexual reproduction, is most obviously irreversible and most obviously short-lived.

[16] cf. Darlington, 1954.

Q

Now in the restrictive systems uncertainty is checked and in the extreme case of obligatory apomixis it is wiped out. Yet these systems are continually arising in all kinds of sexually reproducing organism. They are continually and almost universally present as an alternative to systems of free recombination and high uncertainty. Yet they never supersede free recombination in any large group. Or rather no group in which they supersede free recombination becomes a large group. Thus it is clear that free recombination is itself maintained and multiplied by its success. Its uncertainty is not accidental. It is adaptive. It is universally organised. It is perpetually kept up to the mark by natural selection of the genetic system. But it is perpetually liable to be knocked off the mark by natural selection of the vegetative system.

In a word, just as the regularity or certainty of development is determined and adaptive, so also is the irregularity or uncertainty of recombination.

25

INITIATIVE IN EVOLUTION

i. *Lamarckism*

IT is now a hundred years since Darwin put forward his doctrine of evolution by natural selection, the doctrine which is the main theme underlying this book. Let us make clear in conclusion how far our views agree and how far they disagree with his.

Darwin assumed in the *Origin of Species* that the evolution of living organisms depended on the origin of new forms which varied from old forms by continuous differences in no constant or predictable direction. Crossed together the new and the old showed blending inheritance. To these variations direction was given by a process of natural selection which, like artificial selection, preserved some while it destroyed others. A direction, an adaptive direction, was thus given to variations *after* they arose. This view was intended by Darwin to supplant the alternative view that direction was given to variations *before* they arose, that adaptation is direct and that 'acquired characters' are inherited. Which means, in our terms, that changes in the phenotype which are due to changes in the environment determine corresponding changes in the genotype. That is the view that was held by Lamarck and by almost all other evolutionists before Darwin.

In his later works and in later editions of the *Origin*, Darwin retreated from this bold and definable position. Spontaneous variation with blending inheritance did not seem capable of giving direction or momentum to evolutionary change. Darwin therefore compromised between the two alternative and radically opposed assumptions by adding his doctrine of pangenesis to his theory of natural selection. He was willing to assume that adaptation was partly by selected variation and partly by directed variation.

Now the question of time is crucial in inferring the causes of variation. Lamarck held that hereditary variations were

231

adaptive because they arose as a direct response to a changed environment. The change in the environment occurred first. It led to a change in the body. And this change in the body was passed on to the progeny. It was therefore, as we may say, automatically registered as a change in heredity. It is inherent in this view that responses to the environment are beneficial. Moreover they profit the generation which bears them. This was part of the traditional view of heredity. Darwin took it for granted. He was therefore surprised to discover that the sex ratio varied widely between different races and species of animals. He concluded, rightly as we think, that in each breeding group the sex-ratio is adapted to the needs of reproduction, that is, to the advantage of the following unborn generation.[1] But he found this as much beyond the capacity of natural selection as it was beyond the capacity of Lamarckian adaptation. He considered that an 'individual with a tendency to produce more males than females would not succeed better in the battle for life than an individual with an opposite tendency; and therefore a tendency of this kind could not be gained through natural selection'.

Selection favouring the production of neuter castes in the Hymenoptera is, Darwin held, a slightly different question from that of selection favouring different sex-ratios. In the Hymenoptera the neuters do not differ in a faculty of producing offspring in a new way. They differ in producing no offspring. They are produced by the genetic system not for its own long-term benefit but for the immediate benefit of the community they serve. Darwin consequently accepted caste selection and its anti-Lamarckian implications. But he did not accept sex-ratio selection.

Now the results in these two cases are equally cogent evidence against Lamarckian inheritance. Evidently Darwin was confused by precisely the problem that now confronts us, the problem of selection acting at several levels of integration—the individual, the community and the race. He concluded 'that the problem is so intricate that it is safer to leave its solution for the future'. In the light of our present knowledge of heredity the solution is clear. The sex-ratio is part of the genetic system. Properties of sex determination as well as

[1] Darwin, 1874; *cf.* Fisher, 1929; Crew, 1937.

of all other kinds of heredity are genotypically controlled; that is to say they are inherited, and we have seen many methods of inheritance, some genic, some cytoplasmic, in plants and in animals. Special sex-ratios are therefore capable of being selected for an indefinite number of generations after their origin. To be sure, it is impossible to select them in the generation in which they first arise. But it is also unnecessary.

Our understanding of the evolution of genetic systems depends on the assumption that variations may survive merely because they favour posterity, even a remote posterity. It depends on the assumption that selection can extend from the individual to its descendants and to the group with which its descendants breed. It depends on the assumption that in each connection the field of selection varies according to the subject of selection from something much smaller and shorter than the individual or its life to something much larger and longer, namely the race and the species and their descendants. The capacity for sexual reproduction could have conferred no advantage on the generation which first enjoyed it. No improvement in meiosis can benefit the individual in which it first arises. The elaborate genetic processes of self-sterility and the endless devices securing cross-pollination can yield no reward except in the qualities and the diversity of qualities of the progeny. All these changes anticipate not merely the act of selection but the generations in which selection occurs. They all of them therefore put out of court any assumption of direct adaptation or the inheritance of acquired characters.

If it is true that, in terms of direct adaptation, the evolution of genetic systems is inconceivable, it is also true that these systems themselves are meaningless.

Evolution ceases when the mechanism for recombination is stopped. The self-pollinating pea or apomictic dandelion or orchid keeps the floral apparatus which had developed as an attraction to cross-pollinating insects. It retains the whole sexual system apart from the one detail that has broken down. These things which are now useless are still regularly produced. With the newt in the darkness of its Istrian cave it is quite otherwise. Its pigments and its vision are useless and it becomes colourless and blind. Sexually recombining plants and animals sooner rather than later lose their useless structures or processes.

Disuse has this effect in all respects except when it is a disuse of the mechanism of recombination on which all evolutionary change depends. Thus the primary function of the genetic system is in serving to generate, preserve and recombine differences in the ways in which natural selection will most effectively be able to use them in furthering evolutionary change. When the genetic system breaks down natural selection ceases to have the means of effecting change.

On the genetic view that genotype determines phenotype change must always anticipate its expression and its use. This principle of anticipation or pre-adaptation is not new. It was first expounded epigrammatically by Lucretius. It is however demonstrated over the whole face of evolution on the level of the genetic system.

Pre-adaptation in the evolution of genetic systems is of indefinite extension, and it is on this account that they show from time to time those contradictory vagaries which so often puzzle writers on biological subjects. Sexual reproduction survives because it profits all posterity. The opposite state of apomixis survives because it profits its own·immediate progeny. Permanent hybridity, subsexuality, and even polyploidy are changes made with immediate advantage at the expense of ultimate survival.

The combination of lag in the adaptation of the whole organism with anticipation in the change of its individual genes is responsible for another principle, namely that form overlaps function at both ends of the evolutionary as well as of the developmental time scale. Thus forms usually arise before they have a use; they always survive beyond their use. The principle of lag implies at once the instability of the compromises underlying adaptation, the irreversible character of evolution, the imperfectibility of its products, and the impossibility of stopping them changing.

ii. *The Element of Chance*

In the light of genetics Darwin's view of continuous variation and blending inheritance has been abandoned. There is no blending of genes or super-genes, of inversions or interchanges. There is no blending of X and Y. Even mixtures of plasmagenes are sorted out. But he had another view of variation which we now have to reconsider. He saw variation, inevitably at the time, as of one kind in its determination. It reacted simply and directly therefore with natural selection. Adaptation was, with the special exception of sexual selection, a direct reaction with a changing environment. The motive power in evolution was therefore in the Environment.[1]

On this view many useful ideas were developed by Darwin and his successors. Geographical isolation and disruptive selection were seen as main causes of the splitting and divergence of a species. They were also often seen to be inadequate. For example how was one to understand the enterprise repeatedly shown by species of plants and animals in invading new habitats which demanded a radical re-organisation of structure? How was one to understand the long continued evolutionary changes in one direction which the palaeontologist described as 'orthogenesis'? Or the sudden cataracts of evolutionary change which they also noticed? One of these problems we may examine more closely because it was discovered by Darwin and it has an almost experimental simplicity.

Darwin, in the *Origin of Species*, noticed that the land birds and land molluscs of islands such as Madeira and the Galapagos were split up into many species peculiar to these islands. The sea birds and the sea molluscs on the other hand which were still in contact with their continental relatives had failed to develop such local species or even races. This contrast was most significant in Darwin's view because the evidence was quite inconsistent with the theory of special creation.

This diversification of species following geographical isolation is however also inconsistent with the view which Darwin (and indeed Lamarck) held to be necessary. This is the view that change of heredity is adaptive to change of the environment. For the environments of neighbouring islands are often indistinguishable. The animals in such cases have clearly taken the initiative in evolution.

Two kinds of solution have been found for this difficulty. Both involve, as they must, an introduction of chance or uncertainty into the evolutionary process. One was the mutation theory of de Vries and Bateson and the early mendelians. On their view the initiative for evolution was not in selection but in the

[1] Darwin, 1859.

discontinuous changes they observed in heredity. The other was the invocation by Sewall Wright[2] of sampling uncertainty in small populations subject to strict selection. Both of these theories require to be related to evolutionary processes as we now understand them.

The sampling error theory assumes that mendelian segregation in small populations will lead by chance to the survival of different alleles of a gene in different populations in the absence of any selective discrimination. Such divergence would give rise to what Sewall Wright describes as non-adaptive radiation or drift.

This view has been disputed by Fisher and Ford.[3] Their experimental evidence suggests that major mendelian differences do not establish themselves against a selective disadvantage. Further they argue that the whole of a small population that makes a mistake by sampling will usually be wiped out. This argument may be extended. Diverging populations are often large. On the other hand they can also be extremely small. New populations of single individuals are often arising by genetic isolation, for example as a result of polyploidy. And we cannot doubt that they are usually wiped out. The uncertainty of sampling of mendelian differences, or of any one kind of difference whatever, is not the basis of the uncertainty of evolutionary change and divergence.

iii. *The Breakdown of Classical Theory*

The inadequacy of classical Darwinian and Mendelian explanations of selective adaptation need not however surprise us since the classical theories of variation are also inadequate. Variation cannot be described in either Darwinian or Mendelian terms. In three main respects it breaks through the classical scheme:

(i) It arises on the simplest classification at three levels, genic, structural and numerical. These three primary types of variation have different kinds of effect in regard to quantity, proportion and specificity. But their effects interact. All evolution occurs in interbreeding populations in which all these changes are occurring together. No single difference can be considered independently of other kinds of difference.

[2] Sewall Wright, 1948, 1956.　　　　[3] Fisher and Ford, 1947, 1950.

(ii) A large part of these effects concern the genetic system whose properties have nothing to do with the survival of the individual but only of its posterity. All adaptation of the genetic system is therefore pre-adaptation. It has no relation to any existing environment. Its relations are internal to the species and often, as we have seen in the evolution of sex chromosomes, extremely unstable and subject to their own evolutionary laws.

(iii) In the adaptation of the genetic system all the primary types of variation interact and the genetic system itself reacts on the external form of the individual. These reactions are reciprocal and complex. Thus a change of chromosome number, or a change in an incompatibility gene, or a change in the abundance of a species, may any of them change the size of a breeding group or the character of a breeding system; and this in turn will affect the frequency of mutation, the degree of hybridity, the amount of recombination and so on.

Thus the evolution of the genetic system which is independent of changes in the environment continually reacts on the evolution of the external form. In the Bryophyta the divergence of sex chromosomes leads to a divergence of sexes. In *Oenothera* the divergence of complexes leads to a divergence of species. Equally in plants and animals the occurrence of polyploidy leads to a multiplication of vegetative or apomictic species. None of these situations has any adaptive meaning in relation to the existing environment. They are all internal or spontaneous in their origins. The evolutionary initiative has been with the genetic system and not with the environment.

The effects of this evolutionary initiative on the evolution of the external form, or what we may call the vegetative system, are capricious in a high degree. On the one hand a single major gene mutation may have far-reaching consequences and produce them in rapid succession. On the other hand there are profound changes in the number and balance of a chromosome complement by which for example an 8-chromosome species of *Trifolium* can produce a 6-chromosome race which is externally almost indistinguishable from it.[4] The immediate effect of this change is trivial. Only very slowly will it lead to divergence of

4 Darlington, 1956a.

the two types. But divergence will slowly result. The chromosome change will lead to a selection of different environments and a selection of different mutations advantageous to the two types at a time long after the original cryptic division of the species. Selective divergences thus arise from irrelevant origins by unpredictable sequences. It is thus that they give the appearance that no selection is operating at all.

In all these situations different kinds of change, in genes and in the structure, and number, of the chromosomes, are concerned together. They are, as we have seen, mutually selective. They therefore need to be recombined if the species is to adapt itself. But it is inherent in chromosome differences and structural differences that they hinder or stop recombination of gene differences. They cause genetic isolation, the split up of populations, of individuals or of chromosomes. Any gene changes which inhibit crossing-over, segregation and fertilisation, or even merely cross-fertilisation, have the same effect. They all arise in single individuals on whose merits, owing to the failure of recombination, they frequently depend for their survival.

The modes of species formation are, for these reasons, quite different in different groups, for instance in the diploid *Oenothera*, the triploid *Taraxacum*, and the tetraploid *Rubus*. They may also be quite differently related to the aspect of the environment which most affects the genetic system, namely, geographical position. For example, under marginal conditions a cross-fertilising hermaphrodite plant, *Oenothera*, is forced to become self-fertilising and develop interchange hybridity with blocked recombinations. In similar conditions an obligatorily cross-fertilising animal, *Drosophila robusta*, is forced to be structurally homozygous with full recombination. The one splits into species on the margin; the other is likely to split into species in the centre where it keeps its store of inversion hybridity.[5]

Thus an element of uncertainty is introduced into the process of evolution. Integrated variation, mutual selection and interaction of the vegetative and genetic systems all heighten this uncertainty in a way which is quite foreign to the classical theories either of Darwinism or Mendelism.

The general opinion of Darwinian geneticists which is also the common sense opinion is probably the following:

[5] Carson, 1955.

'Natural selection has certain obvious limitations. It can only produce results which are of immediate biological utility to the species; and being blind and automatic, it is incapable of purposeful design or foresighted planning. In consequence its results will always be relative—to the particular environment in which the particular species of animal or plant is living, as well as to the particular structure and habits of the species.'[6]

What we observe of the evolution of genetic systems is hardly consistent with these views. Mechanisms of heredity never benefit the individuals who first manifest them. They must often be neutral with respect to the immediate posterity. They survive for a vast period because they benefit posterity over a vast period. The infinite variety of mechanisms promoting hybrids and recombination prove themselves worth while when the species is faced not with its present particular environment but with a change to another environment. The species is prepared by its genetic system for what we may call unexpected events. Natural selection has provided it with a system which although automatic is not properly described as blind. On the contrary it has been endowed with an unparalleled gift, an automatic property of foresight.

Turning back we may notice that de Vries ascribed evolution to the kinds of mutation he witnessed in *Oenothera Lamarckiana*. His mutant plants were trisomics, triploids and products of segregation in this very unusual hybrid species. For this reason they were discredited in contrast to the gene-mutants revealed by inbreeding *Drosophila* and maize which have more ordinary genetic systems. But we see that in their integration and their balance as well as in their certainty, they had properties of the building materials of evolution which single gene mutations cannot show. And in the end the one type of analysis has served as an indispensable complement to the other.

These views do much more than explain non-adaptive radiation. They show us the large extent to which evolutionary initiative resides in the genetic materials. Of this initiative the evolution of genetic systems and its characteristic features of pre-adaptation and genetic isolation are one kind of expression. The origin of species with little or no assistance from discontinuity in the environment is another kind of expression. They

[6] J. S. Huxley, 1954.

do not drift apart by chance: they are driven apart by mutation. They show us uncertainty appearing at a higher level than in the origins of changes of all kinds, namely at the level of combinations of these changes. For in these combinations chance opportunity from time to time breaks through the selective control and dominates the evolutionary process.

Just as the Mendelian principle of segregation enables us to predict the results of simple breeding experiments so the Darwinian principle of natural selection enables us to predict the results of simple selection experiments. But in the changing states of natural populations with their alternations of stagnation and crisis, their cycles of stability and breakdown,[7] the initiative often passes to internal conditions, to the genetic system. Inbreeding then does not always purify. Selection, external selection, does not always direct.

To the Lamarckians and early Mendelians natural selection was not complicated enough or positive enough to explain evolution. To us the systems it works on give its results all the complexity we could wish for. In addition there is a selection internal to these systems and invisible to the external observer which supplies what is otherwise lacking, initiative and foresight.

[7] E. B. Ford. 1957.

REFERENCES

ÅKERBERG, E. 1939. Apomictic and sexual seed formation in *Poa pratensis* *Hereditas*, **25**, 359–370.

ANDERSSON-KOTTÖ, I. and GAIRDNER, A. E. 1936. The inheritance of apospory in *Scolopendrium vulgare*. *J. Genet.* **32**, 189–228.

BARBER, H. N. 1941. Chromosome behaviour in *Uvularia*. *J. Genet.* **42**, 223–257.

BARBER, H. N. 1942. The experimental control of chromosome pairing in *Fritillaria*. *J. Genet.* **43**, 359–374.

BARBER, H. N. and CALLAN, H. G. 1943. The effects of cold and colchicine on mitosis in the newt. *Proc. Roy. Soc.* B, **131**, 258–271.

BARIGOZZI, C. 1946. Uber die geographische Verbreitung der Mutanten von *Artemia salina*. *Arch. Klaus-Stift.* **21**, 479–482.

BATE-SMITH, E. C. *et al.* 1955. Chemistry and Inheritance of Flower Colours in the Dahlia. *Nature*, **176**, 1016–1018.

BAUER, H. 1952. Die Chromosomen im Soma der Metazoen. *Verhand. Deutschen Zoologischen Gesellschaft*, 252–268.

BAUR, E. 1909. Das Wesen und die Erblichkeitsverhältnisse der 'Varietates albomarginatae hort.' von *Pelargonium zonale*. *Z.I.A.V.* **1**, 330–351.

BEADLE, G. W. 1933a. Further studies in asynaptic maize. *Cytologia, Tokyo*, **4**, 269–287.

BEADLE, G. W. 1933b. Polymitotic maize and the precocity hypothesis of chromosome conjugation. *Cytologia, Tokyo*, **5**, 118–121.

BEADLE, G. W. 1945. Biochemical-genetics. *Chem Rev.* **37**, 15–96.

BEALE, G. H. 1941. Gene relations and synthetic processes. *J. Genet.* **42**, 197–214.

BEALE, G. H. 1954. *Genetics of* Paramecium aurelia. Cambridge.

BEATTY, R. A. 1956. Melanizing Activity of Semen from Rabbit Males of Different Genotype. *Proc. Roy. Phys. Soc.* **25**, 39–44.

BEERMANN, W. 1952. Chromomerenkonstanz und spezifische modifikationen der chromosomenstruktur in der Entwicklung und Organdifferenzierung von *Chironomus tentans*. *Chromosoma*, **5**, 139–198.

BEERMANN, W. 1955a. Cytologische Analyse eines Camptochironomus-Artbastards. I. Kreuzungsergebnisse und die Evolution des Karyotypus. *Chromosoma*, **7**, 198–259.

BEERMANN, W. 1955b. Geschlechtsbestimmung und Evolution der genetischen Y-Chromosomen bei Chironomus. *Biol. Zb.* **74**, 525-544.

BELAR, K. 1929. Beiträge zur Kausalanalyse der Mitose. II. Untersuchungen an den Spermocyten von *Chorthippus (Stenobothrus) lineatus* Panz. *Arch. EntwMech. Org.* **118**, 359–484.

BENNETT, E. 1938. The origin and behaviour of chiasmata. XIV. *Fritillaria chitralensis*. *Cytologia, Tokyo*, **8**, 443–451.

BERNAL, J. D. 1940. Structural units in cellular physiology. *The Cell and Protoplasm*. *Am. Ass. Adv. Sci. Publ*. **14**, 199–205.

BRACHET, J. 1944. *Embryologie Chimique*. Paris and Liége.

BREMER, G. and BREMER-REINDERS, D. E. 1954. Breeding of tetraploid rye in the Netherlands. *Euphytica*, **3**, 49–63.

BREUER, M. and PAVAN, C. 1955. Behaviour of polytene chromosomes of *Rhynchosciara*. *Chromosoma*, **7**, 371–386.

BRIDGES, C. B. 1922. The Origin of Variations in Sexual and Sex-limited Characters. *Amer. Nat*. **56**, 51–63.

BRIDGES, C. B. 1936. The Bar 'Gene', a Duplication. *Science*, **83**, No. 2148; 210–211.

BRUUN, H. G. 1938. Studies on heterostyled plants, 2. *Svensk bot. Tidskr*. **32**, 249–260.

BUCHHOLZ, J. T. 1922. Developmental selection in vascular plants. *Bot. Gaz*. **73**, 249–286.

BURNET, F. M. 1956. *Enzyme, Antigen and Virus*. Cambridge.

BURNET, F. M. and MCKIE, M. 1929. Observations on a permanent lysogenic strain of *B. enteritidis* Gaertner. *Austr. J. Exp. Biol*. **6**, 277–284.

CALLAN, H. G. 1942. Heterochromatin in *Triton*. *Proc. Roy. Soc. London*, B, **130**, 324–335.

CALLAN, H. G. and MONTALENTI, G. 1947. Chiasma interference in Mosquitoes. *J. Genet*. **48**, 119–134.

CARSON, H. L. 1955. Variation in genetic recombination in natural populations. *J. Cell. Comp. Physiol*. **45** (Suppl. 2), 221–236.

CASPERSSON, T. 1941. Studien über den Eiweissumsatz der Zelle. *Sond. a.d. Naturwiss*. **29**, 3–43.

CATCHESIDE, D. G. 1932. The Chromosomes of a new Haploid. *Cytologia*, **4**, No. 1: 68–113.

CATCHESIDE, D. G. 1951. *Genetics of Micro-Organisms*. London.

CHITTENDEN, R. J. 1927. Vegetative segregation. *Bibliogr. Genet*. **3**, 355–442.

CLELAND, R. E. 1949. Phylogenetic relationships in *Oenothera*. *Hereditas* (Suppl. Vol.), 173–188.

CLEVELAND, L. R. 1949. The whole life cycle of chromosomes and their coiling systems. *Trans. Am. Phil. Soc*. **39**, (1): 1–100.

COOPER, D. C. and BRINK, R. A. 1937. Chromosome homology in races of maize from different geographical regions. *Amer. Nat*. **71**, 582–587.

CORRENS, C. 1927. Der Unterschied in der Keimungsgeschwindigkeit der männchensamen und weibchensamen bei *Melandrium*. *Hereditas*, **9**, 33–44.

CORRENS, C. 1928. Bestimmung, Vererbung und Verteilung des Geschlechtes bei den höheren Pflanzen. *Hb. Vererb*. **2**, 1–138.

CRANE, M. B. and Thomas, P. T. 1940. Reproductive versatility in *Rubus*. *J. Genet*. **40**, 109–128.

CRANE, M. B. and LAWRENCE, W. J. C. 1952. *The Genetics of Garden Plants*, 4th ed. London.

CREW, F. A. E. 1937. The sex ratio. *Nature, Lond.*, **140**, 449–453.

DARLINGTON, C. D. 1929. Ring-Formation in *Oenothera* and other Genera. *J. Genet.* **19**, 345–363.

DARLINGTON, C. D. 1931. Cytologial theory of inheritance in *Oeonthera*. *J. Genet.* **24**, 405–474.

DARLINGTON, C. D. 1932*a*. *Chromosomes and Plant-Breeding*. London.

DARLINGTON, C. D. 1932*b*. *Recent Advances in Cytology*, 1st ed., Chap. 16, The evolution of genetic systems. London (2nd ed. 1937*a*).

DARLINGTON, C. D. 1933*a*. The origin and behaviour of chiasmata. VIII. *Secale cereale* (n.8). *Cytologia*, **4**, 444–452.

DARLINGTON, C. D. 1933*b*. Chromosome study and the genetic analysis of species. *Ann. Bot.* **47**, 811–814.

DARLINGTON, C. D. 1934. Anomalous Chromosome Pairing in the Male *Drosophila pseudo-obscura*. *Genetics*, **19**, 95–118.

DARLINGTON, C. D. 1935*a*. Time, place and action of crossing-over. *J. Genet.* **31**, 185–212.

DARLINGTON, C. D. 1935*b*. The Internal Mechanics of the Chromosomes. I, II and III. *Proc. Roy. Soc. London*, B, **118**, 33–96.

DARLINGTON, C. D. 1936*a*. The External Mechanics of the Chromosomes. I, II, III, IV and V. *Proc. Roy. Soc. London*, B, **121**, 264–319.

DARLINGTON, C. D. 1936*b*. Crossing-over and its mechanical relationships in *Chorthippus* and *Stauroderus*. *J. Genet*, **33**, 465–500.

DARLINGTON, C. D. 1937*b*. The biology of crossing-over. *Nature, Lond.*, **140**, 759.

DARLINGTON, C. D. 1939*a*. Misdivision and the genetics of the centromere. *J. Genet.* **37**, 341–364.

DARLINGTON, C. D. 1939*b*. The genetical and mechanical properties of the sex chromosomes. V. *Cimex* and the Heteroptera. *J. Genet.* **39**, 101–137.

DARLINGTON, C. D. 1940*a*. The Causal Sequence of Meiosis. II. Contact points and crossing-over potentials in a triploid *Fritillaria*. *J. Genet.* **41**, 35–48.

DARLINGTON, C. D. 1940*b*. The prime variables of meiosis. *Biol. Rev.* **15**, 307–322.

DARLINGTON, C. D. 1940*c*. Taxonomic species and genetic systems. (In *The New Systematics*, ed. J. S. Huxley, Oxford.)

DARLINGTON, C. D. 1941. Polyploidy, Crossing-over and heterochromatin in *Paris*. *Ann. Bot.* **5**, 203–216.

DARLINGTON, C. D. 1944. Heredity, development and infection. *Nature*, **154**, 164–169.

DARLINGTON, C. D. 1948. The plasmagene theory of the origin of cancer. *Brit. J. Cancer*, **11**, 118–126.

DARLINGTON, C. D. 1949*a*. On an integrated species difference. *Heredity*, **3**, 103–107.

DARLINGTON, C. D. 1949*b*. Les plasmagènes. *Coll. Int. C.N.R.S.* **8**, 123–130.

DARLINGTON, C. D. 1949*c*. Genetic Particles. *Endeavour*, 8: 51–61.

DARLINGTON, C. D. 1950. Physical and Chemical Breakage of Chromosomes. *Pub. Staz. Zool. Napoli.* **22** (Suppl.), 1–8.

DARLINGTON, C. D. 1952. The cell and heredity under ionization. *Biol. Hazards of Atomic Energy*. Ed. Haddow. 33–45, Oxford.

DARLINGTON, C. D. 1953*a*. Polyploidy in animals. *Nature*, **171**, 191.

DARLINGTON, C. D. 1953*b*. *The Facts of Life*. London.

DARLINGTON, C. D. 1954. Heredity and environment. *Caryologia* (Suppl.), **6**, 370–381.

DARLINGTON, C. D. 1955. The chromosome as a physico-chemical entity. *Nature*, **176**, 1139–1144.

DARLINGTON, C. D. 1956*a*. *Chromosome Botany*. London.

DARLINGTON, C. D. 1956*b*. Natural populations and the breakdown of classical genetics. *Proc. Roy. Soc.* B, **145**, 350–364.

DARLINGTON, C. D. 1957. Messages and Movements in the Cell. *Conference on Chromosomes: Wageningen*, 199–231.

DARLINGTON, C. D. and DOBZHANSKY, TH. 1942. Temperature and 'Sex-Ratio' in *Drosophila pseudoobscura*. *Proc. Nat. Acad. Sci.* **28**, 45–48.

DARLINGTON, C. D. and GAIRDNER, A. E. 1937. The variation system in *Campanula persicifolia*. *J. Genet.* **35**, 97–128.

DARLINGTON, C. D., HAIR, J. B. and HURCOMBE, R. 1951. The history of the garden hyacinths. *Heredity*, **5**, 233–252.

DARLINGTON, C. D. and JANAKI-AMMAL, E. K. 1945. Adaptive isochromosomes in Nicandra. *Ann. Bot.* **9**, No. 267–281.

DARLINGTON, C. D. and KEFALLINOU, M. 1957. Correlated chromosome aberrations at meiosis in Gasteria. *Chromosoma*, **8**, 364–370.

DARLINGTON, C. D. and LA COUR, L. F. 1940. Nucleic acid starvation of chromosomes in *Trillium*. *J. Genet.* **40**, 185–213.

DARLINGTON, C. D. and LA COUR, L. F. 1941. The genetics of embryo sac development. *Ann. Bot.* **5**, 547–562.

DARLINGTON, C. D. and LA COUR, L. F. 1945. Chromosome breakage and the nucleic acid cycle. *J. Genet.* **46**, 180–267.

DARLINGTON, C. D. and LA COUR, L. F. 1950. Hybridity selection in *Campanula*. *Heredity*, **4**, 217–248.

DARLINGTON, C. D. and MATHER, K. 1933. The origin and behaviour of chiasmata. III. Triploid *Tulipa*. *Cytologia*, **4**, 1–15.

DARLINGTON, C. D. and MATHER, K. 1944. Chromosome balance and interaction in *Hyacinthus*. *J. Genet.* **46**, 52–61.

DARLINGTON, C. D. and MATHER, K. 1949. *The Elements of Genetics*. London.

DARLINGTON, C. D. and THOMAS, P. T. 1937. The breakdown of cell division in a *Festuca-Lolium* derivative. *Ann. Bot., Lond.*, **1**, 747-762.

DARLINGTON, C. D. and THOMAS, P. T. 1941. Morbid mitosis and the activity of inert chromosomes in *Sorghum*. *Proc. Roy. Soc.* B, **130**, 127–150.

DARLINGTON, C. D. and UPCOTT, M. B. 1941. Spontaneous chromosome change. *J. Genet.* **41**, 297–338.

DARWIN, C. 1859. *On the Origin of Species by means of Natural Selection etc.* London.

DARWIN, C. 1868. *The variation of Animals and Plants under domestication.* London.

DARWIN, C. 1874. *The Descent of Man and Selection in Relation to Sex*, p. 259. London.

DARWIN, C. 1877. *The Different Forms of Flowers*. London.

DE CASTRO, D. 1954. Instabilidade cromosomica em *Luzula purpurea*. *Agron. lusit.* **16**, 195–214.

DEMEREC, M. 1929. Cross sterility in maize. *Z. indukt. Abstamm.-u. VererbLehre*, **50**, 281–282.

DIPPELL, R. V. 1950. Mutation of the killer cytoplasmic factor in *Paramecium aurelia*. *Heredity*, **4**, 165–187.

DOBZHANSKY, T. 1938, 1941, 1951. *Genetics and the Origin of Species*. New York.

DOBZHANSKY, T. and STURTEVANT, A. H. 1938. Inversions in the chromosomes of *Drosophila pseudo-obscura*. *Genetics*, **23**, 28–64.

DOWRICK, G. J. 1953. The chromosomes of *Chrysanthemum*. III. Meiosis in *C. atratum*. *Heredity*, **7**, 219–226.

DOWRICK, V. P. J. 1956. Heterostyly and homostyly in *Primula obconica*. *Heredity*, **10**, 219–236.

DUNN, L. C. 1953. Variations in the segregation ratio as causes of variations in gene frequency. *Acta Gen. Stat. Med.* **4**, 139–151.

EMSWELLER, S. L. and JONES, H. A. 1945. Further studies on the chiasmata of the *Allium cepa* × *A. fistulosum* hybrid and its derivatives. *Amer. J. Bot.* **32**, 370–379.

EPHRUSSI, B. 1953. *Nucleo-Cytoplasmic Relations in Micro-Organisms*. Oxford.

EPHRUSSI, B. and SUTTON, E. 1944. A reconsideration of the mechanism of position effect. *Proc. Nat. Acad. Sci.* **30**, 183–197.

EPHRUSSI-TAYLOR, H. 1951. Genetic aspects of transformations of Pneumococci. *C. S. H. Symp. Quant. Biol.* **16**, 445–456.

FANKHAUSER, G. 1941. The frequency of polyploidy and other spontaneous aberrations of chromosome number among larvae of the newt, *Triturus viridescens*. *Proc. Nat. Acad. Sci.* **27**, 507–512.

FISHER, R. A. 1929. *The Genetical Theory of Natural Selection*. Oxford.

FISHER, R. A. and FORD, E. B. 1947. The spread of a gene in natural conditions in a colony of the moth *Panaxia dominula* L. *Heredity*, **1**, 143-174.

FISHER, R. A. and FORD, E. B. 1950. The 'Sewall Wright Effect'. *Heredity*, **4**, 117–119.

FORD, E. B. 1945. Polymorphism. *Biol. Rev.* **20**, 73–88.

FORD, E. B. 1957. *Mendelism and Evolution*, 6th ed. Methuen, London.

FRAENKEL-CONRAT H. *et al.* 1957. The progeny of virus reconstituted from protein and nucleic acid etc. in *Chem. Basis of Heredity* ed. McElroy *et al.* Baltimore.

FRANK, H. and RENNER, O. 1955. Über Verjüngung bei *Hedera Helix* L. *Planta*, **47**, 105–114.

FRANKEL, O. H. 1949. A self-propagating structural change in *Triticum*. I and II. *Heredity*, **3**, 163–194 and 293–317.

FRANKEL, O. H., DARLINGTON, C. D. and LA COUR, L. F. 1940. The causal sequence of meiosis. I, II and III. *J. Genet.* **41**, 9–64.

GAJEWSKI, W. 1937. A contribution to the knowledge of the cytoplasmic influence on the effect of nuclear factors in *Linum*. *Acta. Soc. Bot. Polon.* **14**, 205–214.

GEITLER, L. 1934. *Grundriss der Cytologie*. Berlin.

GEITLER, L. 1953. Endomitose und Endomitotische Polyploidisierung. *Protoplasmatologia*, **6**, C, 1–89.

GODWARD, M. B. E. 1954. The 'diffuse' centromere of polycentric chromosomes in *Spirogyra*. *Ann. Bot.*, **18**, 143–157.

GOLDSCHMIDT, R. 1938. *Physiological Genetics*. New York.

GROSS, L. 1956. Viral (egg-borne) etiology of mouse leukemia. *Cancer*, **9**, 778–791.

GRÜNEBERG, H. 1937. The position effect proved by a spontaneous reinversion of the *X*-chromosome in *Drosophila melanogaster*. *J. Genet.* **34**, 169–189.

GUSTAFSSON, A. 1944. The constitution of the *Rosa canina* complex. *Hereditas*, **30**, 405–428.

HADORN, E. 1937. Die entwicklungsphysiologische Auswirkung der disharmonischen Plasmakombinationen beim Bastardmerogon *Triton palmatus* (♀) × *Triton cristatus* (♂). *Arch. EntwMech. Org.* **136**, 400–489.

HADORN, E. 1955. *Letalfaktoren*. Thieme, Stuttgart.

HAGA, T. 1956. Genome and Polyploidy in the genus *Trillium*. VI. Hybridisation and speciation by chromosome doubling in nature. *Heredity*, **10**, 85–98.

HAIR, J. B. 1953. The origin of new chromosomes in *Agropyron*. *Heredity*, **6** (Suppl.), 215–233.

HAIR, J. B. 1956. Subsexual reproduction in *Agropyron*. *Heredity*, **10**, 129–160.

HAKANSSON, A. 1943. Meiosis in a hybrid with one set of large and one set of small chromosomes. *Hereditas*, **29**, 461–474.

HAKANSSON, A. and LEVAN, A. 1957. Endo-duplicational Meiosis in *Allium odorum*. *Hereditas*, **43**, 179–200.

HALDANE, J. B. S. 1931. *The Causes of Evolution*. London.

HALDANE, J. B. S. 1932. The time of action of genes, and its bearing on some evolutionary problems. *Amer. Nat.* **66**, 5–24.

HALDANE, J. B. S. 1936. A search for incomplete sex-linkage in man. *Ann. Eugen., Lond.*, **7**, 28–57.

HÄMMERLING, J. 1953. Nucleo-cytoplasmic relationships in development of Acetabularia. *Int. Rev. Cyt.* **2**, 475–498.

HARLAND, S. C. 1936. The genetical conception of the species. *Biol. Rev.* **11**, 83–112.

HARTMANN, P. E. 1957. Transduction: a comparative review: in *Chem. Basis of Heredity*, Ed. McElroy *et al.* Baltimore.

HASKELL, G. 1953. Quantitative variation in subsexual Rubus. *Heredity*, **7**, 409–418.

HEITZ, E. 1935. Chromosomenstruktur und Gene. *Z. indukt. Abstamm.-u. VererbLehre*, **70**, 402–447.

L'HÉRITIER, PH. 1955. Les Virus integrés. *Ann. Biol.* **31**, 481–496.

HERTWIG, P. 1920. Parthenogenese bei einer Mutation von *Rhabditis pellio*. *Arch. mik. Anat.* **94**, 303–337.

HINDLE, E. and PONTECORVO, G. 1942. Mitotic divisions following meiosis in *Pediculus corporis* males. *Nature*, **149**, 668.

HIORTH, G. 1926. Zur Kenntnis der Homozygoten-Eliminierung und der Pollenschlauch-Konkurrenz bei *Oenothera*. *Z.I.A.V.* **43**, 171–237.

HOARE, C. A. 1954. The loss of the kinetoplast in Trypanosomes, with special reference to *Trypanosoma evansi*. *J. Protozool.* **1**, 28–33.

HOLLINGSHEAD, L. 1930. A cytological study of haploid *Crepis capillaris* plants. *Univ. Calif. Publ. agric. Sci.* **6**, 107–134.

HORNIBROOK, M. 1923. Dwarf and Slow Growing Conifers. *Country Life*, London.

HUGHES-SCHRADER, S. 1948. Cytology of Coccids. *Adv. Genet.* **2**, 127–203.

HUXLEY, J. S. 1955. Morphism and Evolution. *Heredity*, **9**, 1–52.

HUXLEY, J. S. *et al.* 1940. *The New Systematics*. Oxford.

HUXLEY, J. S. *et al.* 1954. *Evolution as a Process*. London.

IKENO, S. 1930. Studien über einen eigentlichen Fall der infektiösen bunt-blättrichkeit bei *Capsicum annuum*. *Planta*, **11**, 359–367.

JACOB, F. and WOLLMAN, E. L. 1957. Genetic Aspects of Lysogeny: in *Chem. Basis of Heredity*, ed. McElroy *et al.* Baltimore.

JANAKI-AMMAL, E. K. 1938. A *Saccharum-Zea* Cross. *Nature, Lond.*, **142**, 618.

JINKS, J. L. 1956. Naturally occurring cytoplasmic changes in fungi. *C. R. Carlsberg* (Physiol.), **26**, 183–203.

JINKS, J. L. 1957. Selection for cytoplasmic differences. *Proc. Roy. Soc.* B, **146**, 527–540.

JOHANNSEN, W. 1903. *Über Erblichkeit in Populationen und in reinen Linien*. Jena.

JOHANNSEN, W. 1911. The genotype conception of heredity. *Amer. Nat.* **45**, 129–159.

JOHN, B. 1957. XY segregation in the Crane Fly *Tipula maxima*. *Heredity*, **11**, 209–215.

JOLLOS, V. 1934. Inherited changes produced by heat treatment in *Drosophila melanogaster*. *Genetica*, **16**, 476–94.

JONES, D. F. 1932. Interaction of Specific Genes determining sex in dioecious maize. *Proc. 6 Int. Cong. Gen.* (Ithaca), **2**, 104–107.

JORGENSEN, E. C. and GEISSMAN, T. H. 1955. Chemistry of flower pigmen-tation in *Antirrhinum majus* color genotypes. III. *Arch. Biochem. Biophys.* **55**, 389–404.

KARPECHENKO, G. D. 1935. *Theory of Distant Hybridisation. Theoretical Bases of Plant Breeding.* I. Leningrad.

KERR, W. E. 1950. Evolution of the mechanism of caste determination in the genus *Melipona*. *Evolution*, **4**, 7–13.

KLINGSTEDT, H. 1938. Failure of anaphase separation in species hybrids. *Nature, Lond.*, **141**, 606.

KOLLER, P. C. 1946. Control of nucleic acid charge in the X-chromosome of the hamster. *Proc. Roy. Soc.* B, **133**, 313–326.

KOLLER, P. C. 1957. The genetic component of cancer. *Cancer*, **1**, 335–403. Butterworth, London.

LA COUR, L. F. 1944. Mitosis and cell differentiation in the blood. *Proc. Roy. Soc.* (Edin.) B, **62**, 73–85.

LA COUR, L. F. 1949. Nuclear differentation in the pollen grain. *Heredity*, **3**, 319–337.

LA COUR, L. F. 1951. Heterochromatin and the organisation of nucleoli in plants. *Heredity*, **5**, 37–50.

LA COUR, L. F. 1953*a*. The *Luzula* system analysed by X-rays. *Heredity*, (Suppl.), **6**, 77–81.

LA COUR, L. F. 1953*b*. The physiology of chromosome breakage and reunion in Hyacinthus. *Heredity*, **6** (Suppl.), 163–179.

LA COUR, L. F. 1956. Variations in the amount of Feulgen stain in nuclei of plants grown at different temperatures. *Nature*, **177**, 272–273.

LAMM, R. 1936. Cytological studies on inbred rye. *Hereditas, Lund*, **22**, 217–240.

LAVEN, H. 1956. Cytoplasmic inheritance in *Culex*. *Nature*, **177**, 141–142.

LAWRENCE, W. J. C. 1931. The genetics and cytology of *Dahlia variabilis*. *J. Genet*. **24**, 257–324.

LAWRENCE, W. J. C. and SCOTT-MONCRIEFF, R. 1935. The genetics and chemistry of flower colour in *Dahlia*: a new theory of specific pigmentation. *J. Genet*. **30**, 155–226.

LEDERBERG, J. 1948. Problems in microbial genetics. *Heredity*, **2**, 145–198.

LEDERBERG, J. 1952. Cell genetics and hereditary symbiosis. *Physiol. Rev*. **32**, 403–430.

LEDERBERG, J. 1955. Recombination mechanism in bacteria. *J. Cell. Comp. Physiol*. **45**, 75–107.

LENNOX, E. S. 1955. Transduction of linked genetic characters of the host by bacteriophage Pl. *Virology*, **1**, 190–206.

LEVAN, A. 1936. Die Zytologie von *Allium Cepa × fistulosum*. *Hereditas, Lund*, **21**, 195–214.

LEVAN, A. 1939. Amphibivalent formation in *Allium cernuum* and its consequences in the pollen. *Bot. Notiser*, 256–260.

LEVAN, A. 1941. The cytology of the species hybrid *Allium cepa × fistulosum* and its polyploid derivatives. *Hereditas*, **27**, 253–272.

LEVAN, A. 1944. A hybrid between *Mahonia* and *Berberis*. *Hereditas*, **30**, 401.

LEWIS, D. 1941. Male sterility in natural populations of hermaphrodite plants. *New Phytol*, **40**, 56–63.

LEWIS, D. 1942. The evolution of sex in flowering plants. *Biol. Rev*. **17** 46–67.

LEWIS, D. 1953. The rogue tomato: a problem in nuclear, cytoplasmic and environmental control. *Heredity*, **7**, 337–359.

LEWIS, D. 1954. Comparative incompatibility in Angiosperms and Fungi. *Adv. Genetics*, **6**, 235–285.

LEWIS, D. 1955. Sexual incompatibility. *Sci. Progr*. **172**, 593–605.

LEWIS, D. and CROWE, L. K. 1955. The genetics and evolution of gynodioecy. *Evolution*, **10**, 115–125.

LEWIS, E. B. 1954. Pseudoallelism and the gene concept. *Proc. 9th Int. Genet. Cong*. 100–105.

LEWIS, K. R. and JOHN, B. 1957. Studies on *Periplaneta americana*. II. Interchange heterozygosity in isolated populations. *Heredity*, **11**, 12–24.

LILIENFELD, F. A. 1929. Vererbungsversuche mit schlitzblättrigen Sippen von *Malva parviflora*. *Bibl. Genet., Lpz.*, **13**, 1–213.

LOCKINGEN, L. S. and GIB DE BUSK, A. A model for intracellular transfer of DNA (gene) specificity. *Proc. Nat. Acad. Sci.* **41**, 925–934.

LORBEER, G. 1934. Die Zytologie der Lebermoose mit besonderer Berücksichtigung allgemeiner Chromosomenfragen. I. *Jb. wiss. Bot.* **80**, 567–817.

LWOFF, A. 1950. *Problems of Morphogenesis in Ciliates.* New York.

LWOFF, A. 1952. Lysogenic bacteria. *Endeavour,* **11**, 72–77, 132–136.

McCLINTOCK, B. 1934. The relation of a particular chromosomal element to the development of the nucleoli in *Zea mays. Z. Zellforsch.* **21**, 294–335.

McLEISH, J. 1953. The action of maleic hydrazide in *Vicia. Heredity,* **6** (Suppl.), 125–147.

McLEISH, J. 1954. The consequences of localised chromosome breakage. *Heredity,* **8**, 385–407.

MAEDA, T. 1937. Chiasma studies in *Allium fistulosum, Allium Cepa,* and their F_1, F_2 and backcross hybrids. *Jap. J. Genet.* **13**, 146–159.

MAEDA, T. 1942. Chiasma studies in *Allium. Jap. J. Bot.* **12**, 163–224.

MAGNI, G. E. 1953. 'Sex-Ratio': a non-mendelian character in *Drosophila bifasciata. Nature,* **712**, 81.

MALY, R. 1951. Cytomorphologische Studien an Strahleninduzierten Konstant abweichenden Plastidenformen bei Farnprothallien. *Z.I.A.V.* **83**, 447–478.

MALY, R. and WILD, A. 1956. Ein Cytologischer Beitrag zur 'Entmischungstheorie' Verschiedener Plastidensorten. *Z.I.A.V.* **87**, 493–496.

MASHIMA, I. and UCHIYAMADA, H. 1955. Studies on the breeding of fertile tetraploid plants of Rice. *Bull. Nat. Inst. Agri. Sci.* **5**, 104–136.

MATHER, K. 1938. Crossing Over. *Biol. Rev.* **13**, 252–292.

MATHER, K. 1943. Polygenic inheritance and natural selection. *Biol. Rev.* **18**, 32–64.

MATHER, K. 1950. The genetical architecture of heterostyly in *Primula sinensis. Evolution,* **4**, 340–352.

MATHER, K. 1954. The genetical units of continuous variation. *Caryologia* (Vol. Suppl.), 106–123.

MATHER, K. 1955. Polymorphism as an outcome of disruptive selection. *Evolution,* **9**, 52–61.

MAYR, E. 1954. Change of genetic environment and evolution. *Evolution as a Process,* 157–180. London.

MECHELKE, F. and STUBBE, H. 1954. Studien an mutablen Genen. I. *Antirrhinum majus* L. mut. *Graminifolia. Z.I.A.V.* **86**, 224–248.

MEDAWAR, P. B. *et al.* 1956. A Discussion on Immunological tolerance. *Proc. Roy. Soc. B,* **146**, 1–92.

MENDEL, G. 1865. Versuche über Pflanzenhybriden. *Verh. naturf. Ver. Brünn,* 10 (1).

MICHAELIS, P. 1935. Entwicklungsgeschichtlich-genetische Untersuchungen an *Epilobium. Planta,* **23**, 486–500.

MICHAELIS, P. 1937. Untersuchungen zum Problem der Plasmavererbung. *Protoplasma,* **27**, 284–289.

MORGAN, T. H. 1926. *The Theory of the Gene.* New Haven.

MORRISON, J. W. 1953. Interchange by misdivision in *Triticum*. *Heredity*, **7**, 446.

MULDAL, S. 1952. The chromosomes of the Earthworms. I. The evolution of polyploidy. *Heredity*, **6**, 55–76.

MULLER, H. J. 1932a. Some genetic aspects of sex. *Amer. Nat.* **66**, 118–138.

MULLER, H. J. 1932b. Further studies on the nature and causes of gene mutations. *Proc. 6th Int. Cong. Genet.* **1**, 213–255.

MULLER, H. J. 1942. Isolating mechanisms, evolution and temperature. *Biol. Symp.* **6**, 71–125.

MULLER, H. J. and PAINTER, T. S. 1932. The differentiation of the sex chromosomes of *Drosophila* into genetically active and inert regions. *Z.I.A.V.* **62**, 316–365.

MULLER, H. J. and PROKOFYEVA, A. A. 1935. The individual gene in relation to the chromomere and the chromosome. *Proc. Nat. Acad. Sci., Wash.*, **21**, 16–26.

NAVASHIN, M. 1926. Variabilität des Zellkerns bei *Crepis* Arten in Bezug auf die Artbildung. *Z. Zellforsch.* **4**, 171–215.

NUTMAN, P. S. 1949. Nuclear and cytoplasmic inheritance of resistance to infection by nodule bacteria in red clover. *Heredity*, **3**, 263–291.

OEHLKERS, F. 1938. Bastardierungsversuche in der Gattung *Streptocarpus* Lindl. I. Plasmatische Vererbung und die Geschlechtsbestimmung von Zwitterpflanzen. *Z. Bot.* **32**, 305–393.

OGAWA, K. 1954. Chromosome studies in the Myriapoda. VII: A chain of 9 sex chromosomes. *Cytologia*, **19**, 265–272.

OMODEO, P. 1952. Cariologia dei *Lumbricidae*. *Caryologia*, **4**, 173–275.

PÄTAU, K. 1935. Chromosomenmorphologie bei *Drosophila melanogaster* und *D. simulans* und ihre genetische Bedeutung. *Naturwissenschaften*, **23**, 537–543.

PAVAN, C. and BREUER, M. E. 1955. Differences in Nucleic Acid content of the loci in polytene chromosomes of 'Rhynchosciara angelae' according to tissues and larval stages. *Symposium on Cell Secretion*, Belo Horizonte, 90.

PONTECORVO, G. 1954. Mitotic recombination in the genetic systems of filamentous fungi. *Caryologia* (Suppl. Vol.), 1–9.

PONTECORVO, G. 1955. Heredity and variation in micro-organisms. *Discovery* (Dec. 1955), 518–522.

PRAKKEN, R. and MÜNTZING, A. 1942. A meiotic peculiarity in Rye, simulating a terminal centromere. *Hereditas*, **28**, 441–482.

PRINGSHEIM, E. G. and O. 1951. Experimental elimination of chromatophores and eye-spot in *Euglena gracilis*. *New Phytol*. **51**. 65–76.

REES, H. 1955a. Genotypic control of chromosome behaviour in Rye. I. Inbred lines. *Heredity*, **9**, 93–116.

REES, H. 1955b. Heterosis in chromosome behaviour. *Proc. Roy. Soc.* B, **144**, 150–159.

RENNER, O. 1921. Heterogamie im weiblichen Geschlecht und Embryosackentwicklung bei den Önotheren. *Z. Bot.* **13**, 609–21.

RENNER, O. 1925. Die faktorielle Konstitution einiger komplexheterozygotischer Oenotheren. *Biblioth. Gen.* **9**, 1–168.

RENNER, O. 1934. Die pflanzlichen Plastiden als selbständige Elemente der genetischen Konstitution. *Ber. Math.-Phys. Kl. Sächs. Akad.* **86**, 241–266.

RENNER, O. 1936. Zur Kenntnis der nichtmendelnden Buntheit der Laubblätter. *Flora, Jena,* **30**, 218–290.

RENNER, O. 1937. Zur Kenntnis der Plastiden und Plasma-Vererbung. *Cytologia, Tokyo,* Fujii Jub. Vol. pp. 644–653.

RHOADES, M. M. 1933. The cytoplasmic inheritance of male-sterility in *Zea Mays. J. Genet.* **27**, 71–93.

RHOADES, M. M. 1938. Effect of the *Dt* gene on the mutability of the *a* allele in maize. *Genetics,* **23**, 377–397.

RHOADES, M. M. 1950. Gene-induced mutation of a heritable cytological factor producing male-sterility in maize. *P.N.A.S.* **36**, 634–635.

RHOADES, M. M. 1952. Preferential Segregation in Maize. *Heterosis,* ed. J. W. Gowan. Ames, Iowa, 1952, 66–80.

RHOADES, M. M. and McCLINTOCK, B. 1935. The cytogenetics of maize. *Bot. Rev.* **1**, 292–325.

RICHARDSON, M. M. 1936. Structural hybridity in *Lilium Martagon* × *L. Hansonii. J. Genet.* **32**, 411–450.

RICK, C. M. 1953. Hybridization between Chicory and Endive. *Amer. Soc. Hort. Sci.* **61**, 459–466.

RICK, C. M. and BARTON, D. W. 1954. Cytological and genetical identification of the primary trisomics of the Tomato. *Genetics,* **39**, 640–666.

RILEY, R. 1955. The cytogenetics of the differences between some *Secale* species. *J. Agri. Sci.* **46**, 377–383.

ROBINSON, R. 1936. Formation of anthocyanin in plants. *Nature, Lond.,* **137**, 172–173.

RUTISHAUSER, A. 1954a. Entwicklungserregung der Eizelle bei pseudogamen Arten der Gattung Ranunculus. *Bull. Schweiz. Akad. Med. Wiss.* **10**, 491–512.

RUTISHAUSER, A. 1954b. Die Entwicklungserregung des Endosperms bei pseudogamen Ranunculusarten. *Mitt. naturf. Ges. Schaffhausen,* **25**, 1–45.

SACHS, L. 1952. Polyploid evolution and mammalian chromosomes. *Heredity,* **6**, 357–364.

SANSOME, E. R. 1933. Segmental Interchange in *Pisum.* II. *Cytologia,* **5**, 15–30.

SCHMIEDER, R. G. and WHITING, P. W. 1947. Reproductive economy in the chalcidoid wasp *Melittobia. Genetics,* **32**, 29–37.

SCHÖTZ, F. 1954. Über Plastidenkonkurrenz bei *Oenothera. Planta,* **43**, 182–240.

SCHÖTZ, F. 1955. Untersuchungen an panaschierten Oenotheren 1. Über die photosynthetische Leistungsfähigkeit der Chloroplasten u.s.w. *Z. Naturf.* **10b**, 101–108.

SCHÖTZ, F. 1956. The process of photosynthesis in various varieties of plumed oenotheres. *Photogr. u. Forsch.* **7**, 12-16.

SCOTT, A. C. 1936. Haploidy and aberrant spermatogenesis in a coleopteran, *Micromalthus debilis* Le Conte. *J. Morph.* **59**, 485–509.

SEARS, E. R. 1937. Cytological phenomena concerned with self-sterility in the flowering plants. *Genetics*, **22**, 130–182.

SHARMAN, G. B. and BARBER, H. N. 1952. Multiple sex-chromosomes in the marsupial Potorous. *Heredity*, **6**, 345–355.

SIMPSON, G. G. 1945. *Tempo and Mode in Evolution*. New York.

SIRKS, M. J. 1931. Plasmatic influences upon the inheritance in *Vicia Faba*. I. The elimination of a whole linkage-group in the plasma of *Vicia Faba minor*. *Proc. Acad. Sci. Amst.* **34**, 1057–1062.

SIRKS, M. J. 1938. Plasmatic inheritance. *Bot. Rev.* **4**, 113–131.

SMITH, B. W. 1955. Sex chromosomes and natural polyploidy in dioecious *Rumex*. *J. Heredity*, **46**, 226–232.

SMITH, K. M. 1952. Latency in viruses and the production of new virus diseases. *Biol. Rev.* **27**, 347–357.

SMITH, K. M. 1957*a*. Transmission of Plant Viruses by Arthropods. *Ann. Rev. Entom.* 30.

SMITH, K. M. 1957*b*. *A Textbook of Plant Virus Diseases*. (2nd ed.) Churchill, London.

SMITH, K. M. and MARKHAM, R. 1954. *Mumps, Measles and Mosaics*. Collins, London.

SMITH, S. G. 1953. Chromosome numbers of *Coleoptera*. *Heredity*, **7**, 31–48.

SONNEBORN, T. M. 1950. The Cytoplasm in heredity. *Heredity*, **4**, 11–36.

SØRENSEN, T. and GUDJONSSON, G. 1946. Spontaneous chromosome aberrants in apomictic *Taraxaca*. *K. Dansk. Vid. Selsk. Biol. Skr.* **4**, (2).

STAIGER, H. and GLOOR, H. 1952. Mitosehemmung und polyploidie durch einen Letalfaktor (LPL = Letal-polyploid) bei *Drosophila hydei*. *Chromosoma*, **5**, 221–245.

STERN, C. 1948. The effects of changes in quantity, combination and position of genes. *Science*, **108**, 615–621.

STOCKER, B. A. D., ZINDER, N. D. and LEDERBERG, J. 1953. Transduction of flagellar characters in Salmonella. *J. Gen. Microbiol*, **9**, 410–433.

STURTEVANT, A. H. 1937. Essays on evolution. I. On the effects of selection on mutation rate. *Quart. Rev. Biol.* **12**, 464–467.

SUOMALAINEN, E. 1953. The kinetochore and the bivalent structure in the Lepidoptera. *Hereditas*, **39**, 88–95.

SUOMALAINEN, E. 1954. Zur Zytologie der Parthenogenetischen Curculioniden der Schweiz. *Chromosoma*, **6**, 627–655.

SWEET, E. D. 1937. Chiasmata, crossing-over and mutation in *Oenothera* hybrids. *J. Genet.* **35**, 397–419.

TARTAR, V. 1954. Anomalies in regeneration of *Paramecium*. *J. Protozool.* **1**, 11–17.

THOMAS, P. T. 1936. Genotypic control of chromosome size. *Nature, Lond.*, **138**, 402.

THOMAS, P. T. and REVELL, S. H. 1946. Secondary association and heterochromatic attraction. I. *Ann. Boy.* **10**, 159–164.

THOMPSON, J. B. and REES, H. 1956. Selection for heterozygotes during inbreeding. *Nature*, **177**, 385–386.

THOMSON, A. D. 1956. Heat treatment and tissue culture as a means of freeing potatoes from Virus Y. *Nature*, **177**, 709.

ULRICH, H. 1957. Die Strahlenempfindlichkeit von Zellkern und Plasma u.s.w. *Zool. Anz.* **19** (Sup. Bd.)

UPCOTT, M. B. 1937. The external mechanics of the chromosomes. VI. The behaviour of the centromere at meiosis. *Proc. roy. Soc.* B, **124**, 336–361.

UPCOTT, M. B. 1939a. The genetic structure of *Tulipa*. III. Meiosis in polyploids. *J. Genet.* **37**, 303–339.

UPCOTT, M. B. 1939b. The nature of tetraploidy in *Primula Kewensis*. *J. Genet.* **39**, 79–100.

VAARAMA, A. 1949. Spindle abnormalities and variation in chromosome number in *Ribes nigrum*. *Hereditas*, **35**, 136–162.

VANDEL, A. 1927. La cytologie de la parthénogenèse naturelle. *Bull. biol.* **61**, 93–125.

WADDINGTON, C. H. 1939. *An Introduction to Modern Genetics*. London.

WAGNER, R. P. and MITCHELL, H. K. 1955. *Genetics and Metabolism*. New York and London.

WESTERGAARD, M. 1940. Studies on cytology and sex determination in polyploid forms of *Melandrium album*. *Dansk Botanisk Arkiv*, **10**, No. 5: 131 pp.

WESTERGAARD, M. 1946. Aberrant Y chromosomes and sex expression in *Melandrium album*. *Hereditas*, **32**, 419–443.

WESTERGAARD, M. 1948. The relation between chromosome constitution and sex in the offspring of triploid *Melandrium*. *Hereditas*, **34**, 257–279.

WETTSTEIN, F. v. 1930. Über plasmatische Vererbung sowie Plasma- und Gen-wirkung. *Ber. dtsch. bot. Ges.* **46**, 32.

WETTSTEIN, F. v. 1937. Die genetische und entwicklungsphysiologische Bedeutung des Cytoplasmas. *Z. indukt. Abstamm.-u. VererbLehre*, **73**, 349–366.

WETTSTEIN, D. v. 1957. Genetics and the submicroscopic cytology of plastids. *Hereditas*, **43**, 303–317.

WHITE, M. J. D. 1937, 1942. *The Chromosomes*. London.

WHITE, M. J. D. 1938. A new and anomalous type of meiosis in a mantid, *Callimantis antillarum* Saussure. *Proc. Roy. Soc.* B, **125**, 516–523.

WHITE, M. J. D. 1946. The Spermatogenesis of Hybrids between *Triturus cristatus* and *T. marmoratus* (Urodela). *J. Exp. Zoo.* **102**, 179–204.

WHITE, M. J. D. 1954. *Animal Cytology and Evolution*. Cambridge.

WHITING, P. W. 1943. Multiple alleles in complementary sex determination of Habrobracon. *Genetics*, **28**, 365–382.

WHITING, P. W. 1945. The evolution of male haploidy. *Quart. Rev. Biol.* **20**, 231–260.

WILLIAMS, H. 1955. June Yellows: a genetic disease of the Strawberry. *J. Genet.* **53**, 232–243.

WILSON, IRENE M. 1937. A contribution to the study of the nuclei of *Peziza rutilans* Fries. *Ann. Bot., Lond.*, **1**, 655–672.

WILSON, C. M. 1952. Meiosis in Allomyces. *Bull. Torr. Bot. Club*, **79**, 139–160.

WINGE, O. 1932. The nature of sex chromosomes. *Proc. 6th Int. Cong. Genet.* **1**, 343–355.

WINGE, O. and DITLEVSEN, E. 1947. Colour inheritance and sex determination in *Lebistes*. *Heredity*, **1**, 65–83.

WRIGHT, S. 1945. Genes as physiological agents. General considerations. *Amer. Nat.* **79**, 289–303.

WRIGHT, S. 1948. On the roles of directed and random changes in gene frequency in the genetics of populations. *Evolution*, **11**, 279–294.

WRIGHT, S. 1956. Modes of Selection. *Amer. Nat.* **90**, 5–24.

YAMAFUJI, H., OMURA, H. and SATO, M. 1954. Injection method for inducing polyhedrosis in Silkworm. *Enzymologia*, **16**, 329–335.

Note: Earlier references may be found in the reviews quoted.

INDEX

s